Gooseberry Falls To Grand Portage

A Walking Guide To The Hiking Trails In Minnesota's North Shore State Parks

Ron Morton and Steve Morse

Rockflower Press
Knife River, Minnesota

Rockflower Press
Box 295
Knife River MN 55609
www.rockflowerpress.com

Gooseberry Falls To Grand Portage
A Walking Guide To The Hiking Trails
In Minnesota's North Shore State Parks

Printed in the United States of America

Cover design by Steve Rodriques
Copy Editor: Nancy Nelson

Cover photograph by Ron Morton and Steve Morse

Although the editors and publisher have researched all sources
to ensure the accuracy and completeness of the information in
this book, we assume no responsibility for errors, inaccuracies,
omissions or any inconsistency herein.

ISBN 978-0-9785998-2-9

Contents

Parks and Walks

Gooseberry Falls State Park

Split Rock Lighthouse State Park

Tettegouche State Park

George H. Crosby Manitou State Park

Temperance River State Park

Cascade River State Park

Judge C.R. Magney State Park

Grand Portage State Park

Acknowledgements

We would like to thank and gratefully acknowledge the dedicated state park employees and enthusiastic volunteers who not only maintain these beautiful, scenic places, but who work very hard to make each and every park a unique and memorable place to visit.

We would also like to acknowledge, as well as pay tribute to, all the geologists and naturalists whose field work in the North Shore state parks provided us with the background information that turned this idea into reality.

Our copy editor, Nancy Nelson, spent many hours with preliminary drafts of this book. She offered numerous suggestions for improvement, and her insight, dedication, and wonderful editing skills greatly influenced and improved the final version of this walking guide. Any remaining editorial errors are strictly due to the authors own misdoings!

Judy Gibbs who, with her dog Sammy, went on many of these hikes. Her enthusiasm for hiking, for all things green, and her willingness to share her knowledge and love of nature is deeply appreciated.

Finally there is Charlie, my wire-haired dachshund, who was with us on each and every walk we did in the eight state parks. His enthusiasm and companionship was really appreciated (and at times very entertaining).

Introduction

The eight state parks located along the North Shore of Lake Superior are a grand showcase for the region's rugged landscape, a landscape with "wilderness-like" qualities dominated by dark volcanic rocks that have been sculpted and molded by powerful rivers to form twisting canyons, steep-walled gorges, and thundering waterfalls. The rivers flow into the largest of the Great Lakes, a lake whose wild storm waves have created stark, rocky cliffs, pebble and cobble beaches, and dramatic headlands with arches, caves, and hidden coves.

The dark rocks, rugged landscape, and powerful waters are the heart and soul of the North Shore as well as the eight state parks located along it. This heart and soul, physically and spiritually, along with the great lake itself, has been created by three of planet earth's most powerful and primeval forces: volcanic fire, glacial ice, and running water. Volcanic fire provided the dark, billion-year-old rocks, glacial ice the ten to twelve thousand-year-old landscape, and running water the rivers as well as the spectacular scenery associated with each of them.

Part of that scenery includes the plants that have taken root in the rocks and soils since the end of the last Ice Age. Within each park are a wide variety of colorful wildflowers along with the green "Canadian carpet" associated with boreal forests. And thinking about forests, the parks have wide stretches of old-growth hardwoods: trees up to 400 years old that put on a brilliant color display every fall for park visitors. The parks also contain groves of great cloud catchers: white and red pines, tall, straight, and majestic.

Though the same geological processes created the setting and landscape of all eight parks, each park, from Gooseberry Falls to Grand Portage, is different, and each park does a great job of showing off these differences to visitors, especially those who get away from visitor's centers and asphalt sidewalks to explore the parks on one of the many walking paths provided for that purpose.

This book is meant for those visitors, people who, regardless of age, want to explore, enjoy, and take in the park's natural beauty while, at the same time, learning about the park's natural history, a history that has been blended together to create such a wonderfully varied and rich landscape.

So whether you are a stroller, walker, saunterer, or serious hiker, eighteen or eighty, in tennis shoes or hiking boots, out for an hour or an entire day, we welcome you to the North Shore and to Gooseberry Falls, Grand Portage, or any of the parks in between. We also hope you will join us and use this book to explore a place where the sidewalk truly does end and the wonder, beauty, and power of planet earth are on display each and every day.

Geology and the North Shore State Parks

Sitting at my desk listening to the wind rush through the trees on this cold October day, I'm dividing my attention between showers and swirls of red and yellow leaves, and a satellite image of the North Shore of Lake Superior. I never realized how easy it is to pick out the major rivers that empty into the lake, from the Gooseberry, just north of the town of Two Harbors, up through the Split Rock, Baptism, Manitou, Caribou, Temperance, Cascade, and Brule, to the most northern and historic, the Pigeon on the Canadian-American border. Each of these dynamic and scenic rivers has a state park centered on it, and each is partly responsible for the landforms seen and rocks exposed in those parks.

Of the eight state parks along Lake Superior's North Shore, five are appropriately named for the river that flows through them, and all owe their origin, landscapes, and scenic beauty to the same trio of dynamic and powerful earth forces: volcanic fire, glacial ice, and running water. Operating over periods of time that virtually defy imagination, these three magi of planet earth provide today's hikers with a wonderful look at the ancient volcanic history of the parks, as well as the beauty, landforms, and newness of the glacial and water-carved terrain they walk over.

The bridge between this "new" terrain and its "old" rocks is geological time. Geological time is the foundation of the eight state parks this walking guide covers as well as of all modern geology. The concept of geological time is believed to be so important it has been called "the greatest contribution of the science of geology to modern western thought." Geological time gets this distinction for three reasons.

First, it allows rocks, fossils, ice ages, ore deposits, mountain ranges, and a zillion other geological events and formations to be placed in their proper sequence so geologists can unravel and understand the evolution of our planet and the many different creatures who have called it home.

Second, geological time shows us that earth processes and events take place over a great range of time periods. For example, mudslides and earthquakes last only a few seconds or minutes, volcanic eruptions a few hours or days, but the building of great mountains and the creeping of continents halfway around the world take tens of millions of years.

These different geological events, and a hundred others, come and go. Some fast, some slow, but over the long length of geological time the same land area, such as that of the parks along Superior's North Shore, can be the scene of a wide variety of these events. Think about it–all the changes that have occurred from Gooseberry Falls State Park to Grand Portage State Park over the long eons of geological time! Great volcanoes, more than once, raged, roared, and ruled the land; hot springs exited onto ancient seafloors and flowed over barren landscapes bubbling with all kinds of life and minerals. Twice, great Alp-like mountains cast their shadows across the land now occupied by the eight parks, and both times they ended up being worn down and washed away to long gone seas.

Speaking of seas, this land has been covered by numerous oceans, each of which was filled with all sorts of strange creatures, most of whom are now extinct. Dinosaurs walked in each of the parks, and during the last Ice Age, there was more than a mile of ice on top of such places as Lookout Mountain, Day Hill, and Carlton Peak. Wooly mammoths, giant beavers, giant sloths, and "dire" wolves lived here at the end of the last Ice Age.

When the ice melted away, it left behind a brand new landscape, one formed and molded in the ice's own image. It was a landscape covered by thick deposits of glacial till and littered with glacial erratics. There were also many new lakes, both small and large. The large included Lake Superior, which is only the last (to date) of the lakes to occupy the Lake Superior Basin, a basin that formed in the dim reaches of geological time. Turns out the Lake Superior Basin sits dead center over an ancient rift valley, one not unlike the East African Rift Valley of today. The rift was active 1.1 billion years ago when Minnesota was really the center of the North American continent. At this time the western part of the continent tried to separate from the eastern part, much like Africa and South America did 200 million years ago. Hot molten magma rose upward from deep within the earth, and as it approached the surface, it caused the crust to arch or bow upward, and then split open like an overcooked sausage. A great crack formed, one that spread from the Lake Superior region down what is now the St. Croix River Valley and on through Minnesota, Iowa, and clear to the edge of the continent, which was somewhere in Kansas. This great crack or rift is referred to as the Mid-Continent Rift.

Hot molten rock poured out of this growing crack year after century, lava flow upon lava flow, thicker and thicker until a pile of basalt lava some 2-10 miles deep covered the Lake Superior region. You would not, however, have needed to strain your neck or use high-powered binoculars to see the top of the lavas, for the rift widened and deepened at about the same rate lava was being extruded. Overall the topography remained pretty flat. The volcanic eruptions went on for about 23 million years and, since lava is about as sticky as wet cement, the greatest amount of lava piled up close to the eruptive source (the rift). The tremendous weight of this rock pile caused the land to sag downward for hundreds and hundreds of feet. This tilted the lavas some 10-20 degrees to the southeast (in Minnesota) and led to the formation of the Lake Superior Basin. It is the lava flows and pyroclastic

4

rocks erupted from this rift that form the vast majority of the rocks exposed in the state parks along the North Shore.

After volcanic activity came to an end, the basin was filled by sediments carried into it by streams. Most of the sediment was derived from exposed lava flows to the east and west of the basin. This sedimentary material compacted and hardened to form a sequence of rocks referred to as red bed deposits: assemblages of continental bedded sandstones, siltstones, and shales that are red or maroon in color because they contain small amounts of oxidized iron in the form of the red mineral hematite. So the basin was filled to the brim to form a flat, swampy plain, and it essentially remained that way for 900 million years. That all changed some 2 million years ago with the start of the last Ice Age. Glacial ice flowed outward from Hudson Bay to cover the land, and it found the red bed deposits much to its liking and scooped them out like children scoop ice cream out of a container. In doing so the ice also deepened the basin by eroding parts of the underlying basalt lava flows.

The basin then filled with ice and pretty much stayed that way until about 18,000 years ago when the ice began its final retreat. As the ice sheet (called the Laurentide) melted back over the southern and eastern edge of the Lake Superior Basin, meltwater became trapped between the edge of the ice sheet and the edge of the basin. This meltwater formed a lake geologists call Glacial Lake Duluth. This lake was smaller but deeper than present day Lake Superior with shorelines at elevations of 1,000 to 1,100 feet (today's Lake Superior is at an elevation of about 600 feet). Glacial Lake Duluth drained to the south through the Brule River Valley (in Wisconsin) and the St. Croix Valley into the Mississippi River. The lake lasted until the ice sheet melted back over Sault Ste. Marie and uncovered a topographically lower area, which allowed the lake to drain to the east. This led to catastrophic floods down what today is the St. Mary's River, a dramatic lowering of water levels in the lake, and the formation of a much larger but shallower body of water called Superior.

 It was running water, over the last few thousand years, that did the final sculpting of the land. Streams along the North Shore flow from west to east, following the slope or tilt of the lava flows, into Lake Superior. These streams cut down through the glacial deposits into the underlying rocks. In doing so the streams tended to follow zones of weakness in the bedrock, such as cracks and fractures, flow or bedding contacts, cooling joints, and tops of lava flows. Because of their opportunistic nature, larger streams have been able to cut deep canyons and twisting gorges and to uniquely sculpt the bedrock to form some of the more spectacular scenery found in the eight state parks along the North Shore.

The third reason geological time is important is because it tells us planet earth is not just old, it is ancient beyond imagination. It is all of 4.6 billion years old–a length of time difficult to imagine let alone comprehend. In dealing with time, our frame of reference is relatively short. For most of us a hundred years is a long time, but take 500 or 1000 years and we're talking ancient history, many times *lost* history.

What we have here in the Lake Superior region is *really* ancient history. The rocks exposed in the parks formed during what geologists call Precambrian time, a time that begins with the formation of the earth and ends with the start of the so-called Cambrian Period, some 544 million years ago. Though this particular time break is a natural one, it is rather lopsided, for the Precambrian represents 88% of all geological time. It's natural because it represents the time when fossils, the remains of prehistoric life, first became abundant in sedimentary rocks. Before the Cambrian, fossils in rocks were few and far between. That doesn't mean there wasn't any life, just that life had not evolved to the point of being able to form or secrete hard skeletons that allowed preservation in sediment. Early life forms, for almost 4 billion years, had bodies that were soft and squishy, and thus nothing much on them to preserve.

Overall, Precambrian time is divided into what is called the Archean, the time from 2.5 billion years ago back to 4.0 billion, the age of the oldest known rock. The time between 2.5 billion and 544 million is called the Proterozoic. The rocks exposed in the parks are Proterozoic in age, varying from about two to one billion years old. Archean-age rocks occur beneath the Proterozoic rocks and are exposed in the Tower-Ely area of northeastern Minnesota (2.7 billon years old) and around the town of Morton in central Minnesota (3.5 billion years old).

The oldest rocks in any of the North Shore state parks are found at Grand Portage State Park, a three hour drive from Duluth. The rocks exposed along the shore of the Pigeon River, about 0.25 miles upstream from the state park visitor's center, are layered; gray horizontal layers alternate with thinner, darker ones. These rocks formed between 1.9 and 1.8 billion years ago, at the same time and in the same narrow basin (called the Animikie) as the iron ore deposits on the Mesabi Iron Range. Called the Rove Formation, this group of sedimentary rocks is composed dominantly of siltstones, shales, and mudstones.

Standing on the shore of the river, looking at these rocks, it is interesting to try and imagine what this area would have been like 1.9 billion years ago. There would surely have been sandy beaches along the shores of the basin, shores located some thirty to forty miles to the west and northwest of the park. Just off shore, in shallow water full of life forms called stromatolites (a type of blue-green algae), the iron minerals that form Minnesota's great Iron

6

Range would have been precipitating out of the warm water. At the same time to stand here deep sea diving equipment would have been needed for the park would have been under hundreds of feet of sea water!

It would also have been a dangerous place, for periodically great turbulent surges of cloudy water would rush down the slope of the basin and cover the flat seafloor in a layer of fine sediment. The surges of water, called turbidity currents, deposited much of the material that ended up forming the rocks of the Rove Formation. These sedimentary rocks vary from about 1000 to more than 10,000 feet in thickness, but they never formed a great range of mountains. Instead something funny happened. Some quirk of plate tectonics caused the bottom of the basin to subside at about the same rate the sediments were being deposited. So the actual thickness of sediment covering the seafloor was never very great. Most of it was buried soon after it was deposited. This particular process of planet earth, the continuous and slow subsidence of an ocean basin and deposition of sediment, went on for one hundred million years. So, as the ancestral North American continent, which extended from Wyoming to Maine and from Iowa to Hudson's Bay, broke apart, a new ocean basin named the Animikie formed. Layers of iron ore and chert, now known as the Biwabik, Cuyuna, and Gunflint Iron Formations, were deposited close to the newly created shores, while the shales and siltstones of the Rove Formation were deposited in the deeper parts of the widening rift.

The state parks along the North Shore are thus underlain by ancient rocks, rocks that formed from the violence of volcanic fire and the chaos of surging turbulent clouds of rushing water. So, whether wearing tennis shoes or hiking boots, walking 1 mile or 5, when visitor's explore the trails in these state parks they become not only time travelers, but ones who occupy two different geological ages at the same moment. The rocks exposed in the parks represent part of the ancient history of our planet. Based on age dates they record over a billion years of geological events, events that began some 1. 9 billion years ago. But the landscape walked over formed after the last great ice sheet melted away, only about 11,000 years ago.

The North Shore state parks are young land with old rocks, and each is a history book containing many different chapters that can be read, seen, and experienced as this guide is used to explore the different hiking trails in the parks–trails that truly wind their way through time.

Book Layout

The walk section for each of the individual walks is divided into two parts. These are:

One: **"Walk Logistics"** gives logistical information about the walk such as start and end points, directions on how to get to these places, walk distance, walk difficulty, and safety concerns.

The distance of the walk is based on GPS track logs and does include spur trails to overlooks.

Two: **"Waypoint-to-Waypoint"** describes the walk itself. In this section you will find detailed descriptions of trail conditions, what there is to see between waypoints, and what each individual waypoint is about. Trail conditions for each section are described under the waypoint number you are walking toward. So, to find out what the trail is like between waypoints 1 and 2 read the material in waypoint 2; conditions between 2 and 3 are found under waypoint 3, and so on.

Individual walk waypoints are based on prominent geological, geographical, historical, or botanical features and are easy to find and identify. They are located on the trail maps by GPS locations, with the accuracy of the GPS unit varying from 10 to 80 feet; the average variation is about 30 feet. If you have a GPS unit, the waypoints for each walk are available for uploading to your GPS unit from Rockflower Press (www. rockflowerpress.com).

Maps: A trail map accompanies each walk. This shows the GPS track of the walk, the locations of waypoints along the track, and prominent geographic and park features.

Glossary: Geological terms and features used in the text are defined and/or explained in Glossary I at the back of the book, and are italicized the first time they are used or encountered in a given walk. In many places these terms are discussed at the waypoint location where they were seen or noted. In this regard we have tried to keep scientific jargon to a minimum and have attempted to use everyday terms and analogies wherever possible. Glossary II gives brief descriptions of many of the plants and wildflowers that can be seen along the walking paths and/or mentioned in the "waypoint-to-waypoint" section. These are also italicized the first time they are encountered in a given walk.

Walk Distances and Ratings: The table on page 11 lists the walks, their distances, and walk difficulty. Difficulty is based on the following:

- **Tennis Shoes**: Generally short hikes of under 2 miles with mostly gentle grades.

- **Walking Shoes**: Walks of 2 to 5 miles with gradual changes in elevation and possibly one or two short steep ascents or descents.

- **Hiking Boots**: Walks of 4 or more miles with some lengthy or steep elevation changes and/or lots of rocks and tree roots on or across the trail.

Please Do: The following is a list of "please do's" before you set out on a walk.

a) Read through the entire walk and use the glossaries to look up terms and definitions that are unfamiliar.

b) Wear the recommended type of shoes, but remember that spring runoff and heavy rain can turn normally dry trails into muddy quagmires. In places the trails are root-crossed and boulder-strewn; they may also be wet and muddy. Walking Sticks are NOT prohibited.

c) Carry a raincoat.

d) If on a longer walk, dress in or carry extra layers of clothing. The trail is close to a huge body of really cold water, and if the wind comes up or changes direction the temperature could rise or fall by many degrees.

e) Always carry water. More is better especially on longer walks. Same goes for food–walking does make you hungry.

f) Take bug dope and sunscreen.

g) Take a camera.

h) If you have one, don't forget your GPS unit, extra batteries, and to upload the waypoints for the walk you are doing.

i) Watch out for wet rocks, slippery clay slopes, and root-crossed trails. Be careful going around fallen trees, and take extra caution whenever you are crossing logs. If uncertain of your ability to balance on a log or large rock, get a walking stick that you can use as a third leg.

The quote used for the introduction to the "Walking Guide to the Superior Hiking Trail" is also most appropriate for the walks in this book: "The trail is the thing, not the end of the trail. Travel too fast and you miss all you are traveling for." Louis L'Amour

That is so true–have fun and good walking.

Map Symbols

| P | Parking Area |

● Waypoint

‒ ‒ ‒ Outline of the Walking Trail

■ Visitor's Center

𝍬 Picnic Site

Ʌ Campground

◿ Shelter

♄ Light House

61 U.S. Highway (Highway 61)

7 County Road

347 Forestry Road

⌒ Other Roads

Lake

River

10

Walk Distances and Difficulty

Abbreviated Walk Name	Distance (Miles)	Difficulty
Gooseberry Falls		
1. Gitchi Gummi	2.0	Tennis Shoes
2. The Estuary	1.0	Tennis Shoes
3. River View and Picnic Flow	2.0	Tennis Shoes
4. Fifth Falls Loop	2.2	Tennis Shoes
5. Nelson's Creek	3.25	Walking Shoes
Split Rock Lighthouse		
1. Little Two Harbors	3.0 or 5.2	Walking Shoes
2. Day Hill	4.0 or 6.0	Hiking Boots
3. Split Rock River Loop	5.0	Hiking Boots
Tettegouche		
1. Shovel Point	1.3	Tennis Shoes
2. Baptism River and High Falls	1.85 or 3.0	Walking Shoes
3. Baptism River Cascades	1.8	Tennis Shoes
4. Tettegouche Lake	4.5	Hiking Boots
5. Nicado and Nipisiquit Lakes	8.3	Hiking Boots
6. Mic Mac Lake	9.1	Hiking Boots
George H. Crosby-Manitou		
1. Humpback Trail	2.9	Walking Shoes
2. Bensen Lake	0.8	Tennis Shoes
2a. Beaver Bog, Matt Willis	3.8	Walking Shoes
3. Beaver Bog, Yellow Birch	4.9	Walking Shoes
4. Manitou River	6.0	Hiking Boots

Abbreviated Walk Name	Distance (Miles)	Difficulty
Temperance River		
1. Carlton Peak	3.3 , 4.7, or 6.5	Hiking Boots
2. Temperance River	2.2	Tennis Shoes
3. Temperance and Lake Superior	1.0	Tennis Shoes
Cascade River		
1. Lakeshore	3.9	Walking Shoes
2. Moose Mountain	3.8	Walking Shoes
3. Cascade River and Creek	1.9	Tennis Shoes
4. Cascade River Loop	7.8	Hiking Boots
Judge C.R. Magney		
1. Devil's Kettle	1.2	Tennis Shoes
1a. Picnic Rock	8.0	Hiking Boots
2. Wild Flower	1.2	Tennis Shoes
3. Gauthier Creek	3.0	Walking Shoes
Grand Portage		
1. High Falls	1.0	Tennis Shoes
2. Middle Falls	5.0	Hiking Boots

Gooseberry Falls State Park

Introduction

Each of the walks described in this section of the book offers great views of one or more of the five waterfalls in Gooseberry Falls State Park. One of my favorite "falls viewing" places is on the bridge across the Gooseberry River just above Fifth Falls. There are places on the trails with better and more spectacular "falls views," and Fifth Falls itself is not as large or as high as Upper Falls and Middle Falls. However, I like this particular spot for two different reasons. First, looking downstream there is the nice waterfall and the rushing, energetic river. Turning around, looking upstream, there is a nice meander and a well-exposed contact between red glacial till and a basalt lava flow. From this vantage point the contact looks knife-sharp making it hard to imagine this thin line represents over one billion years of geological time! The lava flow is part of the North Shore Volcanic Group and is 1.1 billion years old, whereas the glacial till may be all of 10,000 years old. The till rests unconformably on the scoured and abraded lava flow. A billion years in one thin, irregular line, and for a few moments it is kind of scary and awe-inspiring to think about all that has gone on over that period of time and that here, in this one place, all record of these comings and goings has been wiped clean. The other reason I particularly like this spot is that it is the meeting place of two very different rivers. Upstream from here the river gives the impression of being smaller and quieter, while downstream it seems much nosier and bigger, though it is essentially the same size. Upstream the river flows through and over glacial till, leading to slumps, meanders, gravel bars, and river pavement. Here, and on downstream, it has cut through the glacial till into the underlying bedrock forming waterfalls, cataracts, rapids, and roaring water. Waterfalls and raging water make the lower part of the river very popular, much more so than the quiet, meandering upper reaches.

Gooseberry Falls State Park is the southernmost of the parks along Lake Superior's north shore located 13 miles northeast of the town of Two Harbors on Highway 61. The park is named after the river that runs through it, though the origin of the river's name is a matter of conjecture. The name could have come from the "Anglicization" of Groseilliers for the French explorer Sieur des Groseilliers whose name appears on maps of the area as early as 1670; the name could also come from the translation of the Ojibwe name for gooseberry, which is Shab-on-im-i-kan-i-sibi. Either way the name is appropriate, for gooseberries are prevalent all along the riverbanks. These shrubs, which grow up to three feet in height, have pale, palm-shaped green leaves and thin, woody stems covered in thorns. The round berry turns a red to wine-red color when ripe.

The park and the walks included in this section are centered on 1) moving water that includes the Gooseberry River, Lake Superior, and a small creek called Nelson's Creek, and 2) the volcanic rocks exposed throughout the park. The Gooseberry River is the parks main attraction with the various waterfalls as the focal point. However, the walks described in the following pages offer walkers the opportunity to see many other features of the active river from slumps and meanders to potholes, rapids, gravels bars, and even an estuary. Walks 1 and 3 provide spectacular views of Lake Superior and its wave-cut, rocky shoreline; walks 1 and 5 follow Nelson's Creek for part of the way with its wildflowers, Canadian carpet, and, in 2005 and 2006, a family of busy beavers.

Long before the park was established, the great white pine forest along the river was the area's main attraction. In the late 1800s and early 1900s the Nestor Logging Company built its headquarters at the mouth of the Gooseberry River. A railroad line, the Nestor Grade, allowed them to access the white pine. The railroad carried the cut trees to the lake where they were then rafted over to Wisconsin or Michigan sawmills. In fact the record log raft for the entire North Shore came out of here, six million board feet of logs towed to Baraga, Michigan. It took eight days to get them there. Imagine where they might have ended up if a Lake Superior nor'easter had blown up! So the white pine went. But not without a fight. Trying to operate a railroad in white pine country was challenging to say the least. Tracks would simply disappear in thawing swamps, locomotives and cars would get lost in the soupy muck, and rails would actually move or slide down the red clay hills when a train was loaded. Imagine that sensation–a Disney ride at its best. However, even with all the problems, these railroads were efficient, and by 1920 there was virtually no large white pine left on the North Shore.

Imagine a whole forest, hillside to hillside, covered by these magnificent white pines. Grand trees, immense, so large at the base it would take three people to reach completely around them. Up they would rise, great cloud catchers and, in the shade beneath them, would be soft green mosses, spotted ferns, and the skeletons of fallen branches. Two to three hundred-year-old trees of history that are now history themselves.

Tourism took over in the late 1920s, and in 1933 the state legislature authorized preservation of the area around Gooseberry Falls. The following year the Civilian Conservation Corps began to develop the area, and with the construction of roads as well as stone and wooden buildings (including the old visitor's center), hiking trails, a campground, and picnic site, it officially became Gooseberry Falls State Park in 1937.

There are many trails throughout the park designated for hiking and/or cross-country skiing. After hiking all of them, we ended up selecting five walks, each of which allows the walker to see different aspects of the park and its connection to volcanic fire, glacial ice, and running water.

Gooseberry Falls State Park
Walk 1: Gitchi Gummi Trail

Walk Logistics

Start and End: Gooseberry Falls State Park visitor's center

Getting There: The park entrance is just off Highway 61 about 2 miles northeast of Castle Danger. Follow the signs for visitor's center parking and then for the visitor's center. Just past the visitor's center is the junction of two paved trails, this is the starting point for walk 1.

Walk Distance: 2.0 miles   **Difficulty:** Tennis Shoes

Safety Concerns: Waypoints 10 and 11-Steep Cliffs

Worth a Longer Look: Waypoints 3, 8, 9, 10, and 11

Waypoint-to-Waypoint

One: Visitor's Center and Nature Column

The last time we stood at the junction of these two paths we could hear the river booming in the distance; in fact it seemed to shake the very ground we stood on. There had been 2.5 inches of rain the day before, and the river was letting us hear its power. This was only a prelude to seeing the real thing; a brown, angry elemental force that hurled water over the falls like I toss bedclothes off in the morning. Today the river is totally different. There has been no rain for days and thus not so much as a splash is to be heard. The birds seem to recognize and respect the river's silence, for there is not a single song filling the emptiness of the still air. At 7 am on this late August day it is already warm, and the sun looks like a Halloween pumpkin as it rises through the haze-filled sky, a haze that brings with it the faint smell of smoke from the forest fire burning north of here.

Standing just a few feet from the new visitor's center, opened in 1996, take time to examine the hundred-year-old fir timber, called the "nature column," covered by replicas of plants and animals that have been hand-cut out of recycled copper, aluminum, and brass. Each side of the column represents a different habitat in the park; overall there are some fifty animals and numerous plants to be found.

A fifth side could be added to the column and called the "mini-prairie habitat" because some of the plants around the visitor's center are more typical of prairie land than the boreal forest in Gooseberry Falls State Park. There are *brown-eyed Susans*, stiff *goldenrod*, *birdfoot trefoil*, and *tansy*;

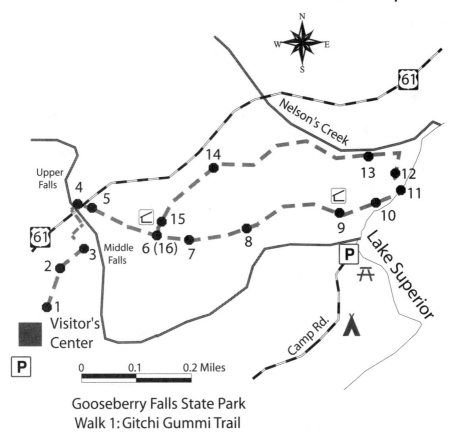

Gooseberry Falls State Park
Walk 1: Gitchi Gummi Trail

some of the trail "regulars" seen here include white and blue *asters*, *wild roses*, and *interrupted ferns*.

One plant here that is rare in the rest of the park is stiff goldenrod, which may have arrived as a component of prairie seed mix. Goldenrods are a major contributor to late summer and fall colors and, with their bright to smoky yellow blossoms, they are starting to show up more often in gardens. Also their reputation has improved. Once considered major contributors to hay fever, goldenrods are now considered minor players. They do produce a lot of pollen, but it is heavy enough that it doesn't stay airborne for a long time. Overall goldenrods are attractive plants and stiff goldenrod is especially good looking. Goldenrods are reliable perennials and, for a gardener, are quite well-behaved.

Two: Castle in the Park

At the junction, take the path to the right to the junction with the Upper Falls and Lower Falls trails, which is waypoint 2. Look uphill for a nice view of the 300-foot-long retaining wall built to look like the side of an English or Scottish castle. It was built in the 1930s by the Civilian Conservation Corps

17

to prevent soil under Highway 61 from washing away. The wall is referred to as the "castle in the park," and we would agree as we look along the top for helmeted archers and listen for the sharp notes of the trumpets that will open the gates and send the knights charging out.

The retaining wall is made out of a dark rock called *gabbro*, which came from a quarry near the town of Beaver Bay just northeast of here. Gabbro is related to the other two rock types found within the park, *diabase* and *basalt*. These three kinds of rocks all have similar mineralogy and chemistry, but the basalt is a lava flow and cooled quickly so it has small crystals and a fine grain size; its crystals are visible only with a microscope. The gabbro is a deep intrusive rock so it cooled slowly and has much larger crystals and a coarser grain size; its crystals are easily seen with the naked eye. The diabase is a shallow intrusive rock so it cooled slower than the lava flows but faster than the gabbro; the crystals are between basalt and gabbro in size and can be seen with a magnifying glass. The gabbro represents part of an old magma chamber from which the lava flows and diabase intrusions were derived.

There are some large birch trees in this area along with goldenrod. Checking out the goldenrod are what appear to be bees or wasps but they are forgeries. These creatures are actually a type of fly that passes itself off as something that stings. With a closer look it can be seen they have two wings instead of four which gives them away.

Three: Middle Falls, Natural Arch, and Cooling Joints

The paved path continues straight ahead to a set of stairs (to the right) that lead down to waypoint 3. This is at the junction between the Gateway Plaza Trail, which goes left and upstream, and the Falls Loop Trail, which goes to the right and downstream. From the viewing platform located at this waypoint there is a great view of Middle Falls, which today has widely separated ribbons and curtains of lacey white water flowing quietly over it. The water spills across and down numerous step-like ledges of dark rock before splashing into a wide pool at the bottom. From here the water glides over a flat, rocky area before toppling over the Lower Falls into another dark pool from which it emerges to begin its final, rather lazy trip through the *estuary* to the lake. This is what I call the Dr. Jekyll River. After a good rainstorm the river turns into Mr. Hyde, filling the entire width of the rocky channel. The water, honey to caramel and cake-frosting white in color, thunders over the top of the falls avalanching straight into a boiling cauldron at the bottom. Here it surges forward, dashing across the flat, rocky area, before hurling itself over the top of the Lower Falls to continue its charge down the estuary and out into the waiting lake.

The dark rocks the river flows over are basalt lava flows not unlike those that are erupting today from Kilauea in Hawaii. The lava flows exposed in the park are 1.1 billion years old and form part of what is referred to as the *North Shore Volcanic Group*. They represent part of the lava extruded from the *Mid-Continent Rift*.

The lava flows within the park (locally known as the Gooseberry Lavas) vary from 5 to 25 feet thick and have very *amygdaloidal* tops. When these flows formed, the flow tops were frothy, much like the foam that develops when warm Pepsi is poured into a glass full of ice cubes. Such tops are easily eroded, leading to the exposure of sparsely amygdaloidal flow centers which, in these particular flows, have well-developed, vertical, six-sided *cooling joints*. The river erodes away the frothy flow tops, then works its way down and along the cooling joints to form a series of widely spaced, step-like features that mark the start of a waterfall. The falls, over time, become higher and steeper as water continues to erode down and through the cooling joints.

From the viewing platform it is easy to see the step-like shape to the falls, and hexagonal cooling joints are visible to the left of the platform. On a day like today, when the water is low and quiet, one can walk across the rocks to the top of the Lower Falls. This is kind of neat because it allows the different parts of a *pahoehoe* lava flow to be seen. From the platform start out on a rock that is dotted with pinhead to dime-size white *amygdules*, the filled in gas cavities of the frothy flow top. This changes about half-way across as the number of amygdules dramatically decreases and, in their place, there are numerous fine cracks through the rock that, when traced out, form six-sided (hexagonal) shapes.

At the top of the flow the amygdules compose 15-40% of the rock and are filled by white *calcite*, cream-colored *chert*, and a grey to pinkish-colored *zeolite* mineral (laumantite). Looking from one side of the waterfall to the other, the top of the pahoehoe flow has a hummocky or billowy shape. This shape is a common feature in pahoehoe lava flows; it is directly related to the viscosity or stickiness of the lava and the fact that the top cools faster than the center parts. The significance of this is that the hot center, as it chugs along, pulls, tugs, and lifts the cooler, more sticky top into these "billowy" shapes. Pretty darn neat–after 1.1 billion years the top of a pahoehoe lava flow so well-preserved it could have been flown in from Hawaii!

In walking toward the Lower Falls the amygdules decrease in abundance and the six-sided fractures, outlining cooling joints, make an appearance. This marks the change from frothy top to more massive and slowly cooled center. There are numerous cooling joints visible, and they give the rock the appearance of a series of patio stones fitted nicely together. If the joints could be seen from the side they would extend down all the way to the flow

19

bottom as distinct six-sided columns.

There is also a small "natural arch" visible on the rocky island between the Middle and Lower falls. The arch has formed at the contact between the frothy flow top and the more massive center, and this zone of weakness in the rock is attacked by water from both sides. With time the arch will get wider and wider until the top eventually becomes unstable and collapses. The other amazing thing about this "island" is how birch and white cedar trees flourish on such a bare, rocky terrain. In fact the river gorge is lined by white cedars, and many of them appear to grow out of the solid rock. Cedars are adept at surviving by using nutrients from the meager soil caught in cracks in the bedrock as long as they have access to moisture.

In looking above Middle Falls a series of "holes" are visible in the basalt that look like cave entrances or the burrows of large animals. These are "horizontal" *potholes*, and they formed from swirling eddies or whirlpools of water which, with the help of the pebbles and cobbles caught up in them, abraded away amygdaloidal-rich areas of the basalt. The "horizontal" potholes are an indication the river once flowed at this elevation and has since cut down through the rock to its present location.

Four: Upper Falls and the CCC Camp

Follow the Gateway Plaza Trail by walking back up the stairs and along the paved pathway to a park information sign on "glacial rebound." At the sign there is a short path that leads to the edge of Middle Falls. Just past the sign walk up the stairs to the left (Gateway Plaza) and at the top turn right and walk along the paved trail to the suspended walkway beneath the highway bridge. From the bridge there is a nice view upriver of the Upper Falls and downriver over Middle Falls to the estuary and Lake Superior. The open area to the left and behind the Upper Falls is the site of the Civilian Conservation Corps camp which was located here from 1934 to 1941. The camp even had a small library named "Gooseberry University."

Waypoint 4 is at the end of the suspended walkway where there is yet another trail junction. The trail to the left goes to the old visitor's center and the start of walk 5, the Nelson's Creek Loop Walk. To continue on walk 1, follow the trail to the right.

Five: Gitchi Gummi Trail

Walk a short distance down the path to a sign for the Gitchi Gummi Trail. This is waypoint 5.

Six: Gabbro Stairway and Loop Trail

Take the wide, gravel trail and cross a small creek before coming to the junction between the Gitchi Gummi Trail and the trail that leads down to the estuary. Stay on the Gitchi Gummi Trail (to the left) and walk along a level, gravel pathway with scattered pieces of amygdaloidal basalt and a small basalt outcrop under a spruce tree. Come to a wooden and stone (gabbro and *monzonite*) stairway with beautifully made retaining walls and nice views of Lake Superior, the Gooseberry River, and the estuary. Waypoint 6 is located just past the top of the stairs at the junction with the Loop Trail.

The forest through here is dominantly spruce, paper birch, and young aspen with white pine found at the top of the gabbro stairway. In the spring there are lots of wildflowers to be seen along this stretch including *bunchberry*, *wood anemones, Canadian mayflower, blue bead lily, starflower*, and *dewberry. Asters* grow all along here at this time of the year.

Seven: Kibbles, Bits, and the Estuary

Take the branch of the Loop Trail that goes straight ahead. Along this section the trail is covered in kibbles and bits (see *diabase weathering*) as well as larger pieces of basalt lava. Kibbles and bits weathering is most common on south-facing slopes. This is due to the fact that these slopes get more sunshine in spring and late fall and thus undergo more freeze-thaw cycles (see *frost wedging*) than north-facing slopes.

There are nice views into the Gooseberry River estuary and out, over the wide expanse of the lake; also seen here are some nice red and white pine along with asters, woodland *sunflowers*, and bush *honeysuckle*, which now have fruit that look like minature elongated rose hips. Continue on to a bend in the trail and the Skeleton White Pine, which is waypoint 7.

Eight: Roses, Mouth of the Gooseberry River, and the Spotted Rock

After the Skeleton White Pine there is a nice view of a river *meander* and the estuary. From here the trail is lined with kibbles and bits before crossing over a long planked section that goes through a wet, grassy area in a birch, spruce, and pine forest with honeysuckle and, in mid-summer, wild roses along the side of the trail. The roses will be pink to white in color, and their sweet scent will fill the air making it seem like a walk through a tropical forest. After the planked section it is back on the kibbles and bits trail passing 2 cut wooden posts (right of trail) to waypoint 8, an overlook of the sand and gravel bar at the mouth of the Gooseberry River, and Agate Beach I on the opposite side of the river.

There is a nice view upriver of the inland forest, and it is easy to pick out all the dead birch trees because they stick out like skeleton fingers against the vibrant green of the rest of the forest. The *outcrop* below the overlook is amygdaloidal basalt, and here the basalt is distinctly spotted. The spots are large *pyroxene* crystals, which enclose much smaller crystals of *plagioclase feldspar*. The large pyroxene crystals are separated from each other by fine-grained areas of plagioclase feldspar with some pale green *olivine* and black *magnetite*. This gives the rock its spotted black and gray look. The larger pyroxenes are more resistant to weathering than the intervening feldspar-rich areas and so end up as "raised lumps" throughout the lava flow. It is this spotted texture that eventually leads to the kibbles and bits seen along the trail. This texture is called *ophitic*, which comes from the Greek and means "a stone spotted like a serpent." Because of this we decided to name this particular lava flow Spotted Rock. Many of the amygdule fillings have been weathered out to give Spotted Rock a rather holey look.

Nine: Tree Zoo, Agate Beach, and a Spit

The trail is relatively flat to gently downhill over kibbles and bits of Spotted Rock with some *cobble*-size-pieces, to a fenced-in area I call a *tree zoo*. The purpose of this zoo is to protect young trees from hungry deer and moose. In this zoo there are mountain maples, balsam poplar, small white pine, and paper birch. Deer and moose love the tops or terminal buds of these trees and will happily snip them off, thus making sure the tree doesn't grow any taller. Moose also love the small, supple branches of the mountain maple, which is also known as moose maple. Perhaps that's why the Ojibwe refer to moose as twig-eaters.

Continue on, keeping an eye on the pieces of rock that cover the trail. Spotted Rock disappears and is replaced by a shiny and smoother weathering basalt without spots; this Spotless Rock breaks into blocky or sharp-angled pieces. A short distance down the trail there is a small outcrop of Spotless Rock located at the top of a low rise. There are more wild rose bushes through this section which, in the summer, add color to the typical green of the *Canadian carpet*; there are also partial views of the river and lake.

From the outcrop of Spotless Rock it is a short walk to a stone shelter and waypoint 9. Just past the outcrop, Spotted Rock again covers the trail. The large, lichen-covered outcrop by the shelter is also sparsely amygdaloidal Spotted Rock. In a "Through the Looking Glass" sense we have walked from Spotted Rock to Spotless Rock and back to Spotted Rock, thus crossing what turns out to be a small *dike* or *sill* that is intrusive into the Spotted Rock.

The shelter is composed of the same beautiful red and black rocks as the old visitor's center and was one of the stone buildings erected in the 1930s by the CCC. Across the mouth of the river is what appears to be an old boat ramp made out of the same dark rock (gabbro).

There are great views of the mouth of the Gooseberry River, the blue, bustling, never-ending lake, and the green forest along its shoreline. Basalt lava outcrops along the edge of the river and estuary. Agate Beach I, a small pebble and cobble-covered beach near the mouth of the river, is directly across from us and down some 100 feet. *Agates* can be found here, especially after a "Superior" storm, but since this is a state park these cannot be collected. Much better (and legal) agates await hikers who investigate the gravel bars further up the river (see walk 2 in the Walking Guide to the Superior Hiking Trail). From the overlook a small *spit* may be visible at the end of the gravel bar where the waters of the Gooseberry River meet the waves of Lake Superior. This looks like a small version of Cape Cod, and it formed in much the same way. Sand and pebbles move along parallel to the gravel bar in longshore currents created by Lake Superior's breaking waves. The currents carry this material beyond the end of the bar and deposit them in the calmer waters of the river. The finger-like hook that bends into the river points in the direction of the movement of the sedimentary material. The spit is transitory, forming in the summer and fall then being eroded away by the fast flowing river in the spring.

Ten: Overlooks and the Sea-Like Lake

Leaving the shelter, walk only a short distance before coming to a path to the left that leads to an old outhouse–not stone but wood–a bit of a disappointment. Personally, I think a gabbro outhouse would be quite the historic landmark.

Just past the junction there is another short path to the right that leads to an overlook of the river mouth. The rock on the trail does its morphing act again, turning from spotted to spotless then back to spotted, indicating another dike or sill. There are great views all along here of Agate Beach I, the river, and Lake Superior. Waypoint 10 is at a series of stone steps that lead to an overlook at the edge of a steep cliff.

Slumping of the cliff to the right of the overlook has led to the creation of what looks like a path down to the gravel bar. The "path" is really steep and dangerous and the park service has placed a wire fence across it. The slumping is due to Lake Superior's storm waves undercutting the cliff bottom and removing support for the upper part of the cliff. Looking to the east and northeast the wave-cut cliff extends into the distance, and along it are numerous areas of active slumping. This is the land in retreat, eroding back, giving way to the constant assault of Lake Superior's waves–an assault that goes on anywhere land meets ocean, sea, or large lake. A constant, never-ending process that has only one outcome–the land always loses.

The outcrop of Spotted Rock found here contains 5-10% chert-filled amygdules that vary from pinhead to dime-size. Many have been weathered out, and it is possible these now form nice wave-washed agates that are carried onto and along Agate Beach I during a Superior storm.

The view from here gets our vote as the "wow" spot of the day. The empty vastness of the lake is stippled with so many changing patterns of light it makes the surface look like a water color painting coming slowly to life. Also neat is the mixing of the brown river water with the blue waters of the lake.

There are mountain ash trees here, and this seems to be a species that likes to live close to the lake. Two species are found in Northeastern Minnesota: the American mountain ash and the European mountain ash, which is also known as the rowan tree. The two species are difficult to tell apart. The rowan tree was planted a lot in Europe because it was believed that it protected people from witches. Birds along the North Shore plant both species willingly and indiscriminately when they eat the fruits and the seeds pass through undamaged.

Eleven: Cliff Views

It is a short walk from waypoint 10 along a level trail that follows the edge of the cliff to waypoint 11, another spectacular overlook with a view along the cliff face to the northeast and southwest. There is a steep drop of 60 feet straight to the lake below. The forest through here is dominantly birch with some mountain ash. The rock exposed here is Spotted Rock.

Twelve: Large Birch

The kibbles and bits covered trail turns away from the vastness of the lake and heads gently downhill to a planked bridge (waypoint 12) that crosses a small creek in a grassy, wet area. Marsh marigolds are abundant here in the spring. There are large birch trees through this section and Spotted Rock outcrops on the trail.

Thirteen: Nelson's Creek, Glacial Till, and Tree Zoos

Going gently up and down, the trail passes over a low ridge to a large white pine stump located at the edge of the Nelson's Creek Valley. The creek has a steep, rocky bank and has, over the years, cut down through the *glacial till* into the basaltic *bedrock* indicating it has been as busy as the Nelson Creek Beavers. There are some individual tree zoos along here to protect young white pines from deer; a couple of these also protect hemlock trees. These very slow-growing and long-lived trees were planted here, but grow naturally in Jay Cooke State Park located south of Duluth.

Continue along and above the creek, passing more white pine stumps before coming to a path that leads down to the water (waypoint 13). Flowing over reddish-colored, sparsely amygdaloidal Spotted Rock, the creek has formed a small cascade that splashes into a little pool. I imagine this would be far more impressive in the spring. To the left is an exposed bank of glacial till jam-packed with *boulders*. The boulders weather out of the till and roll down into the creek where they then have to wait patiently (geologically speaking) for a "superior event" to get them on the move.

Fourteen: Road Cut

Continue along a trail composed of glacial till with cobbles and boulders of basalt, diabase, and pink and grey *granite* and monzonite. Pass more white pine stumps and small tree zoos to a trail marker sign. After the sign we come to the start of a short uphill section where Spotted Rock becomes the dominant trail maker with lots of kibbles and bits. From the hilltop the trail is level as it follows along and above the creek to another short uphill over kibbles and bits to a small Spotted Rock outcrop and a forestry service sign. The sign points in the opposite direction to the one we just past making us unsure of whether we are actually coming or going. Turning away from Nelson's Creek, the trail comes to a large fenced area that represents the back side of the tree zoo seen at waypoint 9. There are lots of white pine through this section as well as paper birch.

From here the level trail passes several smaller fenced-in areas containing white pine to the junction with an old road that heads off to the right (waypoint 14). There are *thimbleberries* here, plants related to *raspberries* and blackberries, that have large, maple-like leaves and tasty red berries that fit over your finger like a thimble. Thimbleberries are a western species, but they occur naturally close to and along the North Shore of Lake Superior; their eastern-most location. The nearest place they occur to the west of here is in the Black Hills.

The road leads out to the Gitchi-Gami State Trail, which runs parallel to Highway 61. The highway runs between two long road cuts of massive Spotted Rock that have long vertical lines down their rock faces. These represent the traces of the drill holes that were used for the blasting of the rock. The rock outcrop has prominent spots with the pyroxene crystals particularly noticeable being shiny black on a fresh surface and grey on a weathered surface. The rock also contains small, round amygdules that are filled by green *epidote*, white *calcite*, cream-colored chert, and a pink zeolite.

At this point the bicycle trail follows the old highway, and the road we followed out to it may once have been an access road to the park.

Fifteen: Old Birch and Spoiled View

The trail continues level and either dirt-packed or kibbles and bits covered as it meanders over the tops of numerous small outcrops of Spotted Rock. The forest is dominantly spruce and birch to waypoint 15, an old, wooden shelter that once had a great view of the lake and the Gooseberry River Valley, but today offers nothing more than the backside of birch trees. The trees have grown big enough to block any view and, if this shelter is a relic of the CCC days, the trees have to be 50 or 60 years old.

Sixteen: Loop Trail and Visitor's Center

From the shelter it is a short walk back to the start of the loop trail (waypoint 6) and then on to the paved pathway back across the suspended walkway. Then it is along the upper paved trail back to the visitor's center and the end of a very nice walk.

Gooseberry Falls State Park
Walk Two: The Estuary Trail

Walk Logistics

Start and End: Gooseberry Falls State Park visitor's center

Getting There: The park entrance is just off Highway 61 about 2 miles northeast of Castle Danger. Follow the signs for visitor's center parking and then for the visitor's center. Just past the visitor's center is the junction of two paved trails; this is the starting point for walk 2.

Walk Distance: 1.0 mile   **Difficulty:** Tennis Shoes

Safety Concerns: Waypoints 9, 11, 12

Worth a Longer Look: Waypoints 3 (from walk 1), 6, 7, 8, and 12

Waypoint-to-Waypoint

Waypoints 1 through 4 are the same as for Walk 1, the Gitchi Gummi Trail Walk.

Five: Trail Junction

Walk a short distance down the path to a sign for the Gitchi Gummi Trail. This is waypoint 5.

Six: Cooling Joints and Potholes

Take the pathway to the right and just past the junction is a sign asking walkers to please keep children in hand. Walk down a wide pathway and wooden stairs to the first open view of Middle Falls (this is directly above the falls); this is waypoint 6. This overlook provides a spectacular view of Middle Falls. If the water is low enough the tops of numerous, closely spaced *cooling joints* are visible, as are the vertical joint columns at the edge of the waterfall. This rock exposure is a good example of how the waterfalls in the park form. First, the river erodes the *amygdaloidal* top of the lava flow exposing the jointed center and base. Water then works its way into the narrow fractures that outline the cooling joints and, with time and continued erosion, down along the joint column. Eventually enough rock material is removed making the column weak enough to allow gravity and rushing water to completely or partly detach it from the adjacent rocks and away it topples into the river. The periodic and partial collapse of the cooling joints leads to the ragged, step-like nature of the waterfalls. This continuous

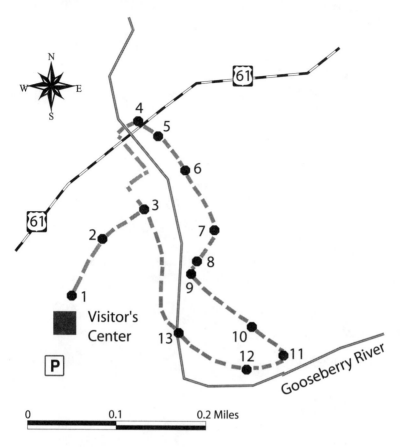

Gooseberry Falls State Park
Walk 2: The Estuary Trail

erosion of the amygdaloidal top and jointed center and base of the lava flows is what causes the falls to slowly migrate upstream.

From the overlook it can be seen how erosion along joint edges has caused the tops of the columns to become slightly raised so that they look like the backs of turtles waiting, like lemmings, to topple over the falls.

Also visible from the overlook are circular or bowl-shaped depressions in the rock; some are so round they look like an ambitious person has come along and drilled out a series of holes. The holes are called *potholes*, and humans had nothing to do with them. The river did it with the help of the sand, *pebbles*, and *cobbles* it carries.

Seven: Glacial Erratics and Slumps

Continue down the stairs and cross a bridge over a small stream before walking by a *glacial erratic* of *diabase*; there are some nice white pines through this trail section. Continue down the wooden stairs and past 2

28

wooden benchs from which there are views of the waterfalls, river, and highway bridge. After we pass the second bench we notice the steep valley side is *slumping* away into the river. As the bank goes, so go the nice red pines that are permanently rooted to it (at least until they reach the river). Come to a trail junction and stay on the wooden walkway, which continues down to yet another bench (waypoint 7). From here there is a lovely view up the river of the waterfalls and the bridge across Highway 61. From the bench it is easy to see the step-like nature of the falls. The flat area below the steps represents the amygdaloidal top of the next lava flow. The bench is surrounded by small balsam fir, cedar, and spruce.

Eight: Glacial Till and River View

Continue downhill toward the river walking under the leaning cedar tree and through a forest of cedar, birch, and spruce over a trail composed of *glacial till*, which is nicely exposed in the bank to the left. This kind of till is referred to as *ground moraine*. Come to a viewing platform (waypoint 8) and bench from which there is a good view of the river and falls. A spur trail, via wooden stairs, leads uphill from this point, and if you make the short but steep climb you will be rewarded with a great view of the Gooseberry River Valley, the estuary, Lake Superior, and the great, green forest that stretches away into the distance.

Nine: Trout, Salmon, and the Estuary

Follow the trail downhill to an iron bridge over a small branch of the Gooseberry River; the main river channel is immediately to the right. Though the tributary doesn't look like much just now, in the spring a visitor might have an entirely different opinion. There is a nice view from the bridge down into the fern, grass, and alder-filled *estuary*. From this spot it is possible to get a glimpse of a steelhead trout (in the spring) or salmon (in the fall) for they come up river from the lake, making it as far as the Lower Falls. This proves to be an unclimbable mountain, so they live and spawn in the waters of the estuary, as well as in pools below the Lower Falls.

The estuary (drowned river mouth) is the result of the changing water levels in the Lake Superior Basin. *Glacial Lake Duluth* formed about 11,000 years ago as the Laurentide Ice Sheet melted. When a new lake outlet formed at Sault Ste. Marie, water levels dropped to elevations even lower than the level of present day Lake Superior. The Gooseberry River was then able to cut down through the basaltic rocks forming a deep canyon near its mouth. As the land rebounded due to melting of the ice and thus the removal of its great weight, water levels began to rise, and some 6,000 to 7,000 years ago the mouth of the river became flooded. Continued movement of sediment from the slumping river banks has led to the infilling of most of the canyon and also to the formation of the gravel bar at the river's mouth. Today the estuary is home to a family of beavers; it is also a great feeding and nesting place for waterfowl and other birds and for animals (like otter and mink) who might prey on their eggs.

The *outcrop* under and just past the bridge is amygdaloidal basalt that contains some large gas cavities; the minerals that once filled these have been weathered out (to possibly form some nice size agates).

Waypoint 9 is just past the bridge at the start of the loop trail around the estuary. Avoid this part of the loop in the spring as the estuary may be full of river debris and large areas of slushy ice.

Ten: Beaver Guards and Log Jams

Follow the trail to the left (falls view loop) paralling the small branch of the Gooseberry River. The ash trees through here have wire guards around their trunks to protect them from the beaver's sharp teeth–not so the birch, which apparently is deemed expendable. Alder and dogwood are also common here. The trail winds through chest-high ferns and *thimbleberries* to an area where the river bank is slumping away. There is a small *meander* at this spot (waypoint 10) and, as with other active slumps along the Gooseberry River, it is along the outside bend of the meander where the slumping occurs. The bend in the meander is presently filled with logs. These were most likely snarled here at the end of the spring runoff when the velocity of the moving water started to decrease. Here the logs will remain until next year when they are swept further downstream in the rampage of the spring snowmelt. However, they will most likely be replaced by more debris as water levels and stream velocity fall in the late spring. Alder and red canary grass are common along the trail.

Eleven: Braided Streams and the Muddy Gooseberry

Leaving the meander, the trail cuts across the estuary going past a small path to the left before reaching a short, boardwalked section. At this point the estuary is filled with grass and/or sand and clay, which has had numerous channels cut into it by the fast flowing waters that move through here in the spring or after a heavy rainstorm. Enough water in these channels and the estuary would be a very wet as well as a very difficult place to walk in.

Crossing the planked section edged with alder, dogwood, and Canadian thistle, it is just a short walk around a meander bend to the main river channel where we meet the wide, muddy-looking, slow moving Gooseberry River. This is waypoint 11.

Standing here watching the water lazily slip by I realize the Gooseberry River, like most North Shore streams, has multiple personalities. I think the Goosberry has three. Upstream the river flows through and over glacial till, leading to slumps, meanders, and *oxbows*. Between Fifth Falls and the estuary it cuts through the till into the underlying *bedrock* to form waterfalls, cataracts, rapids, and roaring water. Finally the river again takes on a quiet, reflective mood as it meanders across the sand-and silt-filled estuary it has created, savoring the final moments before it becomes a small part of a great lake.

Twelve: Missing Bridge and Gravel Bars

Walk up the trail (upriver) through tall grass and *bracken ferns* with clumps of alder; there are small pools and channels all through this trail section. Waypoint 12 is at a log bridge whose purpose is to allow walkers to cross a small stream channel that cuts through the estuary. In 2005 the spring floods removed the bridge, a powerful reminder of just how fierce and fast the water in these overflow channels can be. In the fall the stream is narrow and shallow, and it is easy to cross. Numerous flat-topped, *white asters* appreciate the proximity to water.

Just beyond the bridge an old gravel bar represents a filled in meander bend and shows where the Gooseberry River flowed not so long ago. With the formation of the bar the river has migrated some 70 feet to the south. From the gravel bar there is a narrow path to the left that leads down to the brown-colored river and out onto a new and "active" gravel bar. Here sand, silt, and pebbles are being deposited on the inside bend of a meander with the sediment coming mostly from the undercutting and slumping of the glacial till that forms the river banks further upstream. This gravel bar is rather neat, for it is size-sorted. Fine-grained sand and smaller pebbles occur closer to the river, with cobbles closer to the present river bank. We find small *agates* here. With time and the growth of the gravel bar, the river will continue to migrate further to the south. This is really neat for right here the river, with its migration and building of gravel bars, is a small reminder of how active our planet can be, yet all this activity is barely perceptible to those of us who walk through and enjoy the estuary that was always here and always will be here–at least in the short-term view of the human eye. In the early spring this gravel bar may be completely underwater.

Thirteen: Beaver Drag Ways and the Iron Bridge

Leaving the growing gravel bar return to the loop trail, which continues across the old gravel bar passing a beaver drag way. This is a dirt path along which these energetic animals pull trees or large branches down to the river. From there it is an easy float back to their lodge. From the beaver expressway the trail goes through a deep alder thicket and an area where lots of *clematis* vines have gone to seed. A hop vine adds a little spice to the mix. Hops are not native to this part of the country, but right about now a Gooseberry Falls Hoppy Brew would be welcome if there was such a thing!

The vine probably arrived here via river transport, for river bars and islands are great at collecting that which is carried downstream. We once saw a good growth of tomatoes on a gravel bar on the Root River in southern Minnesota. These seeds likely passed through the human digestive system, a sewage disposal plant, and then along a few miles of river before landing and growing on the gravel bar. I guess life will find a way, sewage plants and all.

The trail is dirt-packed to an iron bridge, which is waypoint 13. The bridge spans the river, and there is a sign for the "Backwater and River Falls Loops." Cross the bridge (depending on the time of year trout or salmon might be seen swimming under the bridge), which is also waypoint 5 from walk 3, the River View and the Picnic Lava Flow Walk. From here take the trail to the right and walk upriver and uphill (passing waypoints 4 through 1 of walk 3, which includes stops below both the Lower and Middle falls) to the junction with the trail that goes back to the visitor's center.

Gooseberry Falls State Park
Walk 3: River View and the Picnic Lava Flow Trail

Walk Logistics

Start and End: Gooseberry Falls State Park visitor's center.

Getting There: The park entrance is just off Highway 61 about 2 miles northeast of Castle Danger. Follow the signs for visitor's center parking and then for the visitor's center. Just past the visitor's center is the junction of two paved trails, this is the starting point for walk 3.

Walk Distance: Just over 2 miles   **Difficulty:** Tennis Shoes

Safety Concerns: Waypoints 6, 14, 15, and 19 (road traffic). In general watch for slippery rocks along lakeshore if wet.

Worth a Longer Look: Waypoints 3 (from walk 1), 4, 6, 8, 11, 12, and 14

Waypoint-to-Waypoint

Waypoints 1 through 3 for this walk are the same as those for walk 1, the Gitchi Gummi Trail walk.

Four: Basalt Boulders and Steelhead Trout

Leaving the viewing platform (waypoint 3, walk 1) walk down the stairs past the Lower Falls to a set of steps to the left that lead out onto a rocky area where there are lots and lots of *cobbles* and *boulders* of *basalt*. Most of these come from the area between the Lower and Middle falls though some have certainly been carried over the Upper and Middle falls to reach this point. The fast moving waters of spring are powerful enough to roll or push rocks of this size along the river bottom until they reach the base of the Lower Falls. Here the velocity of the water decreases dramatically, and the basalt boulders and cobbles are stranded, finding themselves too large and heavy to be moved any further. It is possible the boulders seen here have been accumulating in this spot for many years.

A sign by the stairs provides information about the steelhead trout in the river. The trout come up the river from the lake, making it as far as the Lower Falls. The falls prove to be an unclimbable mountain, so the trout end up living and spawning in the waters of the *estuary* and the pools that form below the Lower Falls.

The forest through here is dominantly northern white cedar, birch, and

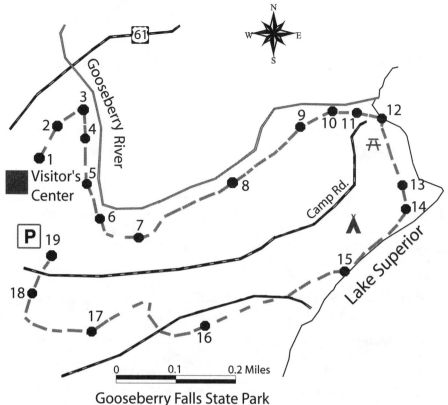

Gooseberry Falls State Park
Walk 3: River View and the Picnic Lava Flow

spruce. Trees close to the river are enclosed by wire around their base to protect them from the industrious beaver that make the estuary their home.

The early name for northern white cedar was arbor vitae which means "tree of life." Legend has it that Native Americans used a tea made from the bark and leaves of the tree to save explorer Jacques Cartier and his crew from scurvy–though some twenty sailors died before they tried it. This was at the present site of Quebec City in the winter of 1535-1536 and led to the northern white cedar being the first tree imported into Europe from North America.

Pilated woodpeckers love this tree and will excavate large, oval holes in the sides searching for carpenter ants. Porcupines eat the thin cedar stems as snack food, and deer and snowshoe hares use it for browse.

Five: Old Flood Plain and Iron Bridge

Continue to walk downriver on a wooden pathway, which now follows an old *flood plain* or terrace of the river. There are lots of stranded boulders along here, and the forest has large spruce trees with cedar, birch, and *thimbleberries*.

Waypoint 5 is at an iron bridge across the Gooseberry River. This waypoint is the same as waypoint 13 from walk 2, the Estuary Walk. Depending on the season a steelhead trout or salmon might be spotted swimming under the bridge.

Six: Sideways Bridge

Leaving the wooden walkway, the trail follows an old river bottom to a new wooden bridge over a small, marshy area (waypoint 6). When I was here last year the old bridge had been turned sideways by the high, fast waters of the spring runoff and offered yet another example of the intermittent power of the river away from the main channel. There is a virtual sea of *horsetails* to the left of the bridge with cattails and wool grass all about.

Seven: Nice Views

From the bridge it is back on the wooden walkway as we pass through an alder swamp with signs of beaver activity (old and new), and then up a long flight of stairs passing some large spruce and cedar trees before reaching the top. From here there is a nice view down the river into the estuary. Remaining well above the river the gravel trail, composed of *glacial till*, follows a large *meander* to a set of stairs to the right of the trail (waypoint 7), which lead back to the visitor's center. There is a great view from here of Middle and Lower falls, the different bridges across the river, the estuary with alders, and of course the meandering, boulder-filled river. *Large-leafed asters*, *honeysuckle*, and *horsetails* can be found along here with some mountain maple.

Eight: The Estuary and Old Birch Tree

Continue straight ahead along a trail composed of glacial till with continuing views of the river and estuary. The forest through here is composed of large birch and spruce trees with some white pine and balsam fir. Along the trail are large-leafed aster, bush honeysuckle, and woodland horsetails. In mid-summer, there will be *wild roses* aplenty.

Pass a trail to the right before coming to a bench from which there is a fantastic view of the estuary, which is filled with alder and reed canary grass. Visible from here are numerous spillover or spring flood channels that criss-cross the estuary. In the distance, upriver, the long road cut of Spotted Rock (see waypoint 14, walk 1) is visible just to the left of the Highway 61 bridge and behind the "castle in the park."

The Department of Natural Resources (DNR) stocks steelhead trout in the estuary. Steelhead, while not native to the area, became a much beloved sport fish when the lake trout population was decimated by the sea lamprey. Steelhead spawn in the streams, and the young trout spend one to three years there before coming downstream to the lake. After two or three years in the lake, they return to the streams to spawn. Steelhead populations have not done well since lake trout populations have recovered, so the DNR has explored various options for enhancing them. Thus, hatchery-raised steelhead "smolts" have sometimes been stocked in the estuary. This is usually an operation that occurs at dusk so the seagulls don't feast on the little guys. The fish transport truck sits up on the hill, and a large diameter hose delivers the young fish to the river.

There are highbush cranberries with berries along this trail section and seeing them brings about thoughts of Thanksgiving dinners to come. Highbush cranberries are not really close relatives of the ones we ordinarily eat with turkey, but the taste is similar. In years when pesticide scares depressed the sale of regular cranberries, highbush cranberries partly filled in the gap. They make wonderful jelly, and if a few greenish ones are thrown into the mix, they don't even require "Sure Jell" or other added pectin to set. However, the bushes that are productive one year may not be so the next. Bears also love these berries, and, being bears, they sometimes knock down the whole bush in the process of eating the berries.

Continue along the gently flowing river to a large, old birch tree with a wire guard around its base (waypoint 8). From its size we estimate that the tree is probably more than 100 years old.

Nine: Spotted Rock and River Terrace

After a short, planked section the dirt trail is again composed of *pebbles* and cobbles as it goes by basalt *outcrops* that form the edge of the trail to the right. The basalt is sparsely *amygdaloidal* and, in places, has distinct spots similar to those seen on walk 1. The spots are large *pyroxene* crystals that enclose much smaller crystals of *plagioclase feldspar*. The large pyroxene crystals (spots) are more resistant to weathering than the intervening feldspar-rich areas and so end up as "raised lumps" throughout the lava flow. This particular texture of the rock has been named ophitic, which comes from the Greek and means "a stone spotted like a serpent." Because of this we have come to refer to this flow simply as Spotted Rock. The trail through this area contains cobbles and pebbles weathered from the spotted rock.

The bank down to the river is steep, and along this section the trail appears to be routed near the top of an old *river terrace*. Continue along the side of the river terrace to waypoint 9, a junction with a rocky spur trail to the right that leads up to the campground road.

Ten: Kayak Campground

Continue down the trail over Spotted Rock, though the way the basalt is weathering makes it difficult to see the spots. Arrive at the junction with a path to the left that leads down to Agate Beach I and a trail straight ahead that goes through a small campground intended for kayakers and canoeists who paddle along Lake Superior's shores. The junction is waypoint 10.

Eleven: Agate Beach I

Take the path to the left down to Agate Beach I, which is a pebble beach that extends to the mouth of the Gooseberry River. There are lots of small *agates* to be found here, from ones that are *jasper* red or *chert* white to a few banded kinds–most are about the size of a dime or smaller.

The area around the beach is very scenic, and in the morning light the color contrasts are wonderful making this a definite "wow" spot. There is the greenness of the campground, the light pink color of the pebble beach, the brownness of the river, and the ominous darkness of the thirty foot basalt cliff across the river with a medieval looking rock shelter at its top. In the distance is the sparkling blueness of Lake Superior.

Take time to walk along the beach enjoying the colors, scenery, and, hopefully, nice weather. At the end of the beach, and tired of agate hunting, walk up the trail to the junction with the path that cuts through the kayak campground. This is waypoint 11.

Twelve: Spits, Beds, and Lake Stacks

Follow the trail to the left toward the lake and waypoint 12, an overlook with a rock picnic shelter and picnic tables. Numerous paths radiate away from this point with some going to the campground, others to the pump house and washrooms, and others back to the beach. The overlook provides a great lake view and today, with the strong northerly wind, white, frothy waves are pounding into the basaltic rocks along the shore and rolling part way up the gravel bar at the mouth of the river. The sound of the breaking waves together with the breath-taking gusts of wind, sends shivers down my back, and serves to remind me of the constant war between the primeval forces of water, wind, and waves versus the rocky shoreline–a war the three W's will always win.

From the overlook there is a nice view of the seasonal spit at the end of the gravel bar that marks the boundary between the river and lake. The spit is a tiny version of the one on Cape Cod, but both formed in a similar manner. Sand and pebbles are transported parallel to the gravel bar by longshore currents created by the breaking waves of Lake Superior. These currents carry the sedimentary material beyond the end of the bar and, when they meet and mix with the less dynamic river water, the sand and pebbles drop to the bottom. The finger-like hook that bends into the river mouth is a common feature of spits and points in the direction of the movement of the sand and pebbles as the longshore and river currents mix. If the longshore currents were stronger they would be able to carry the sedimentary material across the mouth of the river to build what is known as a baymouth bar like Park Point in Duluth (and Wisconsin Point in Superior). The spit is seasonal with the waves of Lake Superior building it in the summer and fall, and the river waters removing it in the spring.

As seen from the overlook, the gravel bar has distinct layers or beds of pebble-rich versus sand-rich material. The beds form from size-sorting of the pieces of rock by storm waves; larger rocks are left high and dry by the vagaries of Lake Superior. It is possible that the next big storm will completely rework the gravel bar and remove all traces of this beautifully layered dream. Immediately to the right of the shelter is a large piece of basalt that is slowly being separated from the land by the erosive power of the lake's storm waves. One day, in the not too distant future, the separation will be complete, and this isolated block will form a feature similar to those along the Oregon and Washington coastlines called "sea stacks." Even though Superior is more like an ocean than a lake, I guess we still need to call this feature a "lake stack."

Straight ahead from waypoint 12 is Agate Beach II, another nice pebble beach where agates may be found. The beach also has small pools of water on the *bedrock* that look like tide pools found along ocean shores. These Lake Superior "tide pools" are due to splash water from the lake, whereas others, farther up from the water line, are from rainwater. Perhaps the most impressive things growing here are among the smallest and most primitive. Thousands of tiny orange lichens cover the bedrock, making it look like the rocks have had a bright orange paint job. The orange rock contrasts strongly with the deep blue of the lake. The beach plant community here includes *tansy*, wild roses with prominent rose hips, and *raspberries*.

Thirteen: Mertensia, Mountain Ash, and a Fire Pit

From the overlook and old anchor take the stairs to the right, which head up toward a pretty stone picnic shelter and some nice red pines. Walk down the open, grassy slope to a triple junction with the path to the left going down to Agate Beach II and basalt outcrops, and the one to the right going to the campground. Follow the path that goes straight ahead to continue this walk.

Walk through a grassy area with lime ferns, raspberries, and a large ash tree to another trail junction. Stay on the path to the left and walk through a grove of mountain ash with birch and spruce–there is a lot of *Mertensia* through here. Come to a stone fire pit and yet another junction, this is waypoint 13.

Fourteen: Picnic Lava Flow

Take the trail to the right and walk just a short distance to a junction with a wide, gravel trail by a large birch tree; there are picnic tables here. From here follow the trail to the left which heads toward the lake and onto a long wide expanse of basalt that is called the Picnic Lava Flow. Waypoint 14 is on the flow at the stone drinking fountain. This *pahoehoe* lava flow has "flagstone-like" sections that represent the tops of *cooling joints* and numerous round *amygdules* that vary in size from pinheads to quarters. The amygdules are filled by chert and banded chert and some are very pretty having colors on a fresh surface that range from milky and pale blue through cream and reddish-white to red. There are also tabular to irregular-shaped plagioclase feldspar crystals ranging from 1.5 to 2 inches in width. They are so abundant in places they may be mistaken for bird droppings, of which there is a plentiful supply. In places the greenish lichen covering the rock makes the agates difficult to see. In looking along the length of the outcrop or across its width the hummocky or billowy nature of the flow top is prominently displayed.

There is a large, reddish-colored *glacial erratic* of basalt sitting on top of the Picnic Lava Flow, and this was left here some 11,000 or 12,000 years ago by the glacial ice as it melted off the land. Over that length of time this lone boulder has been encased in ice, has sat at the bottom of *Glacial Lake Duluth*, has been left high and dry a couple hundred feet above the lake as the waters fell, and now, for the last few thousand years, has been living right here on the beach. Eleven thousand years and, as the world changes around it, the boulder sits, a monument to the power of ice and the loneliness of geological time.

The gabbro pillars to the left of the Picnic Lava Flow mark the edge of a basalt cliff with a steep drop into the cold waters of the lake.

This long expanse of barren lava, home to *harebells* and three-toothed *cinquefoil*, would be a great spot from which to watch the lake on a stormy day–to see, feel, and appreciate the raw power and unforgiving ferocity of a body of water that is not unlike the Atlantic Ocean when it comes to storms, coldness, and an unforgiving nature. On a nice, calm warm day this is a great spot for a picnic lunch or supper.

Fifteen: Breakwater and Jack Pine

Walk along the Picnic Lava Flow parallel to the lakeshore to a steep cliff at the foot of which are huge boulders of basalt that have been broken off the cliff during storm events. There are so many of these they almost form a natural breakwater.

Continue over the Picnic Lava Flow with empty, round amygdules all through the rock. These come from the weathering out of the minerals that once filled them. Other than chert, there could have been *calcite*, laumantite (a *zeolite* mineral), and *epidote*. Pass by some large jack pine and lots of mountain ash to come to the end of the cliff where the trail bears to the right into the woods. This is waypoint 15.

Sixteen: Cart Camping

Follow the trail with mountain ash and raspberries to the camp road and then along the road a short distance to a junction of the road and a wide grassy trail to the left–there is a hiking trail sign here. Walk down the grassy trail a short distance to another junction that goes to the left heading down to a picnic area by the lake. Continue straight ahead for walk 3.

The pathway is straight as it passes through a wet, swampy area with alder, mountain maple, and balsam poplar. Pass the Birch Ridge Group camping site and come to a paved road and parking lot. Campers park their cars here and unload their camping equipment into one of the available carts, which they then wheel to a campsite. The parking area is waypoint 16.

Seventeen: Roses, Mertensia, and Asters

Continue on a wide, gravel pathway to the group picnic/camping area; wild roses, mertensia, *tall buttercups*, and asters can be found all through here with old birch trees. Follow the trail around the campsite through tall grass (which is "sedge lawn" in moister spots) with lots of Mertensia, *hawkweed*, tall buttercups, *chickweed*, and large-leafed aster. Arrive at an opening (waypoint 17) with old *tree zoos*: fenced enclosures around alder and mountain ash. There are lots of *birdfoot trefoil*, tall buttercups, daisies, and hawkweed here.

Eighteen: Kibbles and Bits and a Painters Palette

The wide pathway continues with some sections now composed of kibbles and bits. These dog food size basalt pieces come from weathering of Spotted Rock, which underlies this area. Enter a wet, grassy area with yellow buttercups, orange and yellow hawkweed, white daisies, blue Mertensia, and large-leafed asters. The yellows, whites, blues, and pinks of the flowers mixed with the green and yellowish green of the grasses, make this area look like a moving quilt of many different colors. The woods are dominantly birch and spruce with willow and alder.

After a sharp bend in the trail and a large cedar tree come to a trail junction and waypoint 18. The trail to the left leads to the park entrance road and the visitor's center parking lot, while the trail straight ahead carries on through the wet, grassy area.

Nineteen: Parking Lot

Avoid the wet, grassy trail and take the path up to the road. Use caution to cross the road because this is a busy area with lots of car and truck traffic. Once across the road enter the visitor's center parking lot, which is waypoint 19. From this point, end the walk at the parking lot or continue on back to the visitor's center.

Gooseberry Falls State Park
Walk 4: Fifth Falls Loop Trail

Walk Logistics

Start and End: Gooseberry Falls State Park visitor's center

Getting There: The park entrance is just off Highway 61 about 2 miles northeast of Castle Danger. Follow the signs for visitor's center parking and then for the visitor's center. Just past the visitor's center is the junction of two paved trails; this is the starting point for walk 4.

Walk Distance: 2.2 miles   **Difficulty:** Tennis Shoes

Safety Concerns: None

Worth a Longer Look: Waypoints 2, 7, 10, 11

Waypoint-to-Waypoint

One: Visitor's Center and Nature Column

Today, standing at the junction of these two paved paths, the river is booming in the distance; in fact it seems to shake the very ground we stand on. Over 2 inches of rain fell yesterday, and the river is advertising its power, singing a siren song urging us forward to watch and applaud as it plays the role it was designed for. The sky is a steel grey color, the same color as it has been for the past two days, a dingy undershirt grey that just doesn't want to come clean. And the greyness hangs around us like a wet towel, for it's warm and humid on this August day.

 Standing just a few feet from the new visitor's center, opened in 1996, it is worth the time to examine the hundred-year-old fir timber, called the "nature column" that is decorated with replicas of local plants and animals that have been hand-cut out of recycled copper, aluminum, and brass. Each side of the column represents a different habitat in the park. Overall some fifty animals and numerous plants can be found.

Two: Castle in the Park and the Upper Falls

Take the upper paved trail and walk past the 300-foot-long retaining wall built to look like the side of an English or Scottish castle. It was built in the 1930s by the Civilian Conservation Corps to prevent soil under Highway 61 from washing away. The wall is referred to as the "castle in the park," so we look along the top for helmeted archers and listen for the sharp notes of the trumpets that will open the gates and send the knights charging out.

41

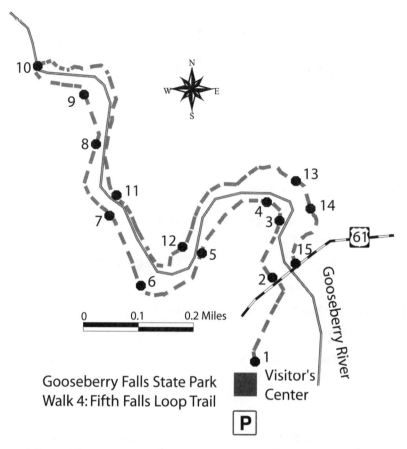

Gooseberry Falls State Park
Walk 4: Fifth Falls Loop Trail

The retaining wall is made out of a dark rock called *gabbro*, which came from a quarry near the town of Beaver Bay just northeast of here. Gabbro is related to the other two rock types found within the park, *diabase* and *basalt*. These three kinds of rocks all have similar mineralogy and chemistry, but the basalt is a lava flow and cooled quickly so it has smaller crystals and a finer grain size; its crystals visible only with a microscope. The gabbro is a deep intrusive rock so it cooled slowly and has much larger crystals and a coarser grain size; its crystals are easily seen with the naked eye. The diabase is a shallow intrusive rock so it cooled slower than a lava flow and faster than a deep intrusion like gabbro; the crystals are between basalt and gabbro in size and can be seen with a magnifying glass. The gabbro represents part of an old magma chamber from which the lava flows and diabase intrusions were derived.

Waypoint 2 is on the left side of the suspended walkway located beneath the Highway 61 bridge. The Upper Falls are truly impressive today. The river is in a state of roaring fury as it sends brown-colored water over the Falls. Forming sheets, fingers, sprays, and frothy mists, the water plunges to the bottom like water from an opened fire hydrant. At the base of the falls a mass of brown churning fury heads down the gorge in a mad rush to repeat this performance at Middle Falls.

Even with all the water and misty spray, the step-like nature of the falls can still be seen. The steps are a testament to both the power of the river and the nature of the Gooseberry Lava Flows. These flows have *amygdaloidal* tops; in fact, when they formed the tops were so gas rich they were frothy, much like the foam that develops when warm Pepsi is poured into a glass full of ice cubes. Such tops are easily eroded, leading to the exposure of sparsely amygdaloidal flow centers which, in these particular flows, have well-developed, vertical, six-sided *cooling joints*. The river erodes away the frothy flow tops, then works its way down and along the cooling joints to form a series of widely spaced, step-like features that mark the start of a waterfall. The falls, over time, become higher and steeper as water continues to erode down and through the cooling joints. The flat area where the Upper Falls begins represents an amygdaloidal flow top that has been completely eroded away.

The rock outcrop just to the right of waypoint 2 is tan-colored, amygdaloidal basalt with the amygdules largely weathered out, giving the rock a pitted look.

Three: Cedar Grove and Basalt

Take the dirt road to the left of waypoint 2. Starting off slightly uphill the road goes by a ledge of basalt and around a *tree zoo* before coming to a set of stone steps that lead down toward the river. Walk down the steps and along a dirt trail to a pair of stone pillars constructed of gabbro. The pillars mark an overlook above the Upper Falls (nice view from here down the river) and were once part of a stone bench, one most likely constructed in the 1930s when the stone buildings and retaining wall were built by the CCC. The reddish-colored rock exposed here is amygdaloidal basalt.

From the bench follow a wide trail that passes by a cement "manhole," before coming to waypoint 3, a small sand and gravel beach located beside a set of small rapids. A solid wall of basalt across the river provides an example of how the water is undercutting the more easily eroded amygdaloidal top of a lava flow. The flow contact is well exposed with the more granular-looking and holey amygdaloidal top overlain by the base of a much more massive-looking, reddish-colored lava flow. The forest here is a mix of birch, spruce, cedar, ash, and balsam fir with some poplar.

Four: Slumps, Meanders, and Polished Rocks

Continue upstream, passing a small waterfall and rapids where the river flows over water-worn and polished basalt. Visible across the river is an extensive area of *slumping*. The hillside is composed of *glacial till,* which here consists of reddish-colored clay and silt with *pebbles* and *cobbles*. The red color comes from the sedimentary rocks that filled in the Lake Superior Basin when volcanism came to an end 1.1 billion years ago (see *Mid-Continent Rift*). The sediments were red bed deposits, and the glacial ice found them much to its liking, for it not only scooped them out of the basin like kids scoop ice cream out of a bucket but, in doing so, pulverized them. The final result was red silt and clay-size particles distributed throughout the glacial till.

The river is actively undercutting the side of the valley along the outside bend of a large *meander*. This causes the river bank to lose support and slump or slide away. This, in turn, removes support for the material above the slump, meaning this stuff will soon slump away as well. This leads to more instability upslope which, in turn, leads to another slump, and on it goes as long as the meander is active and growing.

The small beach at waypoint 3 is located on the inside bend of the same large meander; the sand and pebbles derived from the slumping banks are deposited there as water velocity decreases–the finer red clay and silt continue downstream.

A power line crosses the river at waypoint 4. Another small "beach" as well as an outcrop of sparsely amygdaloidal basalt mark this spot. Small, weathered, feldspar crystals in the basalt stand out as grey-looking "spots" giving the rock a speckled appearance.

Five: Bouldery Till and River Terrace

It is a short walk upriver to a small, sandy beach and nice exposures of *boulder*-rich till that form the riverbanks. This is directly across from a ledge of massive looking basalt. Numerous boulders and cobbles in the river have come from the erosion of the till banks. The river erodes the banks, washing the red-colored silt and clay away. As this happens the boulders and cobbles in the till become less and less secure until, one fine day, they fall, roll, or tumble into the water. The smaller rocks are then moved slowly downstream, but the larger ones remain pretty much where they come to rest. A large flood of high velocity water might move them a short distance, and this is how the boulder pile seen here most likely formed. The composition of the boulders varies from basalt and diabase to pink and gray *granite* and *monzonite*.

From the beach continue along the river, passing through a forest of spruce, alders, and ash; *wild roses* (rose hips are now fat and red), and *columbine* occur along the trail. Waypoint 5 is at a bridge across the river and a trail junction. The trail to the left leads back to the visitor's center, the one to the right leads across the bridge and joins the Superior Hiking Trail, while the Fifth Falls Loop Trail continues straight ahead. The view upstream from the

44

bridge is of a small meander that has formed by the undercutting of the basalt rock. The area from waypoint 4 to 5 is relatively flat and represents an old *flood plain* or *river terrace*.

Six: Basalt Steps and White Pines

The trail narrows and heads uphill over glacial till that is composed dominantly of silt and clay-size material. Some of the *goldenrods* have galls, round swellings on the stalks, which are bigger than a marble but smaller than a ping pong ball. They contain an insect larva. The larvae have been used as bait by ice anglers. It's easier to buy bait, but maybe the fish really like these "gall" darn insects!

The trail proceeds along the power line, uphill, through bush *honeysuckles* and *thimbleberries*, to a set of basalt steps that lead to a junction with a wide, grassy trail to the left that winds back to waypoint 5. The Fifth Falls Loop Trail, composed of bouldery till, continues to the right. Pass by some nice white pines that are scattered through a cedar, birch, spruce forest to another trail junction with the Fifth Falls Loop Trail going to the right along the river. This is waypoint 6.

Seven: Chert Amygdules, Cooling Joints, and the Inside of a Glacier

Walk downhill to the river over boulders of basalt—one boulder has nice, prominent *amygdules* while another has round amygdules filled by chert. The forest is dominantly spruce and cedar, and there are woodland *horsetails* and *bunchberries* along the trail. Continue along the river with a basalt ledge and wall exposed on the opposite side. Cross a small creek (spring overflow channel) and take some time here (at a large white pine) to observe the riverbanks. They are composed of boulder-rich till, and it is interesting to see just how much rock material the till actually contains. Imagine a sheet of ice over a mile thick, stretching from Gooseberry Falls State Park all the way to Hudson's Bay. From the bottom to the top the ice sheet contains pebbles, cobbles, and boulders. With so much rock inside the ice, it is no wonder glaciers are able to abrade, gouge, scratch, and dig up the landscape and, in so doing, create a brand new world.

Along this part of the trail the river is noticeably nosier as it flows over and around the boulders. This noisy aspect of the Gooseberry River is just one of its three personalities. Upstream, above Fifth Falls, the river is quiet, flowing through and over glacial till, leading to slumps, meanders, and *oxbows*. Between Fifth Falls and the estuary it is much noisier and more boisterous as it cuts through the till into the underlying bedrock to form waterfalls, cataracts, rapids, and roaring water. Finally, the river again takes on a quiet, reflective mood as it meanders across the sand and silt-filled estuary, savoring the final moments before it becomes a small part of a great lake.

45

Continue up the trail to a large open area of basaltic rock (waypoint 7); there is a small waterfall and rapids here along with a small pool with cattails in it. Cooling joints are exposed on the vertical rock face of a small ledge just off the trail (to the right). Below the ledge the basalt is sparsely amygdaloidal with many of the amygdules weathered out; however, near the river there are some nice chert-filled amygdules. Above the ledge is the top of the lava flow, and this contains numerous pinhead-size amygdules, many of which are weathered out, giving the rock a pockmarked or frothy look. The exposed top of the flow has a billowy appearance, and this is typical of pahoehoe lava flows

Eight: Old Bar

Continue the river walk over a well-packed trail with a short bouldery section and one really wet, muddy spot. Along this trail section there are *sarsaparilla*, bush honeysuckle, large-leafed *aster*, and reindeer moss.

Waypoint 8 is at a small "island" of cobbles and boulders that is now grassed over: once upon a time this was a gravel bar in the river.

Nine: Horizontal Potholes, Boulder Bar, and Overlook

Muddy sections that mark the location of small seeps leave our boots caked with mud as the trail continues upriver, passing a "wall" of basalt on the opposite side. The basalt contains small, cave-like holes, which are called horizontal *potholes*. These were formed from eddies and whirlpools in the stream when the water flowed at this level. The eddies and whirlpools spun pebbles and cobbles around and around, turning them into efficient drills that cut their way into the side of the amygdaloidal-rich flow top.

On either side of the river there are boulder bars formed during times of high, fast water; the boulders were stranded here as velocity dropped when the river flowed around this meander bend. The large boulders to the left of the trail represent material frost-wedged off basalt outcrops exposed further up the hill. The boulders then rolled or bounced down to their present position.

Just past the bar and a basalt outcrop to the left is a gravel beach and a trail junction (waypoint 9). The path straight ahead goes to a rocky overlook above a small falls and rapids with lots of horizontal potholes; the left branch heads uphill over basalt boulders and is the continuation of the Fifth Falls Loop Trail.

Ten: Fifth Falls and an Unconformity

The trail heads uphill again staying above the river, with the load roar of Fifth Falls ahead. The trail climbs over boulders and small outcrops of sparsely amygdaloidal basalt through a forest dominated by cedar, spruce, and birch. Passing a trail shelter, with blueberries nearby, continue uphill above the river as it flows rapidly and noisily over a small waterfall. Numerous "holes" visible in the side of the lava were formed by erosion as the fast moving water carried pebbles and sand-size material downstream.

Come to a junction between the Fifth Falls Loop Trail (which now follows the Superior Hiking Trail east across the bridge) and the branch of the Superior Hiking Trail that goes west to Wolf's Rock and the Nestor Grade.

Standing in the center of the bridge (waypoint 10), look upstream to see a nice meander. Also visible is a well-exposed contact between glacial till and a reddish basalt lava flow. The contact looks knife-sharp, making it even harder to imagine that this thin line represents over a billion years of geological time! The lava flow is part of the *North Shore Volcanic Group* and is 1.1 billion years old, whereas the glacial till may be all of 10,000 years old. Here the till rests unconformably (see *unconformity*) on the glacially abraded and scoured lava flow.

Fifth Falls is on the downstream side of the bridge and is due, not to glaciers, but to the nature of the lava flows themselves (see waypoint 2 of this walk and waypoint 3, walk 1). There is also a nice view of the balsam, spruce, and cedar trees lining the river bank and hillside.

At the edge of the bridge (east side) there is a path leading upriver to a large exposure of basalt; this is across from the unconformity seen from the bridge. The baslt is amygdaloidal with most of the amygdules empty (weathered out); a few are filled by chert. *Vesicle cylinders* are common near the top of the flow (close to the trees), and the outcrop has lots of well rounded potholes. These are small to large, circular or bowl-shaped holes (up to 3 feet deep). Some are such perfect circles they look like some ambitious person drilled them. Humans, however, had nothing to do with these; the river did it with the help of the sand, pebbles, and cobbles it carries. If you stay on this path it dead ends at a small gravel beach.

Eleven: Potholes

After crossing the bridge over the Gooseberry River take the trail to the right, which goes gently downhill following the river, at times along its side and then climbing above it. Looking back up the river there are several nice views from the trail of lava flows and Fifth Falls. Pass by some nice, large cedars just before reaching Waypoint 11. This is an outcrop of basalt at the waters edge that contains more potholes

Twelve: Signs and Bridges

Continue down the river passing a nice set of rapids, some large white pines, and a small sand and gravel beach before arriving at a trail junction between the Superior Hiking Trail, the 5th Falls Trail, and the trail used for walk 5 (waypoint 12). At this junction a snowmobile bridge crosses the river, and the Fifth Falls Loop Trail continues straight ahead following the river.

Thirteen: River Views and Mertensia

From waypoint 12 the trail descends with the river, which is wider here and full of boulders. There are nice views upriver of tree-lined banks and rocky water; the trail has lots of boardwalked sections. The trail passes above a meander and slump (waypoint 4) before turning away from the river, crossing two small creeks and a not very attractive power line though the mertensia, seen from the bridge over the second small creek, is beautiful (waypoint 13).

Fourteen: Trail Junction

Waypoint 14 is a short distance past 13 and marks a trail junction. The Superior Hiking Trail heads away from the river and towards the old visitor center as it continues on to the Split Rock River Wayside. The Fifth Falls Loop Trail passes by the cut stump as it goes along the river and on toward the lake. There is lots of balsam poplar in this area, a typical tree that is found in wet soils.

Fifteen: Paved Path and Old Visitor's Center

Continue downtream passing cement "manhole" 2 to an overlook above Upper Falls. Here the trail turns to the left and joins a paved trail at the opposite end of the suspended walkway from waypoint 2. This is waypoint 15. About 50 feet from this waypoint is the old park visitor's center. The old visitor's center has cedar shakes on its roof and beautiful red and black rocks for the walls–black gabbro from a quarry near Beaver Bay and red granite from a quarry on Kenwood Avenue in Duluth near the College of St. Scholastica. The red sand and clay for the mortar came from Flood Bay, near Two Harbors.

From waypoint 15 the paved trail leads across the suspended walkway, past the "castle in the park," and back to the new visitor's center where the walk began.

Gooseberry Falls State Park
Walk 5: Nelson's Creek Loop Trail

Walk Logistics

Start and End: Gooseberry Falls State Park visitor's center

Getting There: The park entrance is just off Highway 61 about 2 miles northeast of Castle Danger. Follow the signs for visitor's center parking and then for the visitor's center. Just past the visitor's center is the junction of two paved trails; this is the starting point for walk 5.

Walk Distance: 3.25 miles   **Difficulty:** Walking Shoes

Safety Concerns: Trails are grassy, and in the spring and after a heavy rain they can be wet and somewhat muddy.

Worth a Longer Look: Waypoints 2 (from walk 4), 5, 9, 10, 12, 13

Waypoints 1 and 2 are the same as for Walk 4, the Fifth Falls Loop Walk

Waypoint-to-Waypoint

Three: Old Visitor's Center and the Superior Hiking Trail

Cross the river on the suspended walkway and take the paved path to the left that leads to the old visitor's center. This building is eye catching with cedar shakes on the roof and walls constructed of beautiful red and black rock– black *gabbro* from a quarry near Beaver Bay and red *granite* from a quarry on Kenwood Avenue in Duluth near the College of St. Scholastica. The red sand and clay for the mortar came from Flood Bay, near Two Harbors. A portion of the building has reindeer moss growing on the roof.

Four: Spring Flowers

Just past the old visitor's center is a signpost for the Superior Hiking Trail and a trail junction. Take the branch of the Superior Hiking Trail that goes toward the Split Rock River wayside (straight ahead). The other branch leads to the Fifth Falls Loop Walk.

From the old visitor's center the walking path heads gently uphill following a wide, grassy ski trail that passes under a power line before skirting the edge of a large rocky hill. The hill is composed of *basalt* lava flows that are locally referred to as the Gooseberry Lavas, the same rocks that form the many waterfalls in this park. These 1.1 billion-year old lavas are part of the *North Shore Volcanic Group* that was erupted from the *Mid-Continent Rift*. These rocks form the prominent road cut just east of the bridge on Highway

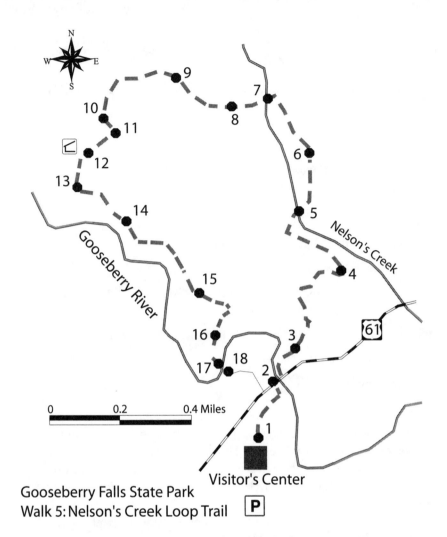

Gooseberry Falls State Park
Walk 5: Nelson's Creek Loop Trail [P]

61.

The forest is dominated by paper birch, many of which are dead or dying.
This appears to be the norm for paper birch trees in northeastern Minnesota.
Through this section the trail, in the spring and early summer, is lined with
horsetails, *wood anemones*, *dewberries*, *trilliums*, *Mertensia*, and *Canadian
mayflowers* as well as what could be Minnesota's state flower–dandelions.

Waypoint 4 is about 0.25 miles from the old visitor's center at a trail
junction where the Nelson's Creek Loop goes to the left and the Superior
Hiking Trail continues straight ahead.

Five: Wildflowers Galore and Nelson's Creek

The trail is wide, grassy, and mostly dry with a couple of short muddy spots
as it follows the edge of Nelson's Creek, which appears as a low, swampy
area to the right. The trail is more for skiing than walking, and it does seem

to be a truism that wherever hiking trails follow cross-country ski-trails there is always a certain amount of mud, wetness, and swamp. Enough snow, however, and this trail would be great.

Waypoint 5 is at a wide bridge across Nelson's Creek. The trail all along this section has a large variety of wildflowers, and their many colors remind me of an impressionist painting, one where the colors all blend together providing a serene and kind of "wow" experience. There are yellow and orange *hawkweed, ox-eye daisies, tall buttercups, chickweed, purple vetch, corydalis, thimbleberries,* and *honeysuckle* to provide the major "colors" for the visual feast. There are also bracken and interrupted ferns and *bunchberries* growing on a big, old stump. Bunchberries like the soil that forms on these decaying stumps. In the spring look for *blue bead lily* and Canadian mayflower.

The forest through here is dominantly spruce, aspen, and birch. Along the creek, in the spring and early summer, there may be *marsh marigolds, blue flag iris, wood anemone, coltsfoot, yellow* and *purple violets,* and, later in the summer, *ostrich ferns*; today there are flat-topped *white asters* and *goldenrod.*

Six: More Wildflowers

The trail heads uphill from the bridge followed by a short, dry section with more wildflowers providing the backdrop to the steel grey sky above and green woods beyond. There are *wild rose* bushes, *strawberries,* and *bracken ferns* along this section in addition to the same kinds of wildflowers seen from waypoint 4 to 5. A ruffed grouse flies across the trail in front of us. This must have startled a deer, for we catch sight of a white tail as it bounds away. Waypoint 6 is at a trail junction. The Nelson's Creek Loop Trail continues to the left.

Seven: Nelson's Creek and the Color Continues

Continue to follow Nelson's Creek (now on the left) on a wide, grassy, dry trail with the sea of wild-flowers continuing. The variety is similar to that on the other side of the creek, but the forest changes gradually from cedar to aspen and poplar to spruce and birch with some cedar. The Nelson Creek beaver have been busy as there are numerous gnawed and half-gnawed trees through this section. Waypoint 7 is at the second crossing of Nelson's Creek. In the spring there are lots of marsh marigolds along with *springbeauties.*

Eight: Kibbles and Bits

From Nelson's Creek it is uphill over a trail composed of red clay with *pebbles* and *cobbles* (*glacial till*). The bright colors of the ox-eye daisies, white daisies, yellow buttercups, and yellow and orange hawkweed appear as small, brightly colored jewels amongst the green of the grass, clover, and bracken ferns. There is also some *pearly everlasting*, bush honeysuckle, and dogwood. In the summer the rose bushes along here are full of fragrant pink and white flowers.

Continuing uphill the wide trail has some wet, muddy sections as it changes from glacial till to kibbles and bits (see *diabase weathering*) of Spotted Rock. This lava flow is also seen on walks 1 and 3. The spots are large *pyroxene* crystals that enclose much smaller crystals of *plagioclase feldspar*. This spotted texture, which eventually leads to the kibbles and bits we see along the trail, is called *ophitic*, which means "a stone spotted like a serpent" in Greek. Because of this we decide to name this particular lava flow Spotted Rock.

Waypoint 8 is at a small outcrop of Spotted Rock with kibbles and bits. There are two large spruce trees here, one on either side of the trail, and the forest is dominantly spruce.

Nine: Aa Lava Flow

After crossing an old logging road the trail goes gently uphill to an outcrop of massive basalt with kibbles and bits. The basalt has veins and fracture fillings of the red mineral *hematite*; this is the same mineral mined for iron ore on the Mesabi Range.

Continue uphill over outcrops of basalt with kibbles and bits to an outcrop at a hillcrest of *amygdaloidal* basalt (waypoint 9). Amygdules compose 15-35% of the rock, are filled by *quartz, calcite,* and/or a cream-colored *zeolite* (laumantite), and are dominantly angular to contorted in shape. This shape is suggestive of a kind of basalt lava flow called *aa*. The basalt has a red matrix (due to the presence of hematite) and contains small plagioclase feldspar crystals.

The kibbles and bits that occur here are found on a south-facing slope, and this is pretty much true wherever we see this particular feature. The reason is that southerly slopes get more sunshine and are warmer in the spring and late fall and therefore go through many more freeze-thaw cycles, which promotes increased *frost wedging* and weathering.

The forest is mixed younger spruce and birch with many of the birch trees dead or dying. Bracken ferns, large-leafed asters, bush honeysuckle, and sarsaparilla carpet the ground. There is some reindeer moss as well.

Ten: Vesicle Cylinders, Pahoehoe Lava, and More Wildflowers

Continue gently uphill over basalt outcrops and more kibbles and bits with the trail covered by thin, reed-like grass that is dotted with hawkweed, daisies, buttercups, purple vetch, and honeysuckle.

Pass a trail to the left and continue on the pleasant walk through the sea of wildflowers. Watch for blueberry bushes through here. To add to the pleasantness there are views to the right (northwest) of the rolling landscape and nice forest. The trail is now crossing solid basalt that is similar to the basalt found at waypoint 9.

Waypoint 10 is at a sharp bend in the trail (old pine stump here) and a large, open area with more basalt and wildflowers. Here, however, the amygdules in the basalt are small, round, and occur in distinct circular or irregular areas to form what are called *vesicle cylinders*. These are hard to see on the weathered surface and are best observed on broken samples under the tree stump or on a clean, fresh surface. The presence of vesicle cylinders and round amygdules, as opposed to the angular and irregular ones of the previous outcrop, suggests this is a *pahoehoe* lava flow.

Eleven: Stop Sign and Four-Way Intersection

The grassy trail with hawkweed continues through a cutover area of small aspen and balsam poplar trees with some red maple and spruce. Waypoint 11 is at a four-way junction with a stop sign. We assume this sign is for skiers or moose, for I doubt hikers walk that fast. The Nelson's Creek Loop Walk follows the trail straight ahead thus avoiding the ephemeral pond to the right of us.

Twelve: Basal Till and Shelter

The trail from the four-way junction is wide, wet, and grassy with a slight rise that goes up and over a section of basal till to a large outcrop of amygdaloidal basalt with a cushion of moss and reindeer moss.

Reindeer moss is a light gray to greenish-gray branched lichen, a favorite food of (you guessed it) reindeer. In Minnesota, their relatives, the woodland caribou, once grazed on reindeer moss. They are now gone, although there have been a couple of unconfirmed sightings in northeastern Minnesota, and the possibility of reintroducing them has been studied. For now, the reindeer moss need not worry. Lichens are a co-operative arrangement between a fungus and an algae in which the algae furnishes sugar via photosynthesis, and the fungus furnishes mineral nutrients. This is an amazing example of the degree to which organisms can evolve to take advantage of opportunities. This is not an arrangement between relatives. Fungi and algae are not closely related–they are not even in the same kingdom in modern classification. In a way, lichens are almost as preposterous as a Jolly Green Giant.

The basal till is boulder-rich (grey granite, pink monzonite, and dark basalt poke up through the grassy trail); it is called "basal" because it was the first till deposited on top of the *bedrock*. The short distance from the basal till to the rock exposure represents over one billion years of geological time and is thus a major *unconformity*. The pahoehoe lava that cooled and hardened to form this rock is 1.1 billion years old, whereas the glacial ice melted away leaving behind this deposit of basal till some 10,000 to 11,000 years ago. A billion years of dynamic, complex, and active earth history, and all that is here to show for it is a few inches of dirt. Even the worms that live in this thin soil don't have a history that goes back half that distance, though the lichens do!

The basalt outcrop is amygdaloidal with the round amygdules varying from pinhead to quarter-size and filled by quartz, calcite, and a cream to white zeolite (laumantite). Many of the amygdules are weathered out.

After the outcrop there is a short uphill walk over amygdaloidal basalt to a three-sided, wooden shelter (with an empty bird's nest and, hopefully empty, a wasp's nest) at yet another trail junction. This is waypoint 12.

Thirteen: Old River Channel

Take the trail to the right and walk downhill through spruce, quaking aspens, and balsam poplars with nice views to the west and northwest over the Gooseberry River Valley. The trail starts out on a basalt outcrop before giving way to basal till and becoming grass-covered. An anthill here serves as a reminder that all life activity is not happening at the surface of the ground. Big anthills, besides being home to lots of ants, loosen the soil below the frost line. Snakes sometimes take advantage of this for hibernation sites.

Come to another trail junction (lots of strawberries here) and take the trail to the left, which goes downhill.

Walk down the wide, grass-covered trail over angular cobbles and boulders from the glacial till, to an area under a large spruce tree with pebbles and cobbles that represent a variety of rock types, but are mainly composed of amygdaloidal and massive basalt. The pebbles and cobbles are round to sub-round and moderately well-sorted. These features suggest the rocks have been reworked by running water. The rock pieces were washed out of the glacial till, then rounded and sorted by the Gooseberry River, then deposited here as part of a river channel or gravel beach. Today we are some 50 feet above the Gooseberry River, which means that at one time in the distant past the Gooseberry flowed over this spot. It is interesting to speculate on the length of time it took the river to erode and cut its way through the glacial till from here down to its present position. At an inch per year it would be 600 years! So about the time Columbus set foot in the Americas, the Gooseberry River might have been right where we now stand.

From the "old river deposits" walk by an outcrop of sparsely amygdaloidal basalt and onto a long outcrop of amygdaloidal basalt with a rocky hillside to the left (waypoint 13). The boulders of basalt found along the trail have been derived from the hillside by frost wedging. The round amygdules in this lichen-covered outcrop are composed of chert, calcite, or a cream-colored zeolite; lots of kibbles and bits here.

Fourteen: Pearly Everlasting

The trail continues downhill passing a spur trail to the right. Stay to the left and from this junction it is a short walk over a flat, dry trail along the edge of the Gooseberry River Valley to another junction and waypoint 14. The Nelson's Creek Loop Trail goes to the right, whereas the trail to the left takes you back to the shelter at waypoint 12. The forest through this section is dominated by birch. There are pearly everlasting flowers that, true to their name, still look like credible flowers weeks after they have made seeds. These plants make their way into many dried flower arrangements.

Fifteen: Trail Junctions

From the junction the trail is wide and grassy as it passes through an old cutover area. Pass by the junction with a spur trail to the right that leads down to the Superior Hiking Trail. Continue to the left along a grassy trail going by a stand of cedar trees and over a small creek to another junction with a ski trail that goes to the left. Keep on the trail to the right and walk down a wide, grassy path lined with the same kinds of wildflowers that have been so abundant all walk long. The forest through here is spruce, balsam poplar, aspen, and birch. Arrive at yet another trail junction (waypoint 15) with the Nelson's Creek Loop Trail continuing to the right.

Sixteen: Swamp Monsters, Ducks, Large Trees

Walk down the grassy trail, crossing a small seep through nice birch woods to an overlook of a green scummy pond surrounded by tall grass. This is the sort of pond that breeds mutant frogs or out of which will rise a large, grotesque creature covered in slime. I was into these thoughts when a couple of ducks decided to take off from the pond at the same time a grouse flew up just to our right. Gothic thoughts, the slate-colored sky, and unexpected noises combined to scare the heck out of me–I spent the rest of the walk looking back over my shoulder.

With my thoughts scattered on the trail like bits of broken glass, we continued past the pond to waypoint 16, which is in a lovely stand of large spruce, white pine, and balsam poplar trees. Quite the contrast to the "black lagoon." There is a junction here with the trail that goes upriver to Fifth Falls.

Seventeen: Bridge

Take the wide, gravel trail to the left, downriver, through quaking aspen and balsam poplar trees with bracken ferns underneath. It is just a short distance to a bridge across the Gooseberry River and the junction with the Superior Hiking Trail and the Fifth Falls Loop Trail (waypoint 17).

Eighteen: Slump and Walks End

Cross the bridge and, in doing so, take time to look downstream. A small *meander* can be seen, and along its outside bend the valley side and the trees growing on it are *slumping* into the river. Upstream there is another meander bend and a long exposure of a basalt lava flow.

After the bridge, come to the junction with the Fifth Falls Loop Trail, which is waypoint 18 of this walk and waypoint 5 of walk 4. Follow the wide, grassy/gravel trail straight ahead to a service road. From here turn left and follow the road back to the paved path at the suspended walkway beneath the Highway 61 bridge. At this point take the paved trail back to the visitor's center.

Split Rock Lighthouse State Park

Introduction

History and geology are the main points of interest at Split Rock Lighthouse State Park. Historically the most important and visually prominent feature of the park is the lighthouse sitting on top of a rocky promontory overlooking Lake Superior. Corundum Point, located about a mile southwest of the lighthouse, was the site of a failed mining venture in the early 1900s, and there was a small settlement and logging campsite at the mouth of the Split Rock River from 1899 to 1906. This "village" had a wharf and coal dock, a general store and post office, and was the terminus of the Split Rock and Northern Railway. The Merrill Railroad Grade heads inland from the river and marks the location of a short line railroad that provided access to the red and white pine located far from the lakeshore. Finally, there was commercial fishing for herring, whitefish, and lake trout from the "Norwegian" fishing village located at Little Two Harbors and Ellington Island (about 0.5 miles south of the lighthouse) from 1900 to 1920.

Geologically the park features an unusual kind of rock called anorthosite, which forms the high promontory the lighthouse is built on, as well as Day Hill and Corundum Point. The spectacular rocky gorge of the Split Rock River is geology in progress as the river continues to cut down through the pink rhyolite lava flow that forms the waterfalls, rapids, cliffs, and tall towers enjoyed by so many people over the years. Finally, there is the constant presence of Lake Superior and its dark, wave-cut shoreline that runs the length of the park.

Split Rock Lighthouse State Park is located just off Highway 61 some 20 miles northeast of Two Harbors and 7 miles northeast of Gooseberry Falls State Park. It is named for the way the pink volcanic rock that forms the river gorge "splits" into shingle-like pieces. This name appears on a lake survey map as early as 1825; since then a river, creek, and a rocky promontory within the park have also been given this name.

The lighthouse, which is the park's main attraction, was built after a November gale on Lake Superior sank seven ships within twelve miles of Split Rock Point. The construction of the lighthouse was quite the engineering feat with all materials and supplies delivered by boat and then transported from the lakeshore to the top of the anorthosite promontory. It was not until 1924 that the first road, the Lake Superior International Highway, was extended past Split Rock and the first visitors arrived by car.

The lighthouse operated from 1910 until 1969, and in 1971 the site was turned into a state park. In 1976 the Minnesota Historical Society took over administration of the station site with the visitor center opening in 1986. The rest of the park, including campsites and trails, is operated and maintained by the Department of Natural Resources.

The walks described in this section of the book all begin near trail center and either end back at the trail center or at the Split Rock River wayside. There are three separate walks, though hikers may do all or part of any one walk or, because of the way the park and trails are laid out, combine parts of walks 1 and 2. Two of the included walks incorporate sections of the Superior Hiking Trail.

The walks are devised to allow different aspects of the park's geology and history to be seen.. The geological aspects reflect more than 1.1 billion years of geological time and were created by the combined effects of volcanic fire, glacial ice, and running water.

Split Rock Lighthouse State Park

Walk 1: Little Two Harbors and the Corundum Mine Trail

Walk Logistics

Start: Trail Center at Split Rock Lighthouse State Park

End: Either Trail Center at Split Rock Lighthouse State Park or the Split Rock River wayside

Getting There: The park entrance is just off Highway 61 about 2 miles northeast of the Split Rock River wayside. Follow the paved road from the entrance towards the parking lot for the lighthouse. After passing the park information and camping registration center, turn right onto the paved road that leads to parking for the campsites and trail center. Park in the trail center parking lot. A current state park sticker is required.

End: Either the trail center parking lot (for a loop walk) or the Split Rock River wayside. The wayside is 2 miles southwest of the Split Rock Lighthouse State Park entrance on the north side of Highway 61. If coming from Two Harbors the wayside is 5 miles northeast of the entrance to Gooseberry Falls State Park, on the left just before crossing the Split Rock River.

Walk Distance: 3 miles from waypoint 1 to the Split Rock River wayside; 5.2 miles return to Trail Center.

Difficulty: Walking Shoes

Safety Concerns: Waypoint 11-steep stairs. When on the Gitchi-Gami State Trail watch out for bicycles.

Worth a Longer Look: Waypoints 1, 4, 6, 7, 11, 14, 16

Waypoint-to-Waypoint

One: Trail Center, Little Two Harbors Trail, and a Glacial Erratic

It is a cool morning in early September with the temperature in the mid-forties and fog lying like a wool blanket over the little coves along the lakeshore. Elsewhere the fog is thinner, more finger-like, and slowly rises upward to vanish like smoke from a dying campfire. We expect the fog to soon be gone with blue sky, light breezes, and a warming sun taking its place. The Little Two Harbors-Corundum Mine Trail is on the lake side of the trail center picnic shelter which is to the left of the parking lot. To begin

59

Split Rock Lighthouse State Park
Walk 1: Little Two Harbors-Corundum Mine Trail

this walk turn left on the paved trail (toward the lighthouse) and walk along it for about 0.25 miles to waypoint 1. The waypoint is at a bench and junction (to the right as you walk up the trail) with a path that leads down to the old pumphouse for the lightstation. Behind the bench is a large *glacial erratic* of *anorthosite,* the same kind of rock the lighthouse is built on.

Just before waypoint 1 pass a sign for the Little Two Harbors Trail, and another glacial erratic of anorthosite.

Note: The pumphouse trail leads down to the lakeshore and the base of the historic tramway. There is a large outcrop of an *amygdaloidal aa lava flow* to the left of the tramway, and the red-colored top of the flow is exposed in the bank above the lakeshore in the direction of the lighthouse. The flow top consists of fragments of aa lava that are held together by red sandstone. The sand-size sedimentary grains were deposited by ancient streams that flowed over and around the fragments of the flow top. Over time the spaces between the fragments were filled by sand after which the flow was buried by succeeding lavas. This flow top is now overlain by a *sill* of *Beaver River Diabase.*

Two: Tortured Basalt and a World of Asters

From the bench walk downhill (toward trail center) over a wide, gravel trail with some larger *cobbles* on it. The gravel and cobbles are round to sub-round in shape and represent part of an ancient beach *terrace* formed by the falling water level in *Glacial Lake Duluth* as the Laurentide Ice Sheet slowly melted back to expose lower and lower outlets for the lake. Today the beach terrace is only 30 or 40 feet above the present level of the lake, and that is due to glacial rebound of the land since the ice melted away.

Walk past another glacial erratic of anorthosite, one which sat on the beach terrace some 9,000-10,000 years ago after lying at the bottom of Glacial Lake Duluth for a thousand years or more. The forest is dominantly birch with balsam fir and spruce to waypoint 2, a bridge over a small and apparently nameless creek.

The round *boulders* in the creek are anorthosite, but the *outcrop* under the bridge and to the left is a kind of basalt lava flow we call *Tortured Basalt*. This is a name given to a distinctive group of lava flows along the North Shore that break into angular or flagstone to step-like surfaces. These form due to weathering along numerous fractures that criss-cross the rock at various angles. The name comes from the fact that the rock ends up looking like it has been given a very rough time by planet earth. This particular flow is really incipient Tortured Basalt because it is in the beginning stages of breaking into sharp edged, blocky pieces. This basalt is part of the *North Shore Volcanic Group* and contains small, round *amygdules* with the mineral fillings largely weathered out. Small *plagioclase feldspar* crystals can also be seen, and these have an unusual brown or pinkish color due to staining by iron-rich water.

In the late summer and early fall this area could also be called "asterville" with large-leafed, white, and purple *asters*. Asters are part of the Daisy Family and large-leafed aster, also called lumber jack's toilet paper, was smoked by Ojibwe hunters before embarking on a hunt because they believed the smoke attracted deer and moose. There is also *bush honeysuckle* which is most abundant where there are lots of birch trees.

Three: Tortured Basalt, Native Copper, and Rock Flowers

From the bridge continue downhill over a wide, gravel trail that follows the old beach terrace. Pass a small *basalt* outcrop to the right before coming to a trail junction and waypoint 3. Large-leafed aster and *sarsaparilla* carpet the ground through this birch and spruce forest.

Take the path down to the beach where there is a large outcrop of Tortured Basalt along the lakeshore. The criss-crossing fractures in the rock are easier to see here, and the rock is breaking along these fractures to form blocky pieces with sharp corners. Close to the lakeshore, round to elongate amygdules are more abundant, and these vary in size from pinheads to quarters–they are more easily seen on a vertical surface. The amygdules are filled by white *calcite*, red *hematite*, a pink *zeolite* mineral, and milky to cream-colored *quartz* (*chert*). A few of the amygdules contain native copper. This is a rare occurrence in the basalt lavas of the North Shore Volcanic Group, but a common feature of the basalt flows that form Isle Royle. The criss-crossing fractures through the rock are filled by green *epidote* and pink potassium feldspar, and the basalt itself varies from pale reddish-brown to gray.

This is a picturesque place with a great view of Lake Superior and of wildflowers (spring and early summer) growing in the rock crevices. These include three-toothed *cinqufoil*, *harebells*, and *butterwort*. Asters as well as sarsaparilla can be found along the path to the beach. Sarsaparilla is part of the Ginseng Family and supposedly was the root used in the original root beer, also called sarsaparilla.

Four: Alien Landscape

Back at waypoint 3 we continue along the old beach terrace to another trail junction and waypoint 4. Taking the path down to the lake we come to a basalt beach and outcrop. Stepping out onto the outcrop, the look of the beach, combined with the wool-like fog blanket hanging over the small bay, makes it feel as though we have been transported to some far off, alien land.

Lake Superior's waves have polished the rock and worn it smooth, so the numerous fractures through it really stand out; here the fractures have a ribbony appearance due to preferential weathering. Some of the fractures are coated by green epidote. We find three-toothed cinquefoil, harebell, and caribou moss in the sunny, rocky, dry areas.

At the edge of the lake is a cobble beach composed of basalt, *diabase*, and anorthosite. The cobbles have been rolled around and knocked together by the waves for so long they are now well-rounded.

Five: Trail Center

Return to the gravel walking path and continue down the trail to the trail center picnic shelter and waypoint 5. In the open areas along here there is *tansy* and the forest is birch, spruce, balsam fir, and balsam poplar with an understory of mountain maple.

Six: Skipper Stone Beach

The walking path is now paved, though it does have bumps in it where either plants or mushrooms have tried to break through. We pass by several picnic tables that overlook the lake but it is too early for lunch so we continue on to waypoint 6, a park sign that describes how rocks are moved about by

Superior's waves, how they become round and polished, and how a shingle beach is made.

From waypoint 6 walk down to the beach in a nice, little cove and compare the size of the rocks found here with those seen at waypoint 4. The ones here are smaller and flatter, and this is partly because the cove provides some protection from the power of Lake Superior's storm waves. Less power means smaller rocks; the waves do not have the speed or force to carry, deposit, and move boulder and cobble-size material. The pebbles you see along this beach have been worn smooth and flat by tumbling and rolling about in the waves over a long period of time, and this makes many of them great skipping stones–so this must be Skipper Stone Beach!

The outcrop down the beach and to the right is part of a *gabbro dike*, which is much smoother looking than the Tortured Basalt. The gabbro contains lath-like plagioclase feldspar crystals that give the rock a "chunky" look on the broken surface. Just offshore is a tree-covered island called Ellington Island.

Seven: Fishing Village, Tombolo, and Diabase

Just past waypoint 6 the paved path leads back to the trail center (to the right); the Little Two Harbors-Corundum Mine Trail continues to the left where it passes two benches before going down into a pretty bay with a cobble beach and Ellington Island just offshore. Waypoint 7 is at a sign that provides information about Little Two Harbors bay and the commercial fishing for herring, whitefish, and trout that went on here from 1900 to 1920.

When the fishing village was here the island was connected to the lakeshore by a narrow pebble and cobble beach that is now partly underwater. Such features are called tombolos with the largest one seen along the North Shore is at Grand Marais. There is now a sign here warning people not to try and cross over it to the island from March 1 to August 15 and never in a storm– unless you want to be not a tombolo but a very tumbled, wave-washed fellow.

Behind the beach is a cliff of Beaver River Diabase with *frost-wedged* and storm wave created talus partly covering the beach. Along here you can still see some of the foundations from the village that occupied this spot some 85 years ago; however, the woods and the lake have reclaimed the rest making it hard to recognize as a former village. The people who fished lake trout and lake herring here would be amazed. Or maybe they wouldn't. Fishermen who must keep a boathouse in good repair at the water's edge, with a slide to get their boat in and out of the water, know how quickly the lake can cancel their carpentry. Keeping the slide and boathouse functional is a constant battle with the lake. The vegetation fights the same battle. On a calm day it seems like the beach is wide and the trees could be growing closer to the water. On a day with a strong east wind it seems incredible that they grow as close to the water as they do.

Eight: Tamaracks, Large Spruce, and Memorial Bench

A short distance from waypoint 7 the trail turns sharply to the right. Just past the curve is the old foundation of a house with large spruce trees growing inside it. The foundation is over 90 years old, and the spruce trees, from their size, have to be at least 80. So it was not long after the village was abandoned that the forest began to reclaim its territory.

The outcrop in the hillside to the left of the trail is Beaver River Diabase.

From the spruce foundation there is a short uphill climb with the trail making a sharp left turn at the top to continue through the campground, passing the campground parking lot and shower house as well as some small *tree zoos*. These are wire enclosures around the small trees to protect them from deer, rabbits, and moose. Tansy and *fireweed* grow in the open spots.

Pass a trail junction; the access trail to campsites 5 through 10 goes straight ahead, and the walking trail goes to the left toward campsite 11. There are a few tamarack trees here, one of my favorites, especially in the fall with their gorgeous yellow needles. Also here are large-leafed aster, *raspberries*, and *wild rose* bushes.

Walk past campsite 11 and over a rocky creek to the junction with a short path that leads to a bench. This is waypoint 8. The bench is a memorial to Reuben Jongewaard; it is a nice spot to sit and watch the lake. The bench brings tears to my eyes for Reuben and my son Chris used to play together as young children. So I sit for a short while and think about sons, hope, free spirits, and just how short life can be; as I do, the lake waves come and go as they have done for thousands of years.

On the pebble beach, in front of the bench, is a large glacial erratic of rounded and polished anorthosite. It almost looks like it has been placed here as a memorial for Reuben!

Nine: Day Hill Trail Junction

From the memorial bench it is a short walk to the junction between the Day Hill Trail (walk 2) and the Little Two Harbors-Corundum Mine Trail. The Day Hill Trail goes to the right and from it you can access the Superior Hiking Trail. The Little Two Harbors-Corundum Mine Trail continues to the left along the lakeshore. The trail junction is waypoint 9.

Ten: Bowling Balls, Talus, and White Walls

Continue to walk through the campground area with Day Hill to the right; there are alder as well as mountain ash, tamarack, mountain maple, and ash trees through here. The hill is covered in birch trees and is composed of anorthosite and Beaver River Diabase. Boulders formed from frost wedging have bounced, fallen, and rolled all the way down to the campsites–imagine the noise and commotion of that on a dark, moonless night!

Come to a triple junction. The trail to the left goes to campsites 16 and 17, the trail to the right goes to campsite 15, and the trial we follow goes straight ahead toward campsites 18 through 20. Campsite 15 is partly enclosed by two large anorthosite boulders, both of which have been split in two by their fall down Day Hill.

Pass a small beach and continue to a junction between the path that leads out to the last campsites and the trail to Day Hill, which goes to the right. We follow the trail to Day Hill.

The trail now becomes considerably narrower and goes gently uphill through some alders, mountain maple, dead birch, and white cedars. As is the case with most white cedar trees in this part of the country, these record exactly how high a whitetail deer can reach. Deer love white cedars and leave them neatly trimmed on the bottom. It is amazing that any little cedars manage to grow beyond their reach and survive. Here, then, is another reason we see so many cedars in stream gorges. They like the water, they are able to grow in cracks in the bedrock, and their cliff-like setting is bad footing for the deer who would otherwise gobble them up.

Cobbles and boulders of Beaver River Diabase and some anorthosite litter the trail as we come to an area from which there is a great view of the very steep, smooth, and white rock wall that ends at the bowling ball-shaped top of Day Hill. The top is 170 feet above us at an elevation of 820 feet.

Waypoint 10 is at the beginning of a long flight of wooden stairs. Nice view from here of Corundum Point.

Eleven: Rock Tripe, Anorthosite, and Native Copper

Walk down the steep flight of stairs that appear to be stuck to the side of the massive, almost vertical rock wall. Rock tripe, a fairly thick leathery lichen, grows on the outcrop, looking a bit like dead leaves glued to the rock. Tripe, for which rock tripe is named, is stomach lining from cows, and is considered delicious by some. Rock tripe is also edible according to some people, but we haven't run across a live person or a written source who claimed it was good, yet alone delicious. We wonder if the person who named rock tripe liked tripe, or hated it? Rock tripe, along with many other lichens, is a pioneer species able to grow on bare rock, making possible later colonization by mosses and eventually a whole variety of plants. The rocks at Stonehenge in England are said to have about ninety species of lichens living on them. Along with the lichens on the outcrop at Day Hill there are mountain ash trees growing in the cracks. Alongside the outcrop are birch, some gooseberry and currant bushes, alders, mountain maples, and *columbines*.

The stairs pass by large anorthosite boulders that were frost-wedged from somewhere above us. They have been here long enough for trees to have taken root and grown up on them. This moss-covered boulder field is quite likely home to one or more species of salamanders. Both blue-spotted and redback salamanders can be found in similar habitats near North Shore streams. The ability to move up or down through air spaces between the rocks make such a habitat favorable for animals like salamanders that must stay moist because they have no lungs, and breath through their skin.

The stairs lead down to a gravel path that overlooks a rocky beach. Also here is a junction with a trail that heads off to the right. If you just want to do the loop around Day Hill this path will take you up to the Gitchi-Gami State Trail and to waypoint 16 of walk 2, the Day Hill Walk.

If continuing on the Little Two Harbors-Corundum Mine Trail, stay on the left-hand trail and walk a short distance to a sign for beach access and waypoint 11. The beach is both beautiful and breathtaking as it begins on a clean and polished anorthosite outcrop (sunglasses would be in order on a sunny day) that has numerous boulders of anorthosite, some as white as bones, sitting on top of it. The outcrop overlooks a pretty bay with rocky points at each end: the one to the right is Corundum Point whereas the one to the left seems to have no name, though on some topographic maps it has been misidentified as Corundum Point.

To the right of the outcrop is a well-exposed and knife-sharp contact between brown-colored Beaver River Diabase and a white to gray anorthosite *xenolith* that forms the outcrop on the beach. The large boulders of anorthosite come from Day Hill, which is to the left and above us. Cobbles of a distinctly spotted dark rock also occur along the beach, and these may come from an *ophitic* diabase intrusion (Beaver River Diabase).

At the end of the beach to the left (facing the lake) is a large outcrop of reddish-colored Tortured Basalt. As we walk toward it we see round structures throughout the outcrop; these are the result of *spheroidal weathering*. The Tortured Basalt seen here is very amygdaloidal with the amygdules filled by white calcite (stained brown to red by iron oxides), green epidote, and clear to milky quartz (chert). Some amygdules are zoned with pinkish-colored centers and green rims; small fractures through the basalt are sealed by epidote.

This lava flow is particularly interesting because it contains large gas cavities. Some are over 6 inches across, and in one spot there are five of these lined up in a row. These particular ones probably represent a place in the cooling flow where gas bubbles were unable to rise any further so they coalesced to form these large structures. Most likely the gas became trapped beneath the thick, crusty, and chilled flow top. On Isle Royale such structures are sometimes filled by native copper–like Easter eggs of copper and what a nice surprise that would be!

The Tortured Basalt is intensely fractured. The fractures are so abundant that the rock, in places, has simply crumbled apart in a rather sharp manner.

Standing on the anorthosite outcrop on a sunny day the beach provides for some really dramatic color contrasts: reddish basalt, white anorthosite, and spotted grey diabase. Each is distinct from the other, and together they are the perfect complement to the greenish-blue of the sparkling water.

Twelve: Potholes and Split Rock Creek

After leaving the beach, cross a wooden bridge to the junction with a trail that leads to a backpack campsite to the left (designed for people walking the Superior Hiking Trail). From this point the trail becomes wide and grassy with a short kibbles and bits section (ophitic diabase) just before the bridge over Split Rock Creek, which is waypoint 12. The outcrop in the creek is massive basalt with incipient *potholes* and a small waterfall. There is bush honeysuckle here.

Thirteen: Sedge Lawn

From Split Rock Creek walk past a big old birch tree to the junction with a trail that leads up to the Gitchi-Gami State Trail (to the right) with the walking path going to the left. There is a large birch tree here with a large gall on it. The path is a mowed "sedge lawn" trail with sedges taking the place of grass, a sight that is fairly common on mowed North Shore state park trails in their wetter portions.

From the junction it is a short uphill walk to the junction between the walking path (to the right) and the spur trail to the Corundum Mine Site (to the left). This is waypoint 13.

Fourteen: Corundum and a Failed Mine

Take the spur trail and walk uphill past an historical sign with information on the mining operation that took place here from 1904 to 1908. A small mining company, called North Shore Abrasives Company, was formed by men who believed they had discovered the mineral corundum at this location. Corundum, Al_2O_3, is the second hardest naturally occurring mineral (after diamond) and is the same mineral that can form rubies and sapphires. Corundum was valuable as an abrasive which, at that time, was principally used in grinding wheels and sandpaper. The company built a crushing plant and loading facility and shipped material out for a few years. Unfortunately what they were mining was not corundum but plagioclase feldspar, which is one heck of a lot softer than corundum and no good as an abrasive. We may never know whether they were pulling the wool over just their investors' eyes, or over their own eyes too. The business, of course, failed. So mining came to an end, and the buildings were destroyed in 1910 by a forest fire.

From the historic sign walk past footings for a mine tramway and then uphill via switchbacks and over anorthosite boulders to the top of Corundum Point. There is a fantastic view from here of the lake, the rocky shore with some actual sand beaches, and the rolling hills to the south and southwest with dead white birch scattered through the otherwise green forest. Waypoint 14 is at the top of the hill. The Split Rock Lighthouse is visible to the left.

Fifteen: Spotted Rock and Yellow Birch

Return to the main trail (waypoint 13) and continue down the lakeshore to backpack campsite #2, which is a lovely spot overlooking the lake. From here proceed on a grass-covered trail through a birch, spruce, and aspen forest with ash trees and some nice yellow birch to a trail junction. The path to the right is a short spur that goes up to the Gitchi-Gami State Trail with the walking trail continuing ahead toward Crazy Bay. As the story goes Crazy Bay is named for two people who, back in the early nineteen hundreds lived in a tree house not far from the bay. They did so because they were deathly afraid of snakes. So the local fishermen thought they were crazy and thus the name of the bay-or so the story goes.

Cross a bridge over a small creek to waypoint 15, which is located on the lakeshore with a view of a boulder beach and a steep basalt cliff behind it. There is a bench here to relax on while enjoying a nice view of Corundum Point and Crazy Bay, the bay to the immediate right. There are quaking aspens through here, but they certainly are not quaking at the moment as there is little or no breeze. This spot also has alders, balsam poplars, birch, spruce, and mountain maples.

The outcrop along the lakeshore has nice *cooling joints* and small amygdules, and represents a type of basalt we have come to call Spotted Rock. The spots in the flow are large *pyroxene* crystals that enclose much smaller crystals of plagioclase feldspar. It is this spotted texture that eventually leads to the kibbles and bits seen along the trail. In places the flow has been so intensely weathered it is nothing but crumbles of rock (see *diabase weathering*). The spotted texture is called ophitic which comes from the Greek and means "a stone spotted like a serpent." For this reason we call a lava flow with this texture Spotted Rock. The flow exposed here is similar to the Spotted Rock seen on walks 1, 3, and 5 at Gooseberry Falls State Park and my indeed be the same lava flow. Fractures through the flow are partly filled by the red-colored mineral hematite.

Sixteen: Split Rock River and Split Rock Point

Leaving the bench and Spotted Rock come to the junction with a path to the left that goes to backpack campsite #3, and one to the right that goes under the power line and up to the State Trail. Continuing on the Little Two Harbors-Corundum Mine Trail walk uphill (a lot of balsam poplar through here have had their tops snapped off) past a large birch tree and a *tree zoo*. It is then downhill past campsite #4 to a sharp bend in the trail with an overlook of the Split Rock River. This is waypoint 16, and the point of land is called Split Rock Point. There is also a white pine tree here with a recent lightning scar down its trunk, so I guess this is not a good place to be in a thunderstorm. There is *Joe-Pye weed* here and quaking aspen.

A short path to the left leads down to an outcrop of Spotted Rock, and here the waves have washed away all the crumbles as well as any kibbles and bits to expose pink to white veins of calcite, hematite, and a white zeolite mineral. There are small chert and calcite-filled amygdules, and if the chert-filled ones were larger, what with the intense weathering of this rock, they would make nice *agates*. Some amygdules and veins are lined by tiny, clear quartz crystals. The flow also contains wave-created potholes, and the basalt at the lakeshore has a hummocky or billowy look suggesting the top of a *pahoehoe* lava flow.

Corundum Point is visible to the left and in profile looks like the bow of a large ore boat. As Fenton Howard wrote in 50 Circuit Hikes "The image comes to life on windy days when waves crash against the base of the sea cliffs–the bow seems to be plunging through cold waters."

Seventeen: Beaches and Logging

Continue to follow the grassy trail through a birch forest before heading downhill followed by a flat section through a low, muddy area and over a small basalt outcrop. Come to a path to the left that leads down to the lakeshore and an outcrop of massive, reddish-gray basalt.

From the junction walk through a dark grove of spruce and birch to a bend in the trail and then on to a sign (waypoint 17) describing the beaches of Glacial Lake Duluth. There is a nice view of the gravel and sand bar at the mouth of the river, and the new bridge across it. The wood pilings along the edge of the cove, where the river empties into the lake, are from a wharf that was part of the logging operation centered here from 1899-1905.

Eighteen: State Trail and Split Rock Wayside

Continue up the trail past a sign with information about the logging settlement to the junction with the Gitchi-Gami State Trail and waypoint 18. If you have left a vehicle at the Split Rock wayside, end the walk by crossing the bridge over the river, and then walk up to and across the highway to the parking area.

Nineteen: Split Rock Creek

If you are returning to trail center, proceed on the state trail, which parallels old Highway 61. Pass a spur trail to the left that leads to the highway. After this pass a trail to the right that leads down to the Little Two Harbors-Corundum Mine Trail and then an outcrop of amygdaloidal, reddish-colored basalt (to the left) with an apple tree growing in front of it. Pass by three glacial erratics of anorthosite before reaching Split Rock Creek and the bridge across it. This is waypoint 19.

Twelve (again): Little Two Harbors-Corundum Mine Trail

There are trails on either side of the bridge. Both follow Split Rock Creek down to the Little Two Harbors-Corundum Mine Trail. Take either one and walk down to the junction with the Little Two Harbors-Corundum Mine Trail. The bridge over the creek will be waypoint 12 from earlier in the walk.

From this point turn left and retrace your path from waypoint 12 back to 5 and the trail center parking lot.

Split Rock Lighthouse State Park
Walk 2: Day Hill Trail

Walk Logistics

Start: Trail Center at Split Rock Lighthouse State Park

Getting There: The park entrance is just off Highway 61 about 2 miles northeast of the Split Rock River wayside. Follow the paved road toward the parking lot for the lighthouse. After passing the park information and camping registration center, turn right onto the paved road that leads to parking for the campsites and trail center. Park in the trail center parking lot. A current state park sticker is required.

End: Either the trail center parking lot (for a loop walk) or the Split Rock River wayside. The wayside is 2 miles southwest of the Split Rock Lighthouse State Park entrance on the north side of Highway 61. If coming from Two Harbors the wayside is 5 miles northeast of the entrance to Gooseberry Falls State Park, on the left just before crossing the Split Rock River.

Walk Distance: 4.0 miles from waypoint 1 to the Split Rock River wayside; about 6 miles return to trail center.

Difficulty: Hiking Boots

Safety Concerns: Waypoints 3, 4, 6, 14, 15, 16, 17 (this walk)

Worth a Longer Look: Waypoints 1, 4, 6, 7 (from walk 1), 3, 7, 8, 10, 13 (this walk)

Waypoint-to-Waypoint

Note: This walk can be started either at waypoint 1 of walk 1 (Little Two Harbors-Corundum Mine Trail), or on the lakeside of the picnic shelter at trail center which is waypoint 5 of walk 1.

One: Trail Junction

From the trail center picnic shelter walk down the Little Two Harbors-Corundum Mine Trail (to the right).

It is a grey, cloudy, fall day with the smell of rain carried on the fresh breeze that blows in off the lake. The waters reaction to the wind is to form long, rolling waves that come thundering ashore like Wordsworth's "galloping white horses." We have our raincoats and hats and expect to get wet.

Waypoint 1 is at the junction between the Little Two Harbors-Corundum

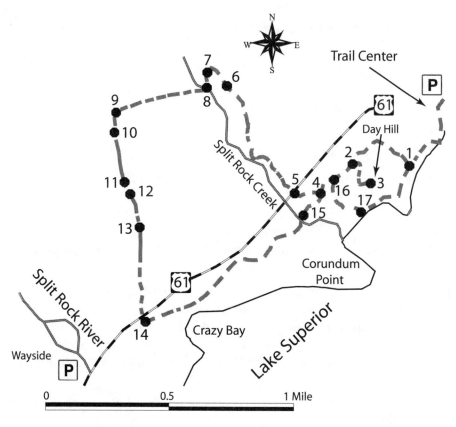

Split Rock Lighthouse State Park
Walk 2: Day Hill

Mine Trail and the Day Hill Trail (this is the same as waypoint 9 of walk 1).

Two: Running Clubmoss

From the junction take the Day Hill Trail, which goes to the right. The trail is wide and composed of gravel and *cobbles* that were once part of an old beach deposit of *Glacial Lake Duluth*. In walking uphill pass an outcrop of *Beaver River Diabase*, a small, rocky creek is to the right.

There are young spruces through here and when we see them we wonder if they will grow up, or be victims of spruce budworm. Budworm has been pretty tough on spruces in northeastern Minnesota. There are some young balsam firs in a boulder field on the left. The ground cover in this area is quite varied, with large-leafed *aster*, bush *honeysuckle*, flat-topped white aster, fringed blue aster, zigzag *goldenrod*, *bunchberry*, woodland *horsetail*, and running *clubmoss* (*Lycopodium clavatum*). The clubmosses look like they belong to another world, which, in a sense, they do. These small plants are descendents of large trees that formed some of the coal deposits we now burn as fuel. Giant versions of today's small ferns and horsetails also were part of ancient swamps and wetlands that were the source of peat that, after deep burial and compression, became coal. These swamps and wetlands go back to a time before the dinosaurs, when amphibians were the scary big predators on the land. Like most modern ferns, horsetails, amphibians, and reptiles, Lycopodium plants are much smaller than their ancestors. Some of them, such as ground-cedar and ground-pine (see clubmoss) look like tiny evergreen trees. Others, like the running clubmoss seen here, look like little evergreen branches growing from "vines" on the ground. They are mostly inhabitants of the coniferous forests. Like mosses and ferns they reproduce from spores. Many produce these spores on small "cones," which are found on the tops of the plants. Highly flammable, the clubmoss was collected and used for the flash powder for old cameras. They were also used for coating pills.

At the hilltop there is an outcrop of Beaver River Diabase, and Day Hill is the prominent feature ahead and to the left. The creek remains to the right with campsites along it, and the *boulders* of *diabase* along the trail come from Day Hill. The forest through here is dominantly birch and spruce.

Continue along the wide trail (once an old logging road) going gently uphill then along a level section to the junction between the Gitchi-Gami State trail and the spur trail that leads to the top of Day Hill. The junction is waypoint 2.

Three: Day Hill

Take the spur trail, which heads uphill through birch, mountain maple, *thimbleberry*, large-leafed aster, and bush honeysuckle as it goes over boulders and cobbles of diabase. Pass an outcrop of Beaver River Diabase in the hillside to the left, before coming to a flat area with "zoos" for white pine trees. *Tree zoos* are places where small trees have been enclosed by wire fencing or mesh. This is done to keep the deer and moose from chomping off the terminal buds of the tree, which they happen to love but stops the tree from growing any taller.

Continue along the level trail, littered with boulders of diabase, to a sharp turn and an *outcrop* of lichen-covered *anorthosite*. The anorthosite outcrop has the typical bowling ball shape exhibited by much of the anorthosite exposed along the North Shore. This round weathering pattern is due mostly to *exfoliation* and *frost wedging*. From the outcrop there is a view of Lake Superior and Corundum Point (straight ahead).

Continue uphill over boulders of diabase and basalt as well as outcrops of anorthosite and diabase to the top of Day Hill and waypoint 3.

The hilltop is a large, open knob of anorthosite (bowling ball weathering) with quite possibly the only anorthosite fireplace and chimney in the world. The view from here is eye stretching and absolutely wow! The vastness of the lake, the lighthouse and rocky promontory it sits on, the rocky shore and green forest stretching inland from it, and, on a clear day, the Apostle Islands, which can be seen across the lake to the southeast some thirty miles away. When satisfied with the view take another look at the fireplace. The story, true or not, is that Frank Day, a partner in a real estate firm that owned Day Hill and the surrounding land, began construction here of a "dream" house for himself and his bride-to-be. Unfortunately the bride-to-be did not want to be, and so the wedding was called off and, in the end, poor Frank was left with nothing but a rare fireplace and a pretty grand view.

The anorthosite is tan to gray with numerous fractures that seem to go every which way. The *calcite* and/or *plagioclase feldspar* and *quartz* that filled the fractures have mostly been weathered out.

There is a path that leads out to a knoll with a steep drop-off at its end. From here we get a spectacular view of the lake and rocky coastline with all its coves and points of land. These coastal features are the result of the differential erosion of the different parts of the basalt lava flows, as well as the difference between *basalt* lava and diabase. In a sequence of tilted lava flows the *amygdaloidal* tops will erode more quickly than the centers or bases and thus recede back faster, forming coves, whereas the centers and bases end up forming points of land. In the case of basalt and diabase the basalt will typically erode quicker than the diabase, and thus be the cove former with diabase on the points.

One large hole is surrounded by a "starburst" shape; this was once the location of a cement post for a spotting telescope.

Four: Trail Junction

From the top of Day Hill walk back to waypoint 3, the trail junction, and from here walk down the bicycle path (to the left). Pass a ski trail to the left (waypoint 16) before coming to waypoint 4, the junction of the Gitchi-Gami State Trail with a trail to the right that leads to Highway 61 and the Superior Hiking Trail. Along here can be found *brown-eyed Susan, raspberries,* yellow sweet clover, *yarrow*, and asters.

Five: Highway 61 and Juneberries

Take the trail to the right, which turns out to be an old road with crushed diabase on it for fill. There are large birch trees through here with alder and lots of Juneberry bushes. Waypoint 5 is at Highway 61.

Six: A North Shore Lawn

Cross the highway then walk on a grassy trail/old road over anorthosite boulders through a forest of birch, spruce, maple, and balsam poplar with lots of the birch and poplar dead or dying. In and amongst the birch are flat-topped white asters, panicled asters, and large-leafed asters which is typical of many aging birch forests along the North Shore. The trail itself is mowed. It is grassy, with white and red clover, sedges, plantain, *strawberries*, and *buttercups*. Outside of the presence of sedges and the scarcity of dandelions and orange *hawkweed* in this particular spot, it's not atypical of many North Shore lawns. Grass, plantain, clover, strawberries, and buttercups–if you mow it, they will come. As the trail continues, it is lined by bush honeysuckle, *bracken fern,* large-leafed aster, and raspberries. Cross over a diabase outcrop and walk through an area full of boulders (one is a dark-colored *schist* with a vein of feldspar through it, another a pink *monzonite* with kibbles and bits around it). Through this section the trail parallels the Split Rock Creek Valley.

Walk through a low, grassy area with *wild rose* bushes, alder, and mountain maple (this will be very wet in the spring) to an opening where there are large boulders of basalt, diabase, pink monzonite, and *granite* to the right of the trail. These are *glacial erratics*; they were piled up here by the road builders during the era of logging.

Arrive at a loop in the trail with birch trees between the two trail segments. Just past the loop cross a bridge over a swampy area. At this point there is a sign proclaiming this to be a scientific study area–scary–for all I can think of is the cloning of trees, as there seems to be not much else going on. Just past the sign there is a large fenced area to the right, which is a deer exclosure, and, to the left, a lot of dead poplar (cloning did not work well here!). Continue on to another bridge over another swampy area and the end of the exclosure (or enclosure if you're a white pine that would like to travel) and the state park boundary, which is waypoint 6. A few white cedars along the trail are all browsed to as high as a deer can reach. Large-leafed asters share the ground with lady ferns and interrupted ferns. The trail is a sedge lawn in the wetter areas.

Seven: Trail Junction

Walk through a grove of old, large cedar trees with smaller balsam poplars and then into a birch, spruce, poplar forest to waypoint 7, which is the junction of the Superior Hiking Trail and the Merrill Railroad Grade with the Day Hill Trail. The old Merrill Railroad Grade goes to the right, and the Superior Hiking Trail follows it for about 0.75 miles before heading off toward Beaver Bay.

Eight: Split Rock Creek and the Beavers

Stay on the Day Hill Trail, which goes to the left. This is also the branch of the Superior Hiking Trail that leads to the Split Rock River Loop and on to Gooseberry Falls State Park. It is just a short walk on this wide, open trail to

Split Rock Creek (waypoint 8), which, at this point, is more of a pond than a creek. This is due to a relatively new beaver dam on the upstream side created by an energetic family of beavers. With all the alder around here these busy beavers have to be happy campers indeed. After crossing the bridge and the new walkway around the flooded area come to the junction between the Day Hill Trail, which goes to the left to follow the Merrill Grade, and the Superior Hiking Trail, which continues straight ahead.

Nine: Dutchman's Breeches and Old Growth Poplar

From here until waypoint 14, the Day Hill Trail is covered by tall grass and is mostly swampy and muddy, so it is best to follow the Superior Hiking Trail.

Leaving beaver central walk through a cedar grove and alder thicket before crossing two small creeks; *Dutchman's breeches* will be abundant here in the spring. After the creek the trail is wet and swampy with some large, old-growth poplar trees mixed in with the cedar, spruce, paper birch, maple, and ash that make up the forest. Waypoint 9 is at a small creek at the base of a long hill.

Ten: Changing Lavas and Clematis

Walk uphill keeping an eye on the rock material making up the trail, for it undergoes some dramatic changes. Pieces of massive basalt give way to amygdaloidal basalt, which in turn gives way to massive basalt. After this, and just before a small outcrop of amygdaloidal basalt, the pieces of rock are again amygdaloidal. What this means is that in walking up the trail we have walked over two separate *pahoehoe* lava flows. We went from the massive base to the amygdaloidal top of one, then over the base and up to the top of the second flow.

After passing the outcrop the material on the trail undergoes yet another change, but this time it is from amygdaloidal lava to kibbles and bits of diabase. The kibbles and bits continue to an outcrop of diabase with purple *clematis* growing around it (waypoint 10).

Eleven: Spring Flowers

From waypoint 10 the trail follows the hillside with lake views appearing and disappearing. Through here, in the springtime, the trail is lined by nodding *trillium*, and wooly blue *violet*. Purplish *hairy rock cress* covers the rocks and yarrow is abundant. The material on the trail again changes only this time it is from kibbles and bits of diabase to massive and fractured diabase indicating the character of the intrusive rock has changed from *ophitic* to massive.

At the top of the hill there is a large outcrop of massive diabase and a nice view of Lake Superior. Continue to the bottom of the hill and this is Waypoint 11.

Twelve: Spruce Forest

Cross a small valley and walk uphill to the top of a long ridge of diabase. The trail parallels the valley through a forest dominated by maple and paper birch.

Taking a turn to the left the trail moves into the open with great views to the east and northeast before entering a spruce forest. Walking through the forest it's sad to see all the dead and dying spruce trees, their demise due largely to the spruce budworm and its happy helper–the red squirrel. As we walk along we see currants and purplish hairy rock cress growing on outcrops of Beaver River Diabase. The pink and white minerals filling cracks in the diabase are *orthoclase* and quartz.

Waypoint 12 is at the edge of the spruce forest just before coming out onto an open, rocky ridge.

Thirteen: Whaleback

Walk along the open ridge with the exposed rock composed of massive and fine-grained Beaver River Diabase. The broken surface of the rock has a reddish color due to oxidation of iron in the minerals that make it up.

In walking along the open ridge there are marvelous views of Split Rock Lighthouse and Day Hill (to the right of the lighthouse). From this viewpoint Day Hill has the appearance of a geological feature called a *whaleback*, a tapered, blunt-nosed hill formed by glacial erosion of rocks that are intensely fractured. It's called a whaleback because, in profile, the hill looks like the back of a whale heading out to sea.

After a short downhill section come to waypoint 13, the junction of the Superior Hiking Trail, which continues ahead for the Split Rock River Loop and a spur trail to the left, which goes downhill toward Highway 61.

Fourteen: Sign and Highway

Heading down the spur trail pass two grassy (at this time of year) ski trails to the left (one is the Merrill Grade) and cross more Beaver River Diabase and an outcrop of *Tortured Basalt* surrounded by pale-pink *corydalis* and *blue-eyed grass.* Cross Highway 61 and walk along a short path that leads to the Gitchi-Gami State Trail and waypoint 14.

Fifteen: Split Rock River Wayside and Creek

If the end point of the hike is the Split Rock River Wayside, turn right and walk down the bike path and across the bridge over the Split Rock River. Doing this provides the opportunity to stop at the shoreline, skip rocks across the water, and possibly wade in the icy waters of Lake Superior. From the gravel beach it is a short walk up the slope and across the highway to the wayside.

If continuing on the Day Hill Trail, turn left and follow the bike path, which here parallels old Highway 61. Pass a spur trail to the right and an outcrop to the left of amygdaloidal, reddish-colored basalt before reaching Split Rock Creek and the bridge across it. This is waypoint 15 and is some 0.8 miles from waypoint 14. The trails on either side of the bridge follow the edge of the creek down to the Little Two Harbors-Corundum Mine Trail.

Sixteen: Trail Junctions

Cross the bridge and continue along the Gitchi-Gami State Trail to the junction of the bike path and the trail up to Highway 61 (waypoint 4). From here continue along the bike path to a trail to the right, which is waypoint 16. This waypoint is just before the junction of the trail that leads up to Day Hill. If you want to skip this part of the walk, and thus avoid the climb up a long, steep flight of wooden stairs that follows the edge of Day Hill, continue on to the junction with the Day Hill Trail (waypoint 3). From here you can retrace your path back to the trail center.

Seventeen: Day Hill and Anorthosite

To continue the Day Hill walk, take the trail to the right, which goes past boulders of anorthosite that have been frost-wedged off Day Hill. The spur trail follows the edge of Day Hill to a nice, round exposure of anorthosite that is full of weathering pits. These most likely formed from rain, ice, and numerous freeze-thaw cycles.

From the outcrop continue down to the junction with the Little Two Harbors-Corundum Mine Trail and waypoint 17.

From this point turn left and take the Little Two Harbors-Corundum Mine Trail up the long flight of stairs that follows the smooth, massive, almost vertical rock wall. From the top walk back to waypoint 1 of the Day Hill Walk (junction of the Day Hill and Little Two Harbors-Corundum Mine trails) and then back to the trail center.

Split Rock Lighthouse State Park
Walk 3: Split Rock River Loop

Walk Logistics

Start and End: Split Rock River Wayside

Getting There: The wayside is 2.0 miles southwest of the Split Rock State Park entrance on the north side of Highway 61. If coming from Two Harbors the wayside is 5 miles northeast of the entrance to Gooseberry Falls State Park, and on the left just before crossing the Split Rock River.

Walk Distance: 5 miles return to parking lot on Highway 61

Difficulty: Hiking Boots

Worth a Longer Look: 2, 3, 5, 9, 12, 13, 15, 16, 18, 19, 20, 21, 23, 28, 29

Safety Concerns: Waypoint 13 (if trail not re-routed)

Waypoint-to-Waypoint

This walk, with some modifications, is taken from the "Walking Guide to the Superior Hiking Trail: Natural History, Scenery, and Other Trail Features," and is walk # 4 in that 2006 book.

One: Sign at South Edge of Split Rock River Wayside

It's an early, summer morning at the Split Rock River Wayside; a gentle breeze blows in off Lake Superior as we stand by the hiking trail sign watching a large orange ball break free of the horizon to float above the quietness of the blue water. As the ball rises, the ground fog, clinging to the rocky shore and covering the highway in feathery patches, lifts upward like smoke from a dying campfire. In eddies and ragged wisps, the fog rises and is gone, vanishing in the glow of the orange sun. This was a special moment in time, and we both recognized, somewhat sadly, that the moment and the vanishing mist have much in common.

Two: The Estuary

After leaving the parking lot it's a short walk uphill to a prominent sign offering various explanations for the origin of the name "Split Rock." Unfortunately, there is no mention of the possibility the name refers to the "shingle-like" way the *Split Rock River Rhyolite*, which forms the spectacular river gorge further upstream, breaks or splits apart. From the sign there is a wonderful view of the Split Rock River *estuary*, a great feeding and nesting place for waterfowl and other birds, and for animals who might prey upon their eggs, like mink and otter.

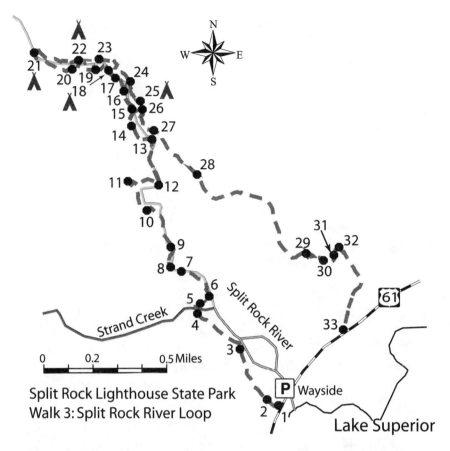

Split Rock Lighthouse State Park
Walk 3: Split Rock River Loop

0   0.2   0.5 Miles

Three: Glacial Till

Leaving the "Split Rock" sign, the wide, graveled spur trail continues uphill offering numerous views of the estuary, before passing an *outcrop* of dark grey *basalt* to reach a nice exposure of *glacial till* that forms the hillside to the left of the trail (waypoint 3). The valley is filled with alder, fir, and cedar. The plants along the trail include *bunchberry, twinflower, strawberry,* and *blue bead lily* (*Clintonia*).

Four: Junction With the Superior Hiking Trail

As it continues uphill, the trail passes through a stand of aspen trees, many of which are missing their upper portions due to a combination of disease (heart rot) and stiff winds. The woods are filled with the lovely pinkish-bluish flower *Mertensia*. It has such a wonderful color for a flower and is so different from the blue bead lily or the white *dewberry*. The trail is partly gravel, courtesy of park personnel, and partly glacial till.

Waypoint 4 is at the junction of the spur trail and the Superior Hiking Trail. The left branch of the Superior Hiking Trail, in about a hundred feet, reaches the top of a beautiful waterfall. When the creek is high enough a small pool forms in the rocky basin behind the falls. This provides a shady place to sit and read or simply watch curtains of water cascade over the falls.

For the Split Rock River Loop take the right branch of the Superior Hiking Trail.

Five: Waterfalls, Grotto, and Aa Lava

From the trail junction we descend a long flight of wooden steps (slippery when wet) to the bridge across Strand Creek (waypoint 5). To the right is a nice grove of cedar trees, and to the left is the waterfall, whose top can be explored just above waypoint 4. From the bridge it is fascinating to watch water tumble some 40 feet over a *diabase* ledge and crash into a rock-surrounded pool. To explore this scenic grotto it's an easy walk up the river bank. Grotto would seem to be the perfect word to describe this spot because it could be a mini version of some remote South Seas Island waterfall. It's lush and green–the rocks are filled with mosses, liverworts, algae, and other plants. With such a wide variety of greens to choose from it is easy to close ones eyes and insert a few palm trees into the picture.

There is also a hikers "happy" book here provided by the Superior Hiking Trail Association in which a hiker can record their impressions of this special place. Last time I was here the book was completely full, so this is obviously a popular place.

To cap off this spectacular spot there is a section through an *aa lava flow.* This 1.1 billion year old flow is exposed on the rock wall immediately across the river from the cedar grove. The once rubbly flow top, pieces and/ or angular chunks of *amygdaloidal* and *massive* basalt "stuck" together by more massive basalt, gives way downwards to a dark, fine-grained basalt that represents the flow center.

Waterfall, grotto, rock wall, and cedar grove, all make for a great place to have a picnic, or just sit and enjoy the view and music of the falling water (a blowdown in the fall of 2005 has temporarily changed this into a somewhat less than perfect place).

Six: Split Rock River

It is difficult to leave this idyllic place but, when we do we follow the trail uphill and cross the narrow ridge separating Strand Creek from the Split Rock River. The trail then descends to an outcrop of dark, massive basalt exposed at the river's edge (waypoint 6). The forest remains unchanged with an understory of mountain maple.

Seven: River View

The trail, now composed of glacial till, rises above the river and crosses a small, rocky stream that flows over pieces of amygdaloidal basalt. From here it's a short walk to waypoint 7, an open view up the Split Rock River flowing over reddish-colored Split Rock River Rhyolite. There is also a small waterfall and rapids here caused by erosion of the rhyolite along vertical *cooling joints* and horizontal fractures.

Eight: Split Rock River Rhyolite and Creeping Cedars

From waypoint 7 it's back to the river and a grove of large cedar trees (waypoint 8) that appear to be having a tough time staying in place. Creep, the imperceptible downslope movement of soil under the pull of gravity (measured in fractions of inches a year), is slowly taking the trees to the river. The "snake-like" curve in the lower part of the trunks represents the cedars attempt to offset this motion and grow straight upward.

The outcrop of rock along the river is the Split Rock River Rhyolite. Here it has a "knobby" weathered top, numerous criss-crossing fractures, and breaks into angular, and/or "flagstone" like pieces. Growing in amongst the rocks is *sweet cicely*, which has a faint licorice smell.

Nine: Waterfall and a Billion Years of Time

It's a short hike from the "creeping" cedars to a small bench and restful view of the river, rhyolite, and tall white pines. From here we can see prominent, closely spaced horizontal fractures in the rhyolite giving the rock the look of saucers or pancakes stacked on top of one another. On the ground there is a tiny, easily passed over plant with a tiny greenish flower–naked miterwort.

Leaving the bench it's a short hike to waypoint 9, a grand view upriver of a small waterfall which, at the present level of the river, has "lace-like" fingers of frothy water flowing lazily over the slick red rock.

The rock outcrop at waypoint 9 is knobby, fractured Split Rock River Rhyolite and, directly across the river, is an *unconformity*, a well-exposed contact between 10,000 year-old glacial till and 1.1 billion year-old rhyolite. A billion years of time and just an inch or two of soil to show for it! We thought about all the comings and goings, all the geological history that thin line represents. There was the coming and going of the dinosaurs, the several different oceans that have covered this area, the wooly mammoths and giant beavers who walked in the park, and the somber fact that the last tenth-of-an-inch represents most of the history of the human race!

Ten: Flint and More Creeping Cedars

Just past waypoint 9 keep an eye out for a large boulder of a black "glassy-looking" rock embedded in the till composing the trail (tree root growing across it). This is *flint,* a fine-grained, dark variety of *quartz* that was used by Native Americans for arrowheads and tools. Waypoint 10 is in a grove of cedar trees that, like their kin at waypoint 8, are slowly "creeping" downhill. Nice view of the river from here. *Coltsfoot* leaves grow all through this section along with some *wild roses* and *rose-twisted stalk*.

Eleven: Two Bridges and Jack-in-the-Pulpit

The trail, still above and away from the river, crosses two rock-filled creeks (no water in either at this time of the year). There are lots of *Jack-in-the-pulpit* along the banks of the second creek, which is waypoint 11. These are coming up through the *thimbleberry* and *columbine*.

Twelve: Frost Wedging and Unloading

It's back to the river's edge and a series of stone steps that lead to the water, which is waypoint 12. On the opposite side of the river is a large, vertical wall of rhyolite with small fan-shaped piles of rock talus at its base. The *talus* forms due to a process called *frost wedging.*

The top of the rhyolite exhibits closely spaced horizontal fractures that grow wider apart from the top of the "wall" to river level. These horizontal fractures form by a process called *unloading* or *exfoliation*. This process gives the rhyolite its "split rock" look in the upper portions. The forest is dominated by birch, and there are lots of bunchberry, *clematis,* and *pyrola* here.

Thirteen: The Rose Garden

The trail continues along, then climbs above the river with nice river views, before heading back to the water, and a large outcrop of knobby, fractured rhyolite. Here the Split Rock River Rhyolite contains small, tabular white feldspar crystals and tiny gas cavities lined with quartz crystals. From the rhyolite outcrop it's a short walk along the river to a nice waterfall and rapids. The rhyolite has nice cooling joints and a "swirled" look which may represent poorly developed *flow banding. Golden Alexanders* grow here.

Head steeply uphill (this section may be rerouted in the future) over rough, broken rhyolite and a set of steep, wooden steps to the top where we literally step into another world. This quieter place (waypoint 13) is dominated by the sight and smell of hundreds of pink and white wild roses that line both sides of the trail. The smell is intoxicating, and the number of blooming roses is amazing. Lots of blue bead lily beneath the roses.

Fourteen: State Park Sign

Leaving "the Rose Garden" the trail heads away from the river but, as we walk along, there are nice views of the steep gorge the river has managed to cut into the fractured and jointed rhyolite. Waypoint 14 is at the "leaving the state park" sign.

Fifteen: Thimbleberries, Glacial Erratics, and the Beehive

Passing through a "forest" of thimbleberries come back to the river where a short path leads down to a large outcrop of knobby, fractured rhyolite and a small waterfall. A large boulder of *Beaver River Diabase*–a *glacial erratic*– sits on top of the rhyolite outcrop. The erratic has probably been in this spot for hundreds of years, simply moving downward as the water slowly eroded and lowered the landscape.

From here the trail heads uphill to an opening (waypoint 15) where there is a nice view of a waterfall and rapids as well as an outcrop that has the shape of a large "beehive." It's a conical mass of fractured rhyolite that has been weathered and eroded along unloading fractures into a beehive shape, this is a small example of the process that forms the "domes" in Yosemite National Park. The "beehive" outcrop is covered by rock talus formed by frost wedging along horizontal fractures.

Sixteen: The Two Towers

From waypoint 15 it's uphill and along the edge of the river to waypoint 16; two 15 foot-high pillars composed of Split Rock River Rhyolite. These represent two large columnar cooling joints that also have numerous, closely spaced horizontal (unloading) fractures. To the right of the Two Towers is the back side of the "beehive," which has nice columnar joints. Weathering along some of these joints shows definite signs of one day producing twins to the Two Towers, and illustrates how they formed. There is abundant polypody fern here–a six-inch tall fern that grows on rocky places such as this.

Seventeen: Nice View and Rock Contact

Leaving the Two Towers the trail is made up mostly of angular pieces of rhyolite all the way to waypoint 17, a large opening in the forest that provides a spectacular view of a waterfall that has several nice steps that curtains of water cascade over and down. There is also a distinct color change in the rocks from one side of the river to the other. Reddish rhyolite outcrops to the right of the falls, while dark grey basalt outcrops to the left. The river has "split" around this outcrop, with the basalt/rhyolite contact along the far fork, the one with the small *meander*-like bend.

Eighteen: Contact Point

It's a short hike to waypoint 18, an outcrop of dark grey basalt to the left of the trail and, to the right, a path down to the river. This leads to an outcrop of basalt, and a nice view up and down the river. This basalt outcrop is similar to the one seen on the trail, but has been polished smooth and shiny by flowing water. The contact between rhyolite, which you can see across the river, and the basalt is in the middle of the river. The Southwest Split Rock River Campsite is located at this waypoint.

Nineteen: Pinhead and Pahoehoe Basalt

Continuing along the river we come to an outcrop of "pinhead" basalt (waypoint 19). The rock is called this because the dark basalt is speckled with white pinhead-to dime-size *amygdules* that are composed of a fine-grained variety of quartz called *chert*. You can also see small, lath-shaped crystals of *plagioclase feldspar* between the amygdules. This outcrop, with its rolling, billowy upper surface, may represent the top of a *pahoehoe lava* flow.

Twenty: Old Bridge and Potholes

It's not far from the "pinhead" basalt to the site of the old bridge across the Split Rock River. The basalt outcrop in the river is what we call "holey" basalt, a rock full of gas cavities (vesicles) that were once filled in by minerals (most likely *calcite*, chert, and *zeolites*) but these have now been mostly weathered out. There are also beautiful *pothole*s in the rock. Some of these are so round they look like someone has spent time here with a rock drill. Some of the potholes contain round and/or oblate, polished rocks that represent, in part, the "drills" that helped make the potholes. One-flowered *wintergreen* and *raspberry* are blooming here.

Twenty-One: New Bridge and Picnic Spot

A thousand feet up the trail from waypoint 20 is the "new" bridge across the Split Rock River (waypoint 21) and the Northwest Split Rock River campsite. Crossing the bridge we hike a few feet upriver to find a lovely picnic spot. Spreading our lunch out over an outcrop of "pinhead" basalt, we sit amongst wild roses beneath a large white pine watching the river glide by. There are potholes in this outcrop and the "pinheads" are difficult to see because of green lichen growing on them.

Twenty-Two: Northeast Split Rock River Campsite and the Old Bridge

From the bridge the trail heads downriver and downhill passing an amygdaloidal and pothole-filled basalt outcrop, before arriving at the site of the old bridge (waypoint 22). This is directly across from waypoint 20. The Northeast Split Rock River campsite is located at this waypoint.

Twenty-Three: Pahoehoe Lava and Forest Glade

Continuing down river we pass another amygdaloidal basalt outcrop. The top surface of the outcrop has "billowy" shapes representing the top of a pahoehoe lava flow. Four hundred feet further on there is a fire ring located in a small opening surrounded by birch and balsam trees. Glacial till is exposed in the bank at the back of the opening, and the outcrop along the river is amygdaloidal basalt. The amygdules vary from pinhead-size to more than two inches in diameter. These are filled by chert, calcite, and zeolites. There are more potholes plus a small waterfall and rapids. The water flowing over the rapids outlines the top to a "billowy" pahoehoe lava flow. The massive basalt seen on the opposite bank represents the base of the flow that overlies the "billowy" lava.

Twenty-Four: Cooling Joint

The trail moves away from the river, crosses a dry creek bed, passes a lot of amanita mushrooms, and continues gently downhill providing nice views of "contact" point and the "split" river which marks the rhyolite/basalt contact. This contact was described at waypoints 17 and 18. Continue downhill crossing a second creek, with rhyolite forming the stream banks, to a large outcrop of rhyolite on the river side of the trail (waypoint 24). This is a large cooling joint, and, given its precarious position, it will soon be river bound! There is also a spectacular, but somewhat scary drop straight to the rushing river some 100 feet below.

Twenty-Five: State Park Sign and Campsite

From waypoint 24 it's a short distance downhill to the Southeast Split Rock River campsite, which is right across the river from the Two Towers. Nice view of the Two Towers and back of the beehive from the campsite. From waypoint 25 continue downward, along and above the river gorge with its rhyolite walls, passing the "beehive" outcrop and crossing a small creek with rhyolite forming the banks and bottom. Waypoint 25 is at a state park sign.

Twenty-Six: Flagstone Rhyolite and White Pine

Not far from waypoint 25 there is a nice view of the river gorge as well as a sharp, steep drop straight to the river. A few feet past this spot is waypoint 26, a great view upriver of the rhyolite-walled gorge. There are nice white pines along the trail and broken "flagstone-like" rhyolite litters the pathway.

Many of the rocky outcrops on this hike have had large white pines attached to them. This makes us wonder if their location made them too hard to cut and so aided in their preservation during the westward migration of logging early in the last century.

Twenty-Seven: Split Rock Junior and a Talus Slope

We continue to walk downhill along and above the river with great views of the "divided" or "split" river along with a small waterfall, rapids, and pool. We also pass a small "split rock" in the making, one with a balsam fir growing out of the "split." The trail passes by some nice six-sided cooling joints in the Split Rock River Rhyolite. Waypoint 27 is at a large talus slope formed by frost wedging. The rhyolite is grayish-green in color due to lichen growth, so it's easy to tell which rocks have been newly turned over by passing critters because the lichens are missing.

Twenty-Eight: Lady Slippers

From the talus slope the trail crosses a small creek and turns inland, passing first through a mixed forest then into one dominated by aspen trees. Waypoint 28 is at the end of a wet section that has cut logs laid over part of it and, along the edges of these and continuing a short distance beyond, are

86

yellow lady slippers (see *orchids*).

Twenty-Nine: Tortured Basalt, Lake View, and Gabbro

The trail continues away from the river heading gently downhill over more "corduroy" or log-covered sections. Just before crossing a small creek with ash trees along it we pass through an area carpeted with Mertensia. From the creek we climb gently upwards to a high, wide opening that affords a great view of the Split Rock River Valley, Lake Superior, and the small bay into which the Split Rock River empties. The rock outcropping in the trail just before the opening looks like knobby, fractured rhyolite, but turns out to be its much darker, similarly weathered and fractured cousin, *Tortured Basalt*.

The rock outcrop at waypoint 29 is Beaver River Diabase. The diabase is smooth and massive and weathers a rusty-brown color. There are nice red and white pines all along this section of the trail as well as some white spruce along the ridge. *Honeysuckle,* columbine, and wild geranium are also found along this section.

Thirty: Shelter and White Pines

The trail follows the open ridge with diabase outcrops along it, and white pine add an elegance to the view which remains spectacular. Waypoint 30 is at a shelter that is meant for day use only. The shelter is surrounded by red pine trees.

Thirty-One: Split Rock Lighthouse

Leaving the shelter, the trail is wide and covered with pine needles to waypoint 31, an opening to the northeast that provides a view of the Split Rock Lighthouse and, to the right, Day Hill, a *whaleback* formed by glacial ice.

Thirty-Two: Junction with the Superior Hiking Trail to Beaver Bay

From waypoint 31 it is a short distance to waypoint 32, a trail intersection with both the Day Hill Trail and the Superior Hiking Trail continuing to the left, and a spur trail to the right (Split Rock River Loop and the Day Hill Trail) that takes us downhill toward the highway.

Thirty-Three: Sign and Highway

Heading down the spur trail, we go by two grassy (at this time of year) ski trails to the left and cross more Beaver River Diabase, and an outcrop of Tortured Basalt with pale-pink *corydalis* and *blue-eyed grass* around it, before reaching the hiking trail sign at Highway 61. From here walk along a grassy path that parallels the highway, crosses the bridge over the Split Rock River (we stay on the river side of the guard rail), and ends at the wayside parking lot and our vehicle. Another option is to cross the highway (this is a continuation of the Day Hill Trail), and follow the new Gitchi-Gami State Trail across the new bridge over the river. Doing this gives us the opportunity to stop at the shoreline and "skip" rocks across the water and cool our feet in icy Lake Superior. We then cross the highway to the parking lot.

Tettegouche State Park

Introduction

Tettegouche State Park has a diverse and impressive combination of natural features that have been created and shaped over more than one billion years by volcanic eruptions, glacial ice, and running water. Today it is running water and Lake Superiors waves that continue this process.

It is the rocky Lake Superior shoreline that is most often seen by visitors, a shoreline that is reminiscent of those found along the wild and starkly beautiful Oregon and Washington coasts. At Tettegouche glacial ice and, over the last 6000 years, Lake Superior's powerful waves have excavated and sculpted the exposed rhyolite and basalt lavas along the lakeshore to form high promontories (such as Palisade Head), bold headlands (like Shovel Point), snug coves, pebble and cobble beaches, and numerous caves, stacks, and arches. The energetic and noisy Baptism River has cut down through deposits of glacial till into the underlying lavas to form waterfalls, cascades, and rapids–the highest waterfall entirely within Minnesota, High Falls, is located here.

Further inland glacial ice, followed by 11,000 years of weathering and erosion, have created rugged ridges out of a dark intrusive rock called diabase, high, open knobs formed by a rock called anorthosite, and long valleys in the more easily weathered and eroded basalt lava flows. In most places the valleys are covered by thick deposits of glacial till. Within the valleys and along some of the ridges are magnificent, mature forests of red and white pine, sugar maple, yellow birch, basswood, white spruce, and white cedar–there are also cedar and black ash wetlands. The yellow birch can be as much as 400 years old, the sugar maples 225 years old, and the white cedar over 300 years old. Six small lakes, accessible only by foot, are found in the interior of the park, and these support walleye and northern pike.

At Tettegouche volcanic fire, glacial ice, and running water have each contributed to the landscape walked across, seen, and experienced. A dynamic and beautiful landscape formed and shaped by dynamic and powerful geological process–processes that would seem to have created something for just about anyone interested in the out-of-doors.

Tettegouche, the largest of Minnesota's North Shore state parks, is located 4.5 miles northeast of Silver Bay with Highway 61 passing through the eastern part of the park. As with Gooseberry Falls and Split Rock Lighthouse state parks, Tettegouche's early history was centered on the logging of the red and white pine forest that covered the land. In 1898 the

Alger-Smith Lumber Company constructed a logging camp on one of the interior lakes. The loggers called the lake Mic Mac after the Mic Mac Indians of their native New Brunswick. They then proceeded to give the other inland lakes Mic Mac names including one they called Tettegouche–a word that is said to mean "retreat."

In 1910, with the virgin pine forest mostly history, the logging company sold the logging camp and surrounding land to a group of business men from Duluth, Minnesota. They turned the camp into a fishing retreat, closed it to hunting, and called themselves the "Tettegouche Club." In 1921 one of the members, Clement Quinn, bought out the others and maintained the camp and land until 1971. In that year Quinn sold the property to the deLaittres family and a few years later, with the aid of the Nature Conservatory, they turned it over to the state. In 1979 Tettegouche became a state park.

The six walks included in this section of the book are designed to allow hikers the opportunity to experience and explore each of the park's complex and diverse landscapes: lakeshore, river, ridges and knobs, valleys, lakes, and old-growth forests. The walks also provide the opportunity to catch a glimpse of some of the park's diverse wildlife and beautiful wildflowers.

Tettegouche State Park
Walk 1: Shovel Point

Walk Logistics

Start and End: Visitor's Center Parking

Getting There: The park entrance is just off Highway 61 about 4.5 miles northeast of the town of Silver Bay, or 0.5 miles southwest of the junction between Highway 61 and Highway 1. Park in the visitor center parking lot and make your way to the picnic tables located at the southeast end of the larger of the two parking lots (straight ahead when entering the rest area). A paved path begins here; this is the starting point for walk 1.

Walk Distance: 1.35 miles   **Difficulty:** Tennis Shoes

Safety Concerns: Steep Cliffs at edge of the lake

Worth a Longer Look: Waypoints 2, 4, 5, 7, 8, 11

Waypoint-to-Waypoint

One: Gulls, People, and Eagles

The parking lot is a busy place on a Friday morning in early July. Trucks, buses, RV's, and cars come and go. There are picnickers, campers, walkers, and a lot of people who are just taking a short break from their trip. This is certainly the most people we have seen at the start of any of the walks, though we expect few will get more than a hundred yards away from the parking lot.

The parking lot is like a carnival come to town–there is the hum of tires, the slam of car doors, the bark of dogs, and the voices and laughter of people ranging in age from young children to one white-haired lady who tells us she is 87 and plans to spend a night at Tettegouche Camp.

Lake Superior is on its best behavior today with barely a ripple on the blue water, which seems to absorb, reshape, and reflect the sunlight in dozens of different ways. Around us the gulls are gathering, and we assume it is the breakfast crew (which probably hangs on for both lunch and dinner). Above us, oblivious to all this human activity, two bald eagles slowly turn, circling higher and higher as they try to find enough wind to send them inland.

Waypoint 1 is at the start of the paved path located next to the picnic tables.

Two: Palisade Head

It is a short walk down the paved pathway to the first overlook, and this is waypoint 2. From here we have a wonderful view of the quiet lake and its

91

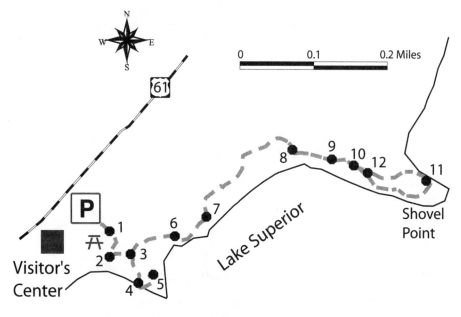

Tettegouche State Park
Walk 1: Shovel Point

spectacular high and rocky coastline with caves and arches cut into the pink and gray *rhyolite* and darker *basaltic* rocks. Palisade Head, with its almost vertical 180-foot-high cliff, dominates the horizon to the south. The vertical lines extending down the cliff side are *cooling joints*, and the rock *talus* at the bottom of the cliff represents "fallen joints," which form from a process called *frost wedging*. When a column or part of a column breaks free, it topples down, slowly gathering speed before plunging into the lake and creating a water spout that would make a blue whale proud. Just imagine the noise, sight, and thrill of watching such an event unfold–a Kodak moment with sound effects.

Palisade Head is also a favorite spot for rock climbers, and it is easy to see why. However, given the tendency of this rock to part along cooling joints like string cheese, I would opt for a safer venue.

Palisade Head is composed of a pink volcanic rock geologists call the *Palisade Head Rhyolite*. This particular rhyolite, which is found from Beaver Bay to Little Marais, a distance of 14 miles, is believed to have a different origin than the rhyolite that forms the gorge of the Split Rock River, or the rhyolite that is exposed at the mouth of the Baptism River (Silver-Beaver Rhyolite). The Split Rock River and Silver-Beaver rhyolites are lava flows whereas the Palisade Head Rhyolite is believed to be a *pyroclastic* rock forming from an explosive volcanic eruption and deposited by *pyroclastic flows*.

Pyroclastic flows are mixtures of pumice, gas, and air that are dense enough to travel over the ground (flow) at high speeds (> 60 mph and up to 300 mph) for great distances (up to 150 miles from source). A large part of the deposit is composed of *pumice*, which ranges from the size of a bread loaf through donut hole to peanut-size with most fragments the size of breadsticks that have been run over several times by a semi-truck (volcanic ash). If the eruption temperature is high enough, the pumice can be so hot on deposition that, in the center of the flow, it welds or fuses together to form a homogeneous glass. The temperatures may actually be hot enough to cause this glass to flow during final cooling. It is thus possible for flow bands and folds to form in this kind of pyroclastic flow.

The Palisade Head Rhyolite is believed to be one of these high temperature pyroclastic flows, and the only evidence of its pyroclastic origin is preserved in the much more rapidly cooled top and bottom of the deposit.

It should be stressed that temperatures high enough to cause this "welding" phenomena and flow folding are far from the norm; most pyroclastic flows retain ample evidence of their origin.

The cooling joints found throughout the Palisade Head Rhyolite are a type of fracture pattern resulting from the thermal contraction of the hot volcanic material as it cooled and crystallized. These elongate, hexagonal columns are oriented perpendicular to the cooling surface. The rock tends to weather and erode along these fractures mainly by frost wedging or by being undercut by Superior's waves.

Three: Large Spruce Tree

From the overlook walk downhill via wooden stairs with mountain maple, bush *honeysuckle*, and asters along the trail. Pass a large spruce tree before coming to a short spur trail to the right that is waypoint 3.

Four: Tortured Basalt and Till Boulders

Take the spur trail and walk down a series of wooden steps, lined with honeysuckle and asters, to a *pebble* and *boulder* beach with a large outcrop of a type of lava flow we call *Tortured Basalt* (waypoint 4). The rock gets this name because of its tendency to break into angular or flagstone to step-like surfaces that form due to weathering along numerous fractures that crisscross the rock at various angles. The name comes from the fact that the rock ends up looking like it has been given a very rough time by planet earth. The intersecting fractures in this particular outcrop give the rock the look of patio stones; as well, in places, the rock has been broken into angular, twisted-looking pieces. *Hematite*, a red iron mineral, seals some of the fractures.

The Tortured Basalt varies from sparsely *amygdaloidal* (to the left of the wooden stairs) to very amygdaloidal (on the beach to the right of the stairs and partly covered by boulders) with the sparsely amygdaloidal rock representing the center of the flow, and the amygdaloidal-rich part the flow top. Amygdules compose up to 40% of the rock, are dominantly round, and are filled by *quartz*, pink and cream-colored *zeolite* minerals, white *calcite*, and green *epidote*.

The large boulders on the beach come from the *glacial till* making up the adjacent hillside. The boulders range from pink *monzonite* and gray *granite* to dark-colored *diabase* and basalt. They have been packed together by the action of storm waves, which washed away the finer clay and silt-size material the boulders were embedded in.

Five: Wave Action and an Arch

Take the narrow, well-worn path across this point of land to the opposite side where there is another pebble beach (waypoint 5) and a beautiful wave-sculpted basalt arch. A sea arch (lake arch here) is a bridge of rock left above openings eroded in headlands or points by waves. The openings are eroded in places where the rock is weaker than normal, such as closely spaced cracks, or lots of amygdules.

The basalt exposed here has a reddish color (due to the oxidation of iron-rich minerals) and elongate, quartz-filled amygdules; in places the amygdules are aligned in the direction of flow. With its smooth weathering surface and lack of fractures this rock would appear to be a different lava flow from the Tortured Basalt of waypoint 4.

There are beautiful boulders of grey and white *banded gneiss* on the beach; they came from the glacial till. Weathering has given these banded rocks a corrugated appearance. It is quite possible these boulders of gneiss were transported from the area of Voyageurs National Park and thus represent material that once formed the roots of a ancient mountain range; one that was (except for its roots) washed to a long-gone sea some 2 billion years ago.

The pebbles on this beach are rounder than those found on the opposite side of the point. On this side the beach is exposed to Superior's fury, which causes lots of wave activity with pebbles continually washed off and onto the beach as well as bumping together as they roll around in the surf. These actions, over time, wear away the irregular and jagged edges, which gives the pebbles a rounder and smoother shape. The opposite side of the point is more sheltered, and so there is not nearly as much wave activity and thus not the dynamic movement of the pebbles that occurs here. From the beach return via the stairs to waypoint 3.

Six: Beach Overlook

Continue to walk toward Shovel Point on a gravel and dirt-packed trail with planked sections over wet areas. The forest is paper and yellow birch with spruce, mountain maple, and mountain ash; large-leafed *aster* and bush honeysuckle form much of the understory. Come to a platform from which there is a great view down to the pebble beach of waypoint 5. From this vantage point it looks like the beach has been size-sorted with larger boulders and *cobbles* at one end, and pebbles at the other, less exposed end. The viewing platform is waypoint 6. Growing on the rock exposed at the platform is rock tripe. This is a kind of lichen that is leathery when wet and brittle when dry. Described as edible by some, I would say you'd have to be starving to try it.

Seven: Basalt Cliff

Continue to follow the gravel pathway with some boulders and the tops of small basalt *outcrops* sticking up, out of the trail. To the right is a long cliff of basalt from which there is a steep drop into the lake. Pass the "not long for this world birch tree" and a bridge over a small creek which, in the spring, is active with a small waterfall and drop pools. The forest is one of spruce and balsam fir with mountain maples and some white cedar with *blue bead lily*, large-leaved aster, *wild rose* bushes, and *raspberries* along the trail. In the spring *Canadian mayflowers*, *dewberries*, and *starflowers* can be seen in this area. Climb a set of wooden stairs to a short, planked path and a bench at a viewing area, which is waypoint 7. From here there is a nice view down the lakeshore of the basalt arch, the dark basalt cliff, and a large "cave" cut into the basalt. *Bunchberry* and a fern-like moss cover the ground.

Eight: Hackly Rhyolite, The Shoreline, and a Gneiss

Continue up the wooden stairs passing the "old cedar rock," a *glacial erratic* of lumpy weathering *Beaver River Diabase* with four cedar trees growing over it. Walk up more wooden stairs, before coming to a wide, gravel trail with boulders and lots of tree roots across it. The forest in this section is dominantly spruce, birch, cedar, and small balsam fir.

The trail continues uphill over a pathway littered with pieces of Palisade Head Rhyolite that have a "hackly" or rough, uneven weathering pattern. The rock pieces come from the cliff ahead; there are also boulders of banded gneiss that come from the glacial till.

Climb a set of wooden steps to an outcrop of reddish-colored, "hackly" rhyolite at the top. Here the Palisade Head Rhyolite contains small, rectangular cream-colored to chalky white *potassium feldspar* crystals along with a few grey, glassy quartz crystals.

The viewing platform just past the outcrop is waypoint 8, and it provides an awesome view of the arch, lake caves, Palisade Head and its talus cliff, and all the coves and points of land making up the shoreline. This is a good place to see how the weathering and erosion of the different volcanic rocks determine whether a cove or headland is formed in the rocky shoreline. In welded pyroclastic flows, like the Palisade Head, the non-welded top and bottom will weather more quickly (cove former) than the welded sections (point and cliff former). In basalt lava flows amygdaloidal tops weather more quickly than massive centers and so, in a series of dipping basalt flows (the basalt lavas consistently dip or are tilted towards the lake at an angle of about 20 degrees), the tops recede to form coves, whereas the centers end up as points or headlands. In the case of basalt and diabase, the basalt typically erodes quicker than the diabase and thus form coves with the diabase forming the headlands. At one time the Palisade Head Rhyolite extended unbroken from Palisade Head to Shovel Point, but erosion by the lake has removed all but the densely welded high promontory and point.

The steep cliff to the left of the viewing area is a popular spot for rock climbing. As one of the climbers there on the day we were told us "the climb down and back up is fantastic, but we really need to be careful and pay attention, for the rock (hackly rhyolite) eats ropes!"

The forest the trail has passed through so far has been classified as aspen-birch by the Minnesota County Biological Survey. Here the trail enters what is called red pine-white pine woodland with white pine making their first appearance. Both types are fire dependent forests, meaning fires are necessary for the tree species to reproduce (ie.get cones to open or produce sunlit areas for growth) with the average interval between catastrophic fires in a red pine-white pine woodland being around 100 years. Here reindeer moss and blueberries grow on the thin soil over the bedrock.

Nine: Plant Restoration

Walk over "hackly" pink and grey rhyolite as the trail heads down slope to a plant restoration area. Here park personnel are planting species that are native to the park such as three-toothed *cinquefoil, bearberry*, poverty oats (Junegrass), and *hepatica* (one of the early spring wildflowers that often blooms in melting snow). Running *clubmoss, wood anemone*, large-flowered *trillium*, and bunchberry can also be found in this area.

Waypoint 9 is located where a short, planked path goes to the right leading to rock climbing decks and a steep cliff of rhyolite. The forest is composed of red and white pine with some cedar and balsam fir.

Ten: Blueberries

The wide gravel trail continues down slope as it follows the southeastern edge of Shovel Point past an outcrop of Palisade Head Rhyolite that contains 5-15% potassium feldspar crystals along with small gray quartz. Waypoint 10 is at yet another wooden planked path leading out to another climbing platform.

This is a great area for *blueberries*. There's little underbrush except young balsam and spruce. The area is reminiscent of many spots in the BWCA that also have bedrock outcrops, spruce and pine growing on thin soil, and lots of blueberries.

Eleven: Shovel Point

Continue down the trail to the junction with the Shovel Point loop trail. Take the branch to the right, which goes by another climbing deck. The trees that grow along this section of the Point are true survivors because there is little soil for them to extend their roots into. They solve this problem by sending the roots outward in a wide, spider web array, and this provides the stability to stand up to the strong winds that blow in off the lake; some small trees are growing right out of the cooling joints on the near vertical southeastern face of the point.

The wide, gravel trail continues downward over rhyolite outcrops to a large open area on the northeast side that is just above the waters of the lake. (waypoint 11). It is worthwhile to spend some time here for this is a place with a much different look and feel than on the southeast side. The barren rock is exposed, open to the wind and the waves and covered by brown, green, yellow, and red lichens. Some of the other plants present are shrubby *cinquefoil*, three-toothed cinquefoil, *bird's-eye primrose,* and blueberries. *Harebells* and *butterwort* also grow here. Butterwort is a purple-flowered, carnivorous plant. Its sticky leaves trap, dissolve, and absorb insects.

This would be a wild and ferocious place in a good storm with huge rollers crashing into the steep cliff and washing over the rocks we stand on. Even the trees have decided this stark place is not for them.

A walkway leads out to a gazebo-like viewing platform, which affords a great view of the rocky, windswept headland with large boulders sitting just beneath the surface of the waves. The boulders, some larger than cars, represent either parts of cooling joints in the rhyolite that have been frost-wedged from the cliff face, or parts of the cliff undercut by the relentless attack of Superior's storm waves. The erosive power of the waves is demonstrated by the presence of caves cut into the rhyolite. From the gazebo we have a great view of the rocky lakeshore to the northeast.

There is an interpretive sign here for the "hiking club" and I really don't like being the one to tell them the information on the sign is incorrect, the Palisade Rhyolite is not a *sill*!

97

Twelve: Sawtooth Mountains and Walks End

Leaving the barren but raw beauty of the pink and grey rocks, continue along a narrow gravel trail over more " hackly" rhyolite–the northeast edge of Shovel Point is to the right. The holes you can see in the rhyolite come from the weathering out of the potassium feldspar crystals. In the far distance, to the northeast, the *Sawtooth Mountains* are visible.

Along this section of the trail the forest is composed of red and white pine, balsam fir, and spruce. Heading uphill over more rhyolite, we can see the branch of the loop trail we walked down to the left. Waypoint 12 is at the junction with the main trail.

From this point return along the trail to the parking lot or, to continue on to walk 2, return to waypoint 2 of this hike. This waypoint, at the overlook, is the start of the walk to the Baptism River.

Tettegouche State Park
Walk 2: Baptism River and High Falls

Walk Logistics

Start: Visitor's Center Parking Lot or Baptism River Parking Lot

Getting There: The park entrance is just off Highway 61 about 4.5 miles northeast of the town of Silver Bay, or 0.5 miles southwest of the junction between Highway 61 and Highway 1. Park in the visitor center parking lot and make your way to the picnic tables located at the southeast end of the larger of the two parking lots (straight ahead when entering the rest area). A paved path begins here; this is the starting point for walk 2.

The other option is to skip the lakeshore part of this walk and begin at the Baptism River parking lot, which is accessed by taking the road past the visitor's center toward the campground and the Tettegouche Trailhead parking lot. The Baptism River parking lot is to the right just before crossing the bridge over the Baptism River. A state park sticker is needed to park here.

End: Visitor's Center Parking Lot, Baptism River Parking Lot, or the Tettegouche Trailhead Parking Lot.

Getting There: The same as above for the Visitor's Center and Baptism River parking lots. For Tettegouche Trailhead Parking proceed from the Baptism River parking lot across the river and then follow the signs to the Tettegouche campground and trailhead parking.

Walk Distance: It is about 3.0 miles from the parking lot at the Baptism River Bridge to Tettegouche Trail Center. From this same parking lot it is 1.85 miles return to High Falls and 0.7 miles from waypoint 7 (this parking lot) back to waypoint 1.

Difficulty: Walking Shoes

Safety Concerns: Waypoint 8, 10, and 13

Worth a Longer Look: Waypoints 2 (from walk 1), 5, 6, 8, 10, 13, 16, 18

Waypoint-to-Waypoint

Waypoints 1 and 2 are the same as for walk 1, Shovel Point.

Three: Visitor's Center Junction

From the overlook at waypoint 2 walk down the paved trail (Rest Area Trail) past a picnic table to waypoint 3, which is at a junction with a sidewalk to the right that goes back to the parking lot and rest center. There is a nice overlook of Lake Superior.

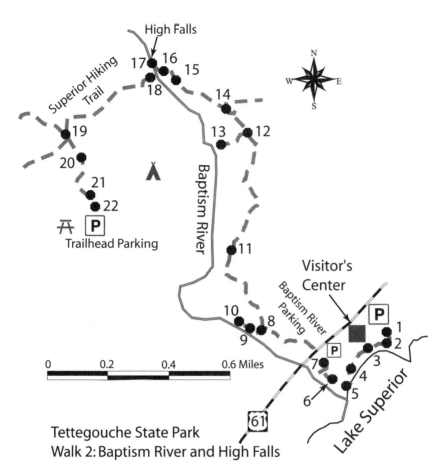

High Falls

Superior Hiking Trail

Baptism River

Baptism River Parking

Visitor's Center

Lake Superior

0   0.2   0.4   0.6 Miles

Trailhead Parking

61

Tettegouche State Park
Walk 2: Baptism River and High Falls

Four: Slumps

Follow the paved trail past a picnic area, through a forest of paper birch, yellow birch, and a grove of quaking aspen; bush *honeysuckle* and large-leafed *aster* provide the ground cover to an overlook of the lake (waypoint 4). In walking down the trail there is a fence on the left that marks the position of the "old" walking path. The fence is needed because the "old" trail has vanished into the lake. There is a large *slump* here, and this is caused by the removal of the rocks and *glacial till* deposits at the base of the slope by the action of Lake Superior's waves. The removal of this material leaves the bank above it unsupported, and eventually it gives in to the pull of gravity and slumps or slides downward as has happened at this location. This loss of slope stability typically happens in stages, leading to a kind of domino effect that, in the end, will produce step-like blocks. As long as wave erosion continues the slumped area will keep on growing.

Five: Gravel Bar and the Silver-Beaver Rhyolite

Walk down a gentle slope on a wide, gravel trail to a set of wooden steps that lead down to a trail junction (waypoint 5) with the path to the left that goes to an overlook and rock outcrop, and the walking path continuing to the right and downhill.

Take the short path to the overlook, which provides a nice view of the mouth of the Baptism River and the gravel bar that extends a good way across it. The name for this river first appeared on maps in the early 1800s. It was written as Baptist, a variation of the French word Baptiste, which is derived from the Greek word bapto and means "to dip." The Baptism River is known to anglers as one of the better game fish streams along the North Shore. Steelhead and rainbow trout spawn in the river each spring, and Chinook salmon and brook trout in the fall. The river is also notable as the place the state's record Atlantic salmon was caught in 1991. The fish weighed 12 pounds 13 ounces and was 35.5 inches long.

The gravel bar across the river mouth forms and grows as *pebbles* and sand are moved in longshore currents created by the breaking waves of the lake. These currents carry the sediment along the growing bar and then out into the more open area where the river enters the lake. Here the longshore current mingles with the river water and, because of this, the velocity of the current decreases and the sand and pebbles are deposited. In this way the bar slowly grows larger and might actually extend clear across the mouth of the river if not for the spring run-off when the increased flow of the river removes much of the deposited material. However, today it is just the opposite, with the low flow reducing the river to a seepage of water through the growing gravel bar.

A large *outcrop* is exposed to the left of the overlook, and this is composed of a light gray to pink-colored lava flow called the Silver-Beaver *Rhyolite*. This rock, which is quite a bit different from the *Palisade Head Rhyolite*, is a nice example of a rhyolite lava flow. In this outcrop there are well-exposed folded and contorted *flow bands*, along with angular fragments of 1) flow banded rhyolite, and 2) very fine-grained gray to reddish-colored rhyolite. The fragments represent the original cooled upper crust of the lava flow, which was pulled apart and broken by the continued movement of the still hot magma beneath it. The fragments were then "cemented" together by this magma, which then cooled and hardened into the rock we see today.

The outcrop also contains 1-15% angular and contorted *amygdules*, which are filled by white *calcite*, clear *quartz*, and a pink to cream-colored *zeolite* mineral. Light-colored veins or fracture fillings cut across the rock.

This is a nice outcrop in which to see features that are typical of the top part of a rhyolite lava flow: angular and contorted amygdules, flow bands and folded flow bands, and a fragmented flow top. The same rock is exposed on the other side of the river mouth, and in the river bank just above the highway where it is overlain by a *basalt* lava flow.

Six: Viewing Platforms

Continue along the trail to a set of wooden steps and then on to a viewing platform that overlooks the river mouth. This is a good viewpoint to see how the lake waves have sorted the gravel bar into different size fractions.

From the platform walk past a set of stairs to the left that goes down to the gravel bar and, to the right of these, a life ring and a sign explaining what to do in the case of emergency (such as someone caught in the longshore current). Continue along the gravel path to another set of steps to the left that also lead down to the river and gravel bar. Just past the stairs is another viewing platform, and this is waypoint 6. At this waypoint the overlook of the river is quite spectacular for the platform has been built upon a rhyolite outcrop that hangs out over the water. Highway 61 can be seen in the distance.

Seven: Baptism River Parking Lot

Walk along the gravel trail to a series of steps that head uphill to the paved parking lot at the Baptism River. The paved road leads either back to the visitor's center and parking lot (to the right) or to the campground and trailhead parking (to the left). In the parking lot there is a sign to High Falls and to the hiking trail and this is waypoint 7.

Eight: Slumps and River Meanders

Leaving the parking lot walk up the steps and down the trail that goes under the Highway 61 bridge. On the other side of the bridge walk up a set of wooden steps and along the gravel path, with boardwalked sections, to a power line. The forest along this trail section is birch and quaking aspen with some yellow birch and a few white pine. *Tansy, thimbleberries*, large-leafed aster, bush honeysuckle, and *yarrow* contribute to the ground cover. In the spring there will be *blue bead lily, Canadian mayflower, wood anemones*, and *trilliums*. Cross under the power line and then over a small, dry creek on a relatively flat trail through a birch, white pine, and aspen forest to a wooden viewing platform. From the platform we have a nice view of the rocky Baptism River and of a large slump on the outside bend of a *meander*. The slump is caused by the erosion and undercutting of the glacial till that makes up the river bank. This erosion, as with the slump along the lakeshore, removes support for the material upslope, and this leads to its slumping or sliding into the river as the meander grows.

Just past the platform is a wooden bench and a long set of stairs that lead down to the river. Take the stairs and walk down all 111 of the steps to the bottom where there is another bench (for a very good reason), which is at waypoint 8. Taking a short rest we look back up the stairs and it appears to be a long, long way to the top!

The river is full of *boulders* that have eroded out of the glacial till as the water cuts down through it.

Nine: Volcanic Siltstone

Follow the path to the right along the river to reach waypoint 9, another small path that leads down to the water and the rock exposed along the shore. Also along the shore are white cedars and, in this more open, sunny area there are *wild rose bushes* with rosehips, *sunflowers*, common *mullein* (also known as Jacob's staff), and *bracken ferns*. In the spring look for *violets*, trilliums, *sessile bellwort*, wood anemone, and blue bead lily.

The outcrop is a grey to pale grey sedimentary rock called a volcanic siltstone, which breaks into sharp, angular pieces along the many fractures that cross through it. The bedding in the rock is difficult to see but it is well-defined in the outcrop on the opposite side of the river. The rock is composed of silt to sand-size quartz and *potassium feldspar* grains and may have been derived from weathering of the Palisade Head Rhyolite exposed further up the river. The rock has round, pinkish spots through it. Though geologists are uncertain how these spots form, they may be related to "reduction spots." Reduction spots occur where a sand grain or small rock fragment causes the iron in the surrounding rock to become chemically reduced thus forming a round or irregular area of a different color.

Ten: Pahoehoe Lava, Anorthosite Xenoliths, and 111 Stairs Again

Continue upriver to a large outcrop of lumpy *Beaver River Diabase* with two nice cedar trees growing from the top. The diabase contains numerous *xenoliths* of *anorthosite*. The xenoliths vary from apple to watermelon-size, are cream to greenish-gray in color, and either have a knife-sharp contact with the diabase or are surrounded by reddish-colored veins that contain feldspar crystals. Small light-colored rhyolite fragments (Silver-Beaver Rhyolite) also occur throughout the diabase along with patches or "blobs" of white calcite.

From the outcrop continue on to the top of the next outcrop (waypoint 10), from which there is a nice view of a small waterfall and the rock of the riverbed (basalt) has numerous *potholes* in it.

From waypoint 10 return along the path to the 111 steps and then up these back to waypoint 8. After the long climb the bench at the top is a welcome sight.

Eleven: Ground Cover and a Glacial Erratic

From waypoint 8 and the bench, which may be hard to leave, continue up the trail through a spruce, white pine, quaking aspen, and birch forest with some large birch trees and a whole assortment of ground cover plants including thimbleberries, bush honeysuckle, lady fern, wood *horsetails*, *raspberries*, dewberry and *baneberry*. Cross a planked trail section before walking up a gentle hill over more boardwalk (this area is wet and muddy in the spring), followed by a *cobble* trail and another short boardwalked section. Bracken ferns with *bunchberries*, large-leafed aster, and blue bead lily can be found through here along with *sarsaparilla.*

The trail continues uphill into a thick and dark forest of young balsam fir with bunchberries and large-leafed aster to a *glacial erratic* of Beaver River Diabase (to the right). From the boulder it is a short walk to a set of wooden stairs with waypoint 11 at the top. It is about 0.33 miles from waypoint 10 to 11.

Twelve: Long Walk

A long walk (0.43 miles) over a trail composed of pebbles, cobbles, and boulders that are part of a kind of glacial till called *ground moraine.* The forest in this section is more open with young aspen, spruce, and balsam fir the dominant tree types; large-leafed aster, bracken ferns, and bush honeysuckle are some of the plants found along the edge of the trail. Just past waypoint 11 pass by an open, circular area with numerous broken balsam fir trees. The trees are snapped off at the base and we have no explanation as to the cause. Come to a set of wooden stairs that lead down to a small creek, then its up, over another small stream, before the trail becomes flat and dirt-packed with short pebble-rich sections to a sign for High Falls. At this point the forest is again thick with balsam fir along with some birch and spruce. In the spring there will be lots of blue bead lily, wood anemone, and Canadian mayflower.

From the sign continue along the dirt-packed trail past another sign for High Falls and then a dead birch with a large growth on it. It is then down a short set of steps, across a small creek to waypoint 12, the junction with a trail to the left that goes down to Two Step Falls. The trail that continues straight ahead goes on to the Superior Hiking Trail and High Falls.

Thirteen: More Long Stairs, Two-Step Falls, and Vesicle Cylinders

Walk down numerous flights of stairs to the river and base of the waterfalls, which is waypoint 13. The stairs descend through a birch, spruce, and thick balsam fir forest with the slope composed of glacial till, which contains a lot of red clay making this a slippery, slimy place when wet. Dogwood and white cedar can be found along the river.

Two Step Falls is just that: two waterfalls with a flat area between them. The outcrop in the riverbank before the waterfall is a reddish-colored basalt that has a very amygdaloidal, rubbly-looking flow top. The amygdules are

104

elongated parallel to the direction of flow and are filled by chert, calcite, and zeolites. Just before this outcrop there are two very unusual boulders. One contains angular fragments of jasper, milky-colored chert, and basalt, the other contains fragments of flint. These boulders have been weathered out of the glacial till but their origin is a mystery (best guess is that they are debris flows of some sort).

The lower step of Two Step Falls is composed of amygdaloidal basalt that contains *vesicle cylinders*. These are round to irregular-shaped areas that contain abundant amygdules. These amygdaloidal areas are separated from each other by sparsely amygdaloidal rock. This part of the flow grades upward into a very amygdaloidal basalt (20-40%) that forms the flat area between the two steps of the falls and represents the top of the lava flow. The amygdules are filled by white calcite, pink and cream-colored zeolite, and clear quartz; many of these minerals are weathered out, giving the rock a pitted or holey look.

This amygdaloidal flow top is overlain by a massive to sparsely amygdaloidal basalt that forms the base and side of the upper step of Two Step Falls. On the opposite side of the river, just past the steep set of stairs that descend from the trail that leads to the campground, there is a nice contact between the two lava flows. The top of Two Step Falls is composed of the amygdaloidal top of this second flow. So Two Step Falls has two steps because it is formed from two separate basalt lava flows.

At this time of year the water comes in long lacey fingers over the upper falls into the rocky pool and then on, to cascade over the lower falls and down the rock-strewn river. This is a serene, beautiful spot with the large glacial erratic of anorthosite sitting in the flat area between the two falls adding to the overall beauty. In the spring one would find no serenity here with the anorthosite boulder most likely hidden beneath the frothing spray of a mad, wild river.

There is a "horizontal" pothole carved into the basalt just below the first step of the falls. Horizontal potholes are carved out of the sides of rocks that form stream banks or water chutes. They form from whirlpools or swirling eddies of water that spin round and round. With the help of pebbles and small cobbles trapped in the spinning water, the surrounding rock is worn away. In basalts these tend to form where the rock is fractured or where there are lots of amygdules (in this case in a vesicle cylinder).

When the exploration of the falls is complete return to the wooden steps and walk back up all 205 of them to the main trail. Let's see, 205 plus 111 equals 316, which is just about the number of calories burned off going up and down them. So this is a good place to rest and have that Snicker bar!

Fourteen: Superior Hiking Trail

From the top of the steps follow the trail (to the left) to the junction with the Superior Hiking Trail and waypoint 14. High Falls is 0.3 miles upriver from the trail junction.

Fifteen: Gravel Bar

Continue upriver on the Superior Hiking Trail, which now follows an old park trail that leads to High Falls. The trail parallels the river to a junction with a short side trail that leads down to a gravel bar that has formed in the slack waters below High Falls. The junction is waypoint 15.

Sixteen: High Falls and the Hanging Joint

It's a short walk upriver to waypoint 16, which is along the side of High Falls and just before the bridge across the river. Waypoint 16 provides a nice view of the falls and the deep pool at its base. The cliff is impressive, and there are lots of logs piled up on the river bank below the falls.

High Falls, 60 feet from the pool to the top, is composed of Palisade Head Rhyolite, and it is the *columnar joints* in this resistant *pyroclastic* rock that led to the formation of the falls. Water works its way down along the joints and, in the fall and spring, may undergo numerous freeze and thaw cycles. Over time this leads to frost wedging of the joints to create a step-like surface. Running water also helps the process along once the broken surface has formed. Such action, over thousands of years, has led to the creation of the waterfall.

The outcrop of Palisade Head Rhyolite contains crystals of potassium feldspar and exhibits nice columnar cooling joints. There is one large joint "hanging" over the river, and this is a small demonstration of how the falls may have formed. We both wonder how many more freeze-thaw cycles it will take before gravity turns the rhyolite rock joint into river debris?

Below, on the northeast side of the river, there is the gravel bar seen at waypoint 15. This formed from deposition of sand to cobble-size material left stranded when water velocity dramatically decreased (and thus the river's carrying capacity) after the long drop into the rocky pool.

Seventeen: Suspension Bridge

From the "hanging joint" continue up to the bridge across the river and a large outcrop of rhyolite, which contains small, square crystals of orthoclase (potassium feldspar) and irregularly shaped grey quartz. Waypoint 17 is in the center of the suspension bridge across the river. The bridge, built with the help of Minnesota Power, has a unique single cable design and is really springy and bouncy. From the bridge we have a nice upriver view of the rapids, and the roaring falls speak for themselves.

From here the options are to either walk back (waypoints 16 to 7) to the

106

Baptism River and/or the Visitor's Center Parking lot, or continue on to the Tettegouche Trailhead parking lot.

Eighteen: Top of the Falls

If continuing on cross the bridge and a small creek to walk along a boardwalk to waypoint 18, a viewing platform that is right over the waterfalls and an outcrop of Palisade Head Rhyolite.

Nineteen: Trail Junctions

Leaving the sight, but not the sound, of the waterfall pass a second viewing platform to the left and continue on to the junction between the Superior Hiking Trail and a park trail that leads to Two Step Falls and back to the campground.

Follow the wide, winding, and graveled Superior Hiking Trail, lined by balsam fir, paper birch and cedar trees, to waypoint 19, the junction between the Superior Hiking Trail and the park trail that leads down to the Tettegouche Trailhead parking lot.

Twenty: Palisade Head Rhyolite

Take the park trail to the left and walk a short distance to waypoint 20, an outcrop of Palisade Head Rhyolite in the center of the rocky trail. The rhyolite contains small, square potassium feldspar and grey quartz crystals in a pale pink rock with hackly or rough-edged weathering. The feldspar crystals are pale pink and weather a chalky white.

Twenty-One: Glacial Till

Continue on the rocky trail through a spruce, balsam, and poplar woods to a stand of white pine and a short downhill section. From this point it is a short walk to the junction with a park ski trail that goes to the right. The footpath along here is composed of glacial till with the larger boulders moved to the side of the trail during its construction. The trail junction is waypoint 21.

Twenty-Two: Tettegouche Trailhead

From the trail junction pass a small white pine zoo (trees with wire enclosures around them to protect them from hungry deer and moose) and go down a gentle hill over a wide, gravel trail to the Tettegouche Trailhead parking lot and the end of one really nice walk.

Walk 3: Baptism River Cascades

Walk Logistics

Start and End: Baptism River Parking Lot

Getting There: The park entrance is just off Highway 61 about 4.5 miles northeast of the town of Silver Bay, or 0.5 miles southwest of the junction between Highway 61 and Highway 1. The walk starts at the Baptism River parking lot, which is accessed by taking the road past the visitor's center toward the campground and Tettegouche Trailhead. The parking lot is to the right just before crossing the bridge over the Baptism River. A current state park sticker is needed to park here.

Walk Distance: 1.8 miles

Difficulty: Tennis Shoes

Safety Concerns: None

Worth a Longer Look: Waypoints 3 ,4, 5, 10

Waypoint-to-Waypoint

One: Baptism River Parking Lot

It's a great day for a walk with a clear blue sky and just the tiniest of a breeze coming in off the lake. The temperature is in the low 60's and is expected to only get to the low 70's–a true northern Minnesota late summer day. Waypoint one is at the sign for High Falls.

Two: Old Channels and Wildflowers

From the parking lot walk down the campground road and, keeping to the left hand side, cross the bridge over the Baptism River. Take a moment to enjoy the nice view downstream of the river mouth and gravel bar. Along here the river is bounded by the steep basalt walls it has cut down through. over the past 7000 to 8000 years.

At the end of the bridge take the steps to the left that head down slope toward the river. Take the next path to the left and walk under the bridge then straight ahead passing an *anorthosite glacial erratic* before walking under the Highway 61 bridge. Large-leafed *asters*, *goldenrod, raspberries, birdfoot trefoil,* Queen Anne's lace (wild carrot), *yarrow,* and *tansy* grow here beside dogwood, alders, and willows.

Pass by a cement culvert, a United States Geological Survey marker (in the trail), and a white rock beach on the opposite side of the river, before coming to waypoint 2, the junction with a trail to the left that goes up to the

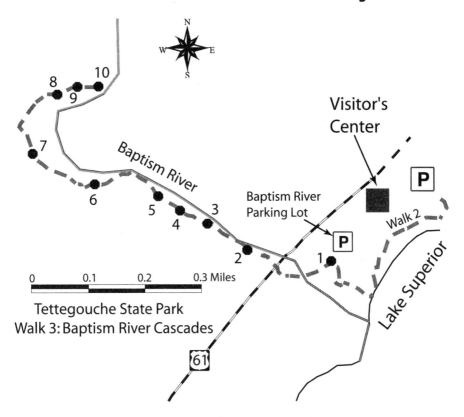

Tettegouche State Park
Walk 3: Baptism River Cascades

campground road and back to the parking lot. The walking path continues straight ahead. *Blue bead lily, bunchberry, twinflower,* bush *honeysuckle, oak fern,* interrupted ferns, and thimbleberries can be found in and amongst the birch and young balsam fir.

The river is filled with *boulders* that have come from the *glacial till* that makes up a good portion of the riverbanks. The flowing water slowly washes away the finer clay and silt-size material in the till and, as this happens, the larger boulders become less and less secure until, on one fine day, they become loose enough to fall, roll, or tumble into the water. The smaller *pebbles* and *cobbles* are slowly moved downstream to form gravel bars; some may make it all the way to the lake. The larger boulders however, remain pretty much where they splashed into the water. The Silver-Beaver Rhyolite outcrops on the opposite side of the river.

Three: Glacial Erratics and River Slump

The gravel trail passes the remains of a large white pine tree and, with some steps and boardwalk sections, follows the river to a glacial erratic of anorthosite (in the river). Occupying this spot since the ice melted off the land more than 10,000 years ago this prehistoric relic has been encased in ice, covered by river water, and slowly descended in elevation as the land around it was eroded away. Alone—but not lonesome—this gift of the Pleistocene has been passed, if not enjoyed, by wooly mammoths, giant beavers, dire wolves, Native Americans (the first humans to live in this area), voyageurs, and thousands of park visitors.

Just past the boulder come to a *slump* in the riverbank (on opposite side) and an abandoned river channel (waypoint 3). The abandoned channel is filled to the brim with boulders derived from the glacial till. There are so many of these they ended up blocking the flow of the river causing the water to flow around this area or *meander* to a different course; the meander led to the active slump. Most likely the river has no trouble using this channel during the spring runoff.

Four: Volcanic Sandstone

The trail follows the old, boulder-filled channel upriver with a pink cliff of rhyolite (Silver-Beaver Lava Flow) on the opposite side. Come to a steep set of stairs that descend to the river and another set that follow the main trail upslope. The bench located at this point is waypoint 4. White cedars are abundant through here along with some alders, paper birch, and balsam firs. Lady ferns, bush honeysuckle, and large-leafed aster carpet the ground.

Take the stairs to the river. The rock exposed in the riverbank is the same spotted sedimentary rock, a volcanic siltstone, that is seen across the river. The siltstone is well-bedded or layered and has the same pink spots throughout it as the outcrop on the other side. The origin of the spots is uncertain, but they may represent what are referred to as reduction spots. These occur where a sand grain or small rock fragment causes the iron in the surrounding rock to become chemically reduced thus forming a circular area that is a different color than the surrounding rock.

The volcanic siltstone is fine-grained and, with a jewelers loop, we can see small pink feldspar and clear *quartz* grains that seem to be cemented together by white *calcite* and *zeolite* minerals. The composition of the rock suggests it is made up of particles that came from the erosion of the *Palisade Head Rhyolite* that is exposed upstream and forms High Falls. The layers in the rock vary from silt to sand-size, and the rock is cross-cut by veins of green *epidote* and pink-colored *potassium feldspar*.

Walking upriver along the outcrop come to a shiny pink rhyolite *dike* and, on the other side of this, an outcrop of *Beaver River Diabase*. The dike has intruded along the contact between the diabase and the volcanic siltstone.

Five: Sculpture Garden

Return to the bench and continue up the stairs with the volcanic siltstone and rhyolite exposed in the bank to the right. The trail is relatively flat and composed of glacial till with cobbles and boulders to waypoint 5, a set of steps that leads to the river. This spot is opposite waypoint 10 of walk 2 which was an outcrop of Beaver River Diabase. On this side of the river the exposed rock is a *basalt* lava flow which is part of the *North Shore Volcanic Group* that formed 1.1 billion years ago. The lava flow has large, round *amygdules*, which are filled by either clear quartz or red *jasper*. Some of the amygdules are zoned with clear quartz centers and pink zeolite rims. The amygdules are sparsely distributed and vary in size from pinheads to more than 1.5 inches long.

A small waterfall and rapids is located here, and the rocks at and above the falls have numerous "flowing" and dynamic-looking convex, concave, or rounded shapes. They look like a modern sculpture garden, especially given the flatness of the basalt outcrop on top and to the left of the falls. This exhibit, constructed by flowing water and the sediment it carried, is worth not only a few pictures but also each "piece" in the exhibit can be given a name based on its shape. At least we think so and spend some time trying to do this. One of the "pieces" has been turned onto its side to expose a beautiful pothole that has been eroded clear through the rock. There is a nice white pine tree here.

Six: River View

The trail, composed of gravel and boulders, goes gently up and down as it passes by the sculpture garden to waypoint 6, a wooden railing from which we have a nice view down the boulder-packed river. All of the boulders come from the glacial till, and it's really hard to imagine just how much rock the glacier must have carried to provide all of these boulders. Upriver the water branches around a rocky island, and there is a small, grass and alder-covered island below us.

Seven: Fern Heaven

Continue upriver and down a set of wooden steps before coming to a low, swampy area with large cedar trees and a bridge over a small creek. The trail continues through birch and balsam fir with long beech ferns making their first appearance. Lady ferns, *Polytrichum* moss, *Atrichum* moss, interrupted ferns, and *ostrich ferns* live here too. Maybe this is fern heaven? What has apparently happened is that we have crossed into a different forest type, an area that the Minnesota County Biological Survey has classified as black ash conifer swamp. Makes sense to me, for it is quite wet through here. The profusion of ferns is a definite contrast to the aspen-birch forest that has dominated most of this trail. Some other ground cover plants here include zigzag *goldenrod*, blue bead lily, large-leafed aster, bush honeysuckle, *thimbleberries*, *dewberries*, *baneberry*, and bunchberries.

The trail goes past the rocky island following a large meander in the river. Walk up a set of wooden stairs and through a cedar grove to waypoint 7, a bridge across a boulder and cobble-filled creek.

Eight: Hackly Rhyolite and Wildflowers

Continue around the meander bend and walk up a flight of stairs to a dirt packed trail. Walk up more stairs and cross a small creek before heading down yet another set of stairs to another creek that is absolutely jam-packed with boulders–any more and this creek will need to change its course. The forest is dominantly birch, cedar, and spruce with alder and mountain maple as the understory. The trail is lined by a variety of wildflowers from bunchberry, blue bead lily, and *Canadian mayflower* to honeysuckle, primrose, and *blue fringed aster*; at the right time of year, *strawberries* and thimbleberries appear to provide the energy food.

From the creek go up a steep set of stairs to a flat but short trail section that is well above the boulder-filled river. Then it is downhill, via more stairs, to another small boulder-filled creek with a bridge across it. Just before reaching the bridge we come to a boulder (glacial erratic?) of "hackly" weathered Palisade Head Rhyolite, which we name the Hedge Hog rock. This is waypoint 8.

Nine: River View

Leaving the bridge walk down a set of wooden steps and along the river on a mostly overgrown trail with thimbleberries, honeysuckle, and some dogwood and mountain maples. Come to a bridge over a small creek and an open view down the river. There is a small set of rapids here with a gravel terrace on the opposite side. This is waypoint 9.

Ten: Vesicle Cylinders and Mergansers

Continue downhill via wooden steps to a wide pebble, cobble, and boulder beach with a rock *outcrop* and the Baptism Cascades at its far end–this is also the upstream end of the large meander that the trail has been following. At this spot we are at the inside bend of the meander, the place where the water flows the slowest and the place where the deposition of the rocks carried down the Baptism Cascade occurs.

On the opposite side of the river is a large, bear-size cave (horizontal *pothole*) carved out of the basalt by swirling water.

From this point the trail goes around and over rocks (including a large outcrop near a nice cedar tree) all the way to the cascades, which is waypoint 10. The rock outcrop at the Cascades is amygdaloidal basalt that contain numerous *vesicle cylinders*. Vesicle cylinders are large to small, round to irregularly shaped areas that are chock-a-block full of amygdules, which are filled by quartz; patches of calcite fill fractures and amygdules.

The cylinders are separated by sparsely amygdaloidal rock. The basalt also contains potholes and, in places, intersecting fractures through the rock outline hexagonal *cooling joints*.

Cascades is a good name for this place for the river does indeed "cascade" through a narrow gorge over the basalt in a series of closely spaced steps before it splashes into a small pool at the bottom. The cascades are ringed by dark green cedar trees, which contrast nicely with the black basalt and the white, lacey-looking water. Cream-colored boulders of anorthosite sitting on top of the basalt add to the color and beauty of the entire setting.

It was an exciting afternoon at the Cascades watching a mother and three baby mergansers swim in the pool (looking for fish?) and dive. The water is so clear we could see the little ones chasing each other as they zoomed back and forth crossing the pool in a series of delighted turns and spirals.

According to local fishermen the ducks were after pink salmon (sometimes called "humpies" because the spawning males have a hump on their back). These were "accidentally" introduction into Lake Superior in 1956. There is considerable fog surrounding the exact circumstances of this event, but the story is that either adult fish ended up in the lake when a seaplane transfer spilled; or about 21,000 fingerlings or fry (young, or newly hatched fish) from a Thunder Bay hatchery ended up swimming downstream into the lake. Amazingly, they survived, reproduced, and have been a part of the system ever since, although not a very large part. A few North Shore streams get small runs in the fall, and the Baptism River gets one of the better ones. The rain over the last couple days has caused the river to break through the bar at its mouth, and the fish seem to have found their way upstream to the base of the Cascades much to the delight of the local duck population. From the cascades return to the Baptism River parking lot by following the trail back down the river.

Walk 4: Tettegouche Lake and Camp

Walk Logistics

Start and End: Parking lot on the Lax Lake Road (Lake County Road 4)

Getting There: From the Tettegouche State Park entrance take Highway 61 north for 0.5 miles to the junction with State Highway 1. Turn left on Highway 1 and drive for about 4 miles to the Lax Lake Road (Lake County Road 4). Turn left (southwest) onto the Lax Lake Road and travel along it for 3 miles to the parking lot on the left, which is just before Nicado Creek and Lax Lake.

The other way to reach the parking lot is take Highway 61 to Beaver Bay and just southwest of the bridge across the Beaver River turn onto the Lax Lake Road (Lake County Road 4). Follow this for 7 miles, passing Lake County Road 5 and Lax Lake. Just after crossing Nicado Creek watch for the parking lot which is on the right-hand side of the road.

Walk Distance: 4.5 miles   **Difficulty:** Hiking Boots

Safety Concerns: Waypoints 10, 11, 15

Worth a Longer Look: Waypoints 5, 6, 7, 8, 9, 14, 16, 17

Waypoint to Waypoint

One: Charlie

On this fall morning the wind throws the mist at us in damp, stinging bursts. Leaves swirl about in all directions, a kaleidoscope of colors against the low, gray, clouds: bloated water carriers whose mission, I fear, is to make certain we get properly soaked.

My dog, a wire-haired dachshund named Charlie, has no such worries and is gone, up the road poking in and out of the tall, wet underbrush with great expectations of flushing out a chipmunk or squirrel.

Waypoint 1 is in the parking lot by the information sign where there is yellow sweet clover and primrose.

Two: Mare's Tail and Singing Frogs

Leaving the parking lot, bypass the gate that blocks vehicles from using the wide, gravel road. Walk along the road and across a shrub wetland with alders, willows, and dogwood. Here there is an interesting aquatic plant that's not common in Minnesota–mare's tail. It's on the left side of the road in the water, near a culvert. This plant grows mainly in the water, but it sends up aerial stems that look a bit like clubmoss, with lots of little closely

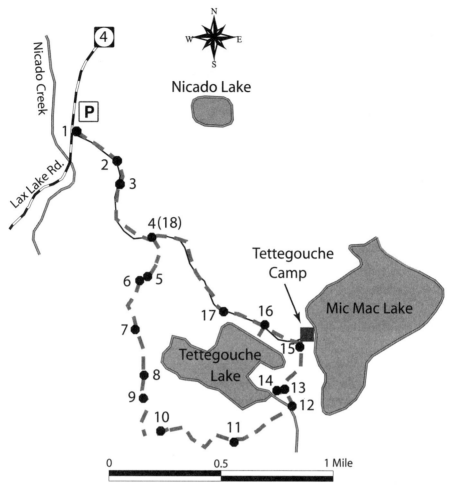

Tettegouche State Park
Walk 4: Tettegouche Lake and Camp

packed leaves coming directly off a thin central stalk. Mare's tail often grows in shallow water over unconsolidated sediments. What this means for the practical-minded is: don't wade out to grab this plant. The bottom may be visible a foot below, but it will not support a human. The extremely loose sediments may extend many feet further down.

Today the frog population is in full song, and together they sound like a band with washboards, kazoos, banjos, and one long, sorry duck. I think I even see a turtle raise its head above the murky waters and give forth a burp worthy of a great tenor.

Pass a snowmobile trail that goes to Lax Lake before starting uphill through a birch, spruce, and balsam fir forest with *thimbleberry*, *raspberry*, and bush *honeysuckle* along the roadside. Waypoint 2 is at the first bend in the road where a deeply weathered rock is exposed; a rock geologists would call "grungy." In fresher form this is part of the Lax Lake *Gabbro*, an igneous intrusive body that extends from just south of here to Finland, Minnesota. Here it has undergone *spheroidal weathering* and is mostly falling apart.

The forest is diverse, with yellow birch and ash joining the more typical paper birch, spruce, and balsam fir. Mountain maple is also abundant, as are the tracks of the moose who consider its branches a great delicacy. Also growing here are raspberries, bush honeysuckle, *bracken fern*s and thimbleberries.

Three: Glacial Till and Ground Moraine

The hill and road become steeper as we climb to a bench (waypoint 3) and a park sign that gives information on the *anorthosite outcrops* seen further down the trail. *Boulders* of Lax Lake Gabbro occur along the road, and a nice exposure of a kind of *glacial till* called *ground moraine* can be seen in the bank to the right.

Four: Gypsy Moth and Oak Trees

Continue uphill through a yellow and paper birch, sugar maple, spruce, and balsam fir forest with scattered white pine and the rare basswood. Lady ferns, large-leafed *asters*, *goldenrods*, blue fringed aster, and *pearly everlasting* make up the ground cover. A small cardboard insect trap is hanging near the road. Some insects use chemicals called pheromones to communicate or to attract mates. They can detect these chemicals in very small amounts, so a sticky trap using the proper pheromone can capture insects even when they are very scarce. Our best guess is that this trap is part of an early warning system to detect the presence of a problem insect (ie, gypsy moth).

Pass a large *glacial erratic* of *Beaver River Diabase* before arriving at the intersection of the gravel road and the walking path that goes around Tettegouche Lake. The walking path is across the road to the right. There are hiking trail signs and a wooden post with a "J" carved into it which we guess is the park designation for the trail. Large-leafed aster grows along the road and through the woods along with *rose-twisted stalk, sarsaparilla, blue bead lily*, and *pipsissewa*. Maple seedlings are abundant here, but these will have to wait a decade or so before they have the chance to become real trees. Apparently maples can spend 40 or more years as two to three-foot-tall saplings. It is only when an older, nearby tree dies or is blown over that the saplings, thanks to the increased sunlight, are able to reach toward the sky.

Oak trees are abundant, and a sign provides information on acorns and explains how popular they are with black bears who come from miles

116

around each fall to sample them. I wonder what the local squirrels think about that!

Waypoint 4 is at a park bench by the information sign.

Five: Ophitic Rocks and Wildflowers

Cross the road and walk along the narrow, dirt pathway through a beautiful sugar maple, birch, oak, and balsam fir forest. As the trail enters the woods there is an abundance of large-leafed aster, blue bead lily, rose-twisted stalk, and sarsaparilla. In the spring, there will be *Canadian mayflowers*, *twin flowers*, *bunchberries*, and coralroot *orchids*; there are also lots of sugar maple seedlings. The forest is a breathtaking sight, even in the mist and grayness, with the fire engine red, salmon red, burnt orange, lemon yellow, and rusty yellow color of the maple, oak, and birch leaves sharply punctuated by the dark green of the balsam fir and the stubborn flutter of the few remaining green maple and oak leaves. It's a scene for an Impressionist painter, even more so with the green, yellow, and brown ground cover of the large-leafed aster, sarsaparilla, and bracken and interrupted ferns. Leaves litter the trail, layer upon layer, and the heavy mist carries the aroma of wet, decaying organic material.

The trail goes gently uphill past glacial erratics and an outcrop of *diabase* to a junction with a spur trail (waypoint 5) to the left. Take the spur trail and, after a short walk over lumpy Beaver River Diabase, come to a large outcrop of the diabase from which we have a great view of Tettegouche Lake and the red, yellow, brown, orange, and green forest below. Nice red pines grow on the overlook with some red oak and bush honeysuckle.

The lumpy nature of the diabase is due to what geologists call an *ophitic* texture. Ophitic comes from the Greek and means "a stone spotted like a serpent." The spots or lumps are composed of dark *pyroxene* crystals (augite) that enclose much smaller crystals of *plagioclase feldspar*. It is this texture that gives many of the diabases, and some of the basalts seen on the trail, their interesting weathering characteristics (see *diabase weathering*).

Six: Sugar Maple Forest

After the junction and waypoint 5 it's downhill over a trail composed of bouldery glacial till. Pass the "kinked" oak tree before walking down a set of wooden steps to an area with a large pile of *frost-wedged talus* from the cliff to the left; the top of the cliff is the overlook we just visited.

Frost wedging is a process by which water fills fractures and cracks in a rock, freezes, and expands in volume by as much as 10%. This causes the cracks or fractures to enlarge a tiny bit, and, after hundreds or thousands of freeze-thaw cycles, the rock breaks into angular fragments. These fragments then slide, fall, or roll to the bottom of a cliff to produce the kind of rock debris seen here. The debris may provide good habitat for species like the red-backed salamander that breathe through their skin and require high humidity.

Continue around "overlook cliff" with its stand of leaning pines at the top to waypoint 6, which is at an opening in the forest with a nice view up the forty-foot-high cliff.

The Minnesota County Biological Survey classified the forest around Tettegouche Lake as "Sugar Maple Forest (North Shore)," and as we look around, this sort of speaks for itself. The classification doesn't mean that it is all sugar maple, but rather that sugar maple is the dominant tree in most areas and has a specific set of other ground layer and shrub layer plants that go along with it. Younger forests of this type tend to have some balsam fir and paper birch, but these species die off as the forest ages. So this area, which does have some balsam fir and paper birch, is probably a younger example of this forest type. The ground plants here include large-leafed aster, sarsaparilla, lady fern, rose-twisted stalk, bracken fern, and *Polytrichum* moss.

Seven: Views, Orchids, and Feed Me

Continue to walk along the narrow trail through the dense, thick, and beautiful fall forest of maple, birch, and oak with balsam fir. Pass a large, ugly spruce tree which, with its bare, uplifted limbs, looks like it's waiting to eat us—all I can think of when I look at it is "feed me, feed me" from the "Little Shop of Horrors."

Go by a diabase outcrop and a trail section that has coral root orchids before reaching the junction with a trail to the right that seems to go nowhere (though I think it eventually leads back to the "feed me" tree). From here it is a short walk over a trail of glacial till to a spur trail to the right that leads to an overlook of Lax Lake. Lax Lake was once called Scaff's Lake, but for some reason the name was changed to the name of a small railroad station.

The overlook is on a high cliff of lumpy weathering basalt. The rock is wet and lichen-covered, making it hard to see any of its features. The rock contains round to elongate, pinhead to dime-size *amygdules*, and these have been filled by *chert* (forming raised lumps on the surface of the flow) and *calcite* with a cream-colored *zeolite*. Fractures in the basalt are filled by orthoclase, a pink potassium feldspar mineral.

The basalt is part of the *North Shore Volcanic Group,* which formed 1.1 billion years ago from eruptions out of the *Mid-Continent Rift*. The Beaver River Diabase is intrusive into this basaltic rock.

Lax Lake is a long, skinny lake, and it appears dark gray and lonely in the mist with the adjacent wetland of black spruce and white cedar adding to the gloomy picture. The hills around the lake are covered by wet-looking maple, birch, spruce, and balsam fir trees. To the west and southwest are nice views over the Cedar Creek and Palisade Creek valleys and their headwater areas. Red pines and a small white pine grow along the overlook.

Eight: More Orchids and the Fall Forest

Leaving the overlook it is a long, gentle downhill walk through a dominantly maple forest to a flat area where the woods seem to change magically with oak and birch becoming mixed with the maple; suddenly the red, orange, and brown changes into a sea of yellow with polka dots of red.

Waypoint 8 is at an outcrop of Beaver River Diabase with coralroot and spotted *orchids* growing here. If these flowers bloomed in the fall they could add their pink, red, and white to the array of leaf colors.

Nine: Wetland Trees

The trail winds around a cliff of anorthosite with an outcrop of Bowling Ball Anorthosite to the immediate left. This is waypoint 9. The anorthosite gets this round shape from a weathering process called *exfoliation* with the help of frost wedging.

There is a trail junction at this point with a spur trail to the right that goes out to Cedar Lake overlook. The overlook is on an anorthosite outcrop with a nice view to the right of Lax Lake and, in the distance, a small pond that is the headwater of Cedar Creek. A large swampy area (coniferous wetland) extends from the pond toward the overlook and, to the southeast, is Round Mountain, another anorthosite knob.

Generally speaking, a swamp is a wetland with trees. Many trees die when their roots are flooded, while others tolerate having their feet wet for a good part of the year. One of the trees in this region that doesn't mind having wet feet is the black ash, which is common in the wetlands around here.

The anorthosite is lumpy, and this texture is caused by water getting into small depressions in the rock and undergoing numerous freeze-thaw cycles. This deepens the depression giving the rock a pitted or lumpy look. Reindeer moss and *blueberries* help to decorate the anorthosite.

Ten: Poison Ivy and Star Flowers

Continue downhill from the junction passing another anorthosite outcrop followed by a large exposure of lumpy Beaver River Diabase to some nice, large birch trees. The trail is composed of glacial till with boulders of pink *monzonite*; large-leafed aster, sarsaparilla, rose-twisted stalk, thimbleberries, blue bead lily, and lady ferns occur along the trailside. Along with them is the odd patch of poison ivy so stay on the trail! The poison ivy seems out of place in this area because it is too shady and wet for this plant, but here it is anyway.

The trail levels out as it winds its way through a multicolored forest with a green, yellow, and brown understory. This is quite different from what is seen in the middle of summer, which is nothing but green, green, and more green in all directions. I can imagine it being somewhat claustrophobic, with the dense forest and mountain maples, hazel, and ferns seeming to crowd out the trail.

Waypoint 10 is at a large pile of round to sub-angular boulders of varied compositions, with pink monzonite and darker diabase and basalt the most abundant. The boulder pile may represent a deposit of rocks left by an ancient stream, possibly a meltwater river that once flowed away from the Laurentide Ice Sheet over 10,000 years ago.

There are *starflower* and twinflower plants along this trail section along with rose-twisted stalk, blue bead lily, and more lady ferns.

Eleven: Ground Pine and Sphagnum Moss

Follow the bouldery trail across a small creek in a swampy area with planked sections to aid in crossing. Beware–the planks are really slippery when wet (like today)! Past the creek the rocky trail heads uphill going by an outcrop of Beaver River Diabase before reaching the top. Now comes a short, flat section before the trail, with lots of tree roots across it, heads downhill. The dense forest continues with blue bead lily, sarsaparilla, *interrupted ferns*, and ground pine (see *clubmoss*) as ground cover. There are also small patches of sphagnum moss. This is usually found in bogs, but it can grow in other places if the soil is consistently wet.

Waypoint 11 is at a small creek full of pink monzonite boulders with large yellow birch trees to the left.

Twelve: Palisade Creek

The trail continues downhill past outcrops of moss-covered diabase. In fact, most of the rocks along this section are covered in moss, a good indication of the wetness of the forest. With the grayness and the misty rain, this section of woods is dark, so much so that when we do emerge into a more open area it is a real shock to the eyes and takes a few seconds to get used to.

Crossing a large slab of anorthosite the trail continues downhill to Palisade Creek, which is waypoint 12. The headwaters of the creek are in Tettegouche Lake which is just to the left. The creek is rocky with nice drop pools and a small waterfall that should be a lot larger in the spring. *Joe-Pye Weed* (now gone to seed), tall meadow *rue*, large-leafed aster, blue bead lily, and honeysuckle can be found in this area.

120

Thirteen: How Did That Get There

The trail bends to the left and goes over Bowling Ball Anorthosite passing a sign for Tettegouche Camp before coming to a T junction (waypoint 13). The trail to the left goes to a floating fen and the one to the right continues on toward Tettegouche Camp. Straight ahead is a very large anorthosite boulder, a glacial erratic also known as one of those "how did that get there" rocks.

Fourteen: Floating Fen

Take the trail to the left to the floating fen (waypoint 14) which is right on the edge of Tettegouche Lake. A large outcrop of anorthosite occurs here and is surrounded by blueberry bushes.

In front of us is an "island" connected to the mainland by a floating mat classified by the Minnesota DNR County Biological Survey as belonging to the "Northern Poor Fen Complex," a fen being a floating bog that has completely grown over and filled down to form enough of a substrate for trees to grow on. On the mat are black spruces and tamaracks. Due to the poor soil and acidic environment the trees grow so slowly the black spruces seen here may be 60 to 80 years old! Across the lake there's an "island" of sugar maple forest tenuously joined to the mainland by the fen on the left and a white cedar forest on the right indicating better and more nutrient-rich soil. Where the spur trail ends on the shore, there are blueberries, bristly *clubmoss* (*Lycopodium annotinum*), and bunchberries. In hunting around we find bog *Solomon's seal*, *bog laurel*, *Labrador tea*, and *leatherleaf*. There will be many more wildflowers here in the spring.

To the left is a small beaver pond and dam, which is separated from the lake proper by a grassy marsh and another beaver dam; this is the headwaters of Palisade Creek. No beaver are about in the rain and mist, but we see lots of indications they are still happily active in this part of the world.

Fifteen: Fall Colors

From the T junction and the large anorthosite boulder continue along a dark, closed in trail before coming into a more open area where the forest is dominantly maple and birch (some yellow birch here), both of which are wearing their finest colors. This opening is brief as the trail closes in again to follow a rocky hillside before coming to a three-way junction which is waypoint 15. The trail to the right goes around the southwestern edge of Mic Mac Lake and the one to the left continues on to Tettegouche Camp.

Sixteen: Tettegouche Camp

From the trail junction it is just a short walk to the access road where this walk started. From this junction Tettegouche Camp is just to the right. The camp is a collection of four cabins along with showers and restrooms. The cabins are available for daily rental (through the visitor's center at Tettegouche State Park) and are open most of the year. However, they are all walk in–not so bad in the winter on skis, but on a day like this-no thank you.

Once on the access road go to the left and uphill through maples, basswoods, red oak, and young balsam with outcrops of anorthosite and Beaver River Diabase sticking up. These have been partially exposed by gullying from rain and snow melt.

Waypoint 16 is where a small path heads off to the left toward Tettegouche Lake. Along the path are lots of zig-zag *goldenrod* alive with bright yellow flowers. There are some very nice white pines visible on the opposite side of the lake.

Seventeen: Ent of the Forest

Continue up the road lined by small basswoods, balsam firs, maples, and red oaks to a beautiful white pine tree, a cloud catcher especially on a day like today. There are two or three more members of the same family back in the woods and these are surely the "Ents" of this forest. Large-leafed asters, thimbleberries, bracken fern, lady fern, raspberries, and woodland horsetails are common along the roadside. These plants make use of the extra sunshine that they find along the open road.

From the "Ents" of the forest continue on to a wooden bench (waypoint 17) and a sign with information on the white pine forest that once covered a large part of this land–a small remnant can be seen across the lake to the left. The white pine here are over 200 years old and are more than 100 feet tall.

Eighteen: Wire Road Banks and a Rainy End

Keep walking (we are hurrying as the bloated clouds suddenly decide to open their hulls and turn the mist to pouring rain) up the road and uphill through a forest of sugar maples, paper birches, balsam fir, basswood, and a few oak trees. Some of the maples and basswoods are very large. Walk past a large glacial erratic of Beaver River Diabase along with outcrops of the same material with the roadside lined by large-leafed asters, lady ferns, thimbleberries, and some Indian tobacco plants. The banks of glacial till exposed along the roadside are covered by wire mesh to prevent them from slumping or sliding across the road and thus blocking it. The hilltop is waypoint 18; this is the same as waypoint 4 and represents the point where the Tettegouche Lake Trail and the access road meet.

From here it is 0.7 miles back down the access road to the parking lot and the end of a wet, though delightful hike.

Tettegouche State Park
Walk 5: Nicado and Nipisiquit Lakes

Walk Logistics

Start and End: Parking lot on the Lax Lake Road (Lake County Road 4)

Getting There: From the Tettegouche State Park entrance take Highway 61 north for 0.5 miles to the junction with State Highway 1. Turn left on Highway 1 and drive for about 4 miles to the Lax Lake Road (Lake County Road 4). Turn left (southwest) onto the Lax Lake Road and travel along it for 3 miles to the parking lot on the left, which is just before Nicado Creek and Lax Lake.

The other way to reach the parking lot is take Highway 61 to Beaver Bay and just southwest of the bridge across the Beaver River turn onto the Lax Lake Road (Lake County Road 4). Follow this for 7 miles, passing Lake County Road 5 and Lax Lake. Just after crossing Nicado Creek watch for the parking lot which is on the right-hand side of the road.

Walk Distance: 8.3 miles   **Difficulty:** Hiking Boots

Safety Concerns: Waypoints 11, 12, 13, 18, 22

Worth a Longer Look: Waypoints 9, 10, 13, 14, 15, 18, 19, 21, 25, 28, 31

Waypoint-to-Waypoint

Waypoints 1 through 3 are the same as for walk 4, the Tettegouche Camp Walk

Four: Oak Trees and Black Bears

Waypoint 4 for this walk is the same as waypoint 4 for walk 4 and is 0.7 miles from the Lax lake Road parking lot.

The trail for walk 5 is to the left of the bench; we follow it toward Nicado Lake.

It is a gorgeous, sunny, blue sky fall day and the absolute opposite of the last time we were here. The red squirrels are busy in the oak trees, and we suspect they are trying to get ahead of the black bears (they must have read the information sign).

Five: Fall Forest and Bowling Ball Anorthosite

Walk through a lovely birch and maple forest with some basswood and red oak. There are some really impressive large birch trees here that are screaming yellow against the powder blue of the sky.

The trail is dry but not well maintained as it goes up a small hill to waypoint 5, a large *outcrop* of *Beaver River Diabase* that is covered in lichen. The

123

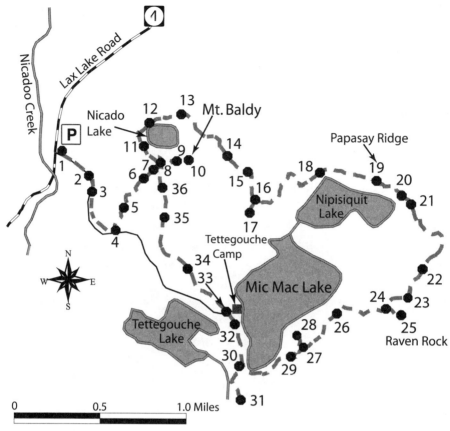

Tettegouche State Park
Walk 5: Nicado and Nipisiquit Lakes

rock exposed along the trail to waypoint 5, and on the hillside to the left, is *anorthosite*. In the sunlight the crystals of *plagioclase feldspar* that compose most of this rock sparkle like gemstones. The anorthosite is gray to white, contrasting greatly with the darker colored, more somber *diabase*.

The anorthosite outcrop exposed on the hillside exhibits the typical bowling ball weathering pattern that seems so typical of this rock. This round, smooth weathering pattern is due to a process called *exfoliation* working in combination with its good friend *frost wedging*.

Large-leafed *aster* decorates the trail along with lady and *bracken ferns*.

Six: Bear Post and a Color Extravaganza

The trail is relatively flat as it goes over *boulders* of anorthosite, *basalt*, *gabbro*, and diabase. The boulders are part of the *glacial till* and here the fine silt and clay-size sediment they were once embedded in has been removed by erosion. Passing an outcrop of Bowling Ball Anorthosite the trail goes through a forest with large maple and birch trees with some red

124

oak, spruce, and balsam fir. The fall color extravaganza continues with various shades of red, orange, brown, and yellow along with quite a bit of green from the hangers-on, and all of this is nicely framed against the deep blue of a cloud free sky.

Going gently up and down come to a bear-mauled signpost to the left. We guess the bear who did this missed out on the acorns and took it out on the post! There would be a nice view to the east if the leaves were off the trees.

Walk past another sign to the right with an outcrop of Beaver River Diabase to the left, and this is waypoint 6.

Seven: Trail Junction

A short distance from waypoint 6 there is another diabase outcrop and a sign with an orange arrow on it. This is at the point where the trail takes a sharp turn to the right, and there is a small anorthosite outcrop trying to hide under a birch tree.

From this point walk downhill to trail junction G (which is the letter inscribed on the signpost), and this is waypoint 7. The trail to the left goes to Nicado Lake and Mt. Baldy and is the continuation of this walk; the path to the right goes to Mic Mac Lake and Tettegouche Camp.

The forest remains beautiful with maple, birch, oak, and now some large basswood trees.

Eight: Spur to Mt. Baldy

It is a short walk to trail junction F (on the signpost) and waypoint 8, which is at the spur trail that goes to the top of Mt. Baldy.

Nine: Great View and Red Oak Trees

Take the spur trail and walk uphill with the aid of some old cut log steps over and past diabase outcrops. Waypoint 9 is at the top of Mt. Baldy on an outcrop of smooth weathering anorthosite; there are white pine trees along this trail section. From the overlook we have a great view of a beaver pond with a dam at the far end (to the southeast), which is chock full of dead birch and aspen trees. Beyond this is Mic Mac Lake and, in the distance, Lake Superior sparkles in the sun. The high hill east of Mic Mac Lake is another knob of resistant anorthosite.

Around the overlook are red oak trees and dogwood with bush *honeysuckle,* and bracken ferns. In the spring the types of wild flowers found here and along the trail include *wood anemone, sessile bellwort,* nodding *trilliums,* purple and yellow *violets,* and *springbeauties.*

Ten: Anorthosite Potholes

Continue along an overgrown trail to the end of the hill and waypoint 10, an outcrop of Bowling Ball Anorthosite. The views from here are eye-stretching and similar to those from waypoint 9. The anorthosite has round weathering pits that look a lot like small *potholes*. Potholes, however, are formed by flowing water using sand grains and *pebbles* as grinding and cutting tools. A combination of a natural depression in the rock (such as a fracture, joint, or gas cavity) and eddies of swirling water provide the opportunity for sand and pebbles to get into the depression and be rapidly spun around and around by the water. This turns the sand and pebbles into effective drills. Over time the depression grows larger and deeper. The anorthosite weathering pits most likely formed from water collecting in small depressions and then undergoing numerous freeze-thaw cycles. Rain then washed out the loose rock particles before replenishing the deepened hole with fresh water to start the whole process over again. Ground pine (see *clubmoss*), *blueberries*, and large-leafed aster grow in the thin soil.

From the "pothole" anorthosite return to waypoint 8, the trail junction (F on the sign).

Eleven: Ant Hills and the Spear Tree

From the junction continue straight ahead toward Nicado Lake. There is a sign that informs us this is a minimum use trail and to expect poor conditions. The trail for walk 4 was not in very good shape and there was no warning sign, so we wonder exactly what waits ahead. We both think "minimum" maintenance really means none, which is a shame, for with a bit of work the trails back here would be superb walking paths.

The overgrown and rocky trail goes downhill passing several ant hills and a large slab of diabase with an anthill on top of it. The diabase has nice *cooling joints,* which would be really pretty and more impressive looking if the rock were wet (which we really don't want).

Continue down the gentle slope over diabase outcrops and boulders through a forest that now has a lot more spruce, balsam fir, and balsam poplar in it. Mt. Baldy and its impressive wall of anorthosite is to the right, and to the left we have a large boulder of anorthosite that has been *frost-wedged* from the wall and then fell, bounced, and/or rolled to where it now sits. You can just imagine the path of destruction it probably created.

We walk hesitantly under the death tree. This is a dangling "spear" of a tree hanging directly over the trail waiting for the right moment to become a lethal projectile and launch itself earthward–scary and noisy as it sways back and forth in the wind. Rushing safely underneath it we breathe a sigh of relief. We walk a short distance uphill before the trail becomes level as it passes over diabase outcrops before arriving at the edge of Nicado Lake and waypoint 11. Mt. Baldy is directly across the lake, and the forest is once again dominantly maple red and birch yellow. Blue bead lily, ground pine, and bracken fern grow along side the trail.

Twelve: Beaver Dam

It is a short walk over anorthosite boulders (from Mt. Baldy), and gabbro boulders (glacial erratics of the Lax Lake Gabbro) to the end of Nicado Lake. At this point we can't help but notice that the walking path is now even less than minimal maintenance, it's gone–buried under several feet of mud and sticks that form a relatively new, 30-foot-long beaver dam. The start of the dam is waypoint 12. Blue flag iris grows along the shore.

Thirteen: Treacherous Crossing and the Miniature North Shore

We cross the dam watching our steps and our heads. I manage to get most of the way across when a beaver out in the lake makes a huge "smack" with its tail. This scares a big animal somewhere ahead of us–we hear it noisily crashing through the bushes. Startled I come close to toppling into the lake, but my big feet (handy things those) keep me firmly rooted to the dam and I hastily cover the few remaining feet to the end. Steve, who was well ahead of me, had no such problems.

Safely on the opposite side, I get to catch my breath by looking at an outcrop of Beaver River Diabase with beautiful blocks (*xenoliths)* of anorthosite in it. The anorthosite blocks have knife-sharp edges against the diabase, which means the melting temperature of the anorthosite is much higher than that of the magma that formed the diabase. In looking at the grey blocks of anorthosite in the darker diabase I imagine the North Shore from about Beaver Bay up to Lutsen. The larger blocks could represent places like Split Rock, Carlton Peak, Day Hill, Mt. Baldy, and Raven Rock while the smaller ones could be any of the bowling ball-like outcrops we have walked by. These are all xenoliths in the Beaver River Diabase, so here, in one small outcrop, is a snapshot of the much larger geological picture.

From the miniature North Shore continue along the trail over a metropolis of anthills, a couple of which have had their tops recently ripped open. This makes us wonder if the beaver slapping its tail warned off a bear who was settling down for a mid-morning snack.

Continue around Nicado Lake (passing more unopened anthills) on a bouldery trail of glacial till. The boulders are dominantly basalt, diabase, pink-colored *monzonite*, anorthosite, *gneiss*, and *granite*–quite the mixture of rock types. It's interesting to think about where these boulders may have come from. The gneiss's home could have been Voyageurs National Park. These kind of metamorphic rocks underlie the entire park and represent the roots of a long gone range of tall, alp-like mountains: mountains that were washed to the sea more than 2.0 billion years ago. The granite may be from the Giants Range, which is a large intrusive body exposed north of the

Mesabi Iron Range. The other rock types are most likely locally derived, coming either from Tettegouche Park itself or from within a few miles of the park. And that's the nature of a glacier–some rocks travel 100s to 1000s of miles in the belly of the beast, while others travel only a few miles.

The forest remains maple red and orange with yellow birch and some stark, bare ash trees. Large-leafed aster is abundant along the trail with lady and *bracken ferns*, blueberries, and *thimbleberries*. Waypoint 13 is at a dry, boulder-filled streambed.

Fourteen: Old Trees

It is a long walk to the next waypoint (0.4 miles) through a beautiful maple and birch forest; the trees are tall, old, and majestic. The trail remains overgrown with thimbleberries and ferns and has some low, wet, swampy areas. Waypoint 14 is in a low, wet area at a birch tree that has numerous roots exposed, and many of these roots snake their way across the trail.

Fifteen: Carpeted Trail and Basswoods

From waypoint 14 the trail is flat and dry with boulders that have weathered out of the glacial till. The forest is magnificent, an old-growth maple forest that is open and simply alive with the colors of the season. It is getting harder and harder to find adequate words to describe these woods let alone their display of fall colors–I guess WOW will have to be as good as it gets! In places a thick carpet of leaves covers the trail, and the muffled crunch and shuffling under our feet adds to the whole fall effect.

Waypoint 15 is at a small pond with a large basswood tree beside it. Basswoods, or American linden, can reach over 130 feet in height with trunks that have diameters in excess of 3 feet. The crown is commonly rounded, and the bark is furrowed with large "S" shaped ridges going up the trunk. The leaves are heart-shaped. A few large birch and a couple of lonesome cedars and yellow birch are scattered through the woods.

Sixteen: Spur Trail

Just past waypoint 15 is an outcrop of Beaver River Diabase, followed by a nice walk on a flat, bouldery trail through the maple-birch forest to another outcrop of diabase. A bench sits here, and it looks so lonesome we decide to sit on it while considering whether or not to take the spur trail to an overlook called Mosquito Creek. The bench and trail junction is waypoint 16.

Seventeen: Mosquito Creek and a Bull Moose

At another time of year we would have skipped this side trip, but it's fall and there have been no mosquitoes around for weeks. Turns out it's a short walk to the overlook, which provides a bird's-eye view of a small creek (probably more mosquitoes than water in the summer) that winds through a floating

128

bog. The overlook is waypoint 17.

It really must be animal day here in Tettegouche. The side trip to the overlook turns out to be more than worth it, for standing on the opposite side of the bog, paying us no attention, is a big, brown bull moose with a great rack of horns. He is busy munching on something green and succulent and, after a couple of minutes watching him, we make a quiet exit. Steve is a bit put out because he is interested in venturing down to the bog to see if there are any *pitcher plants* and *sundew*. He decides seeing the moose is good enough.

Eighteen: Bouldery Trail and Junction E

Excited about what kind of animal we might see next, we hurry on through the lovely maple woods, passing two large white pine and two white spruce just after looking at a diabase outcrop on the left side of the trail.

From the outcrop the trail continues through colorful woods with large boulders of Beaver River Diabase and pink monzonite to a boulder-filled creek with planks across it.

Another planked area takes us through what must normally be a wet, swampy place but at the moment is rather dry. After the "swamp" it is back into the maple-basswood forest. Go by an outcrop of diabase before heading gently downhill over a bouldery trail. The boulders are of mixed lithologies, with the diabase coming from the hill to the right (frost-wedged), the others from weathering and erosion of the glacial till.

The nice maple and basswood forest continues all the way to waypoint 18, which is at a trail junction labeled E. One trail heads off to the right, following the western side of Nipissiquit and Mic Mac lakes to end up at the Tettegouche Camp (to shorten this walk, proceed along this trail using the waypoints from walk 6.)

We follow the trail straight ahead.

Nineteen: Sawtooth Mountains

The bouldery trail passes through a cedar grove with small spruce and balsam fir before reentering the open, dry, maple forest with paper birch. Pass a wide, grassy ski trail to the left, and continue on through the blaze of fall colors to a set of diabase steps that lead to the hilltop.

From the hilltop it is a short walk to the junction of the walking path and the spur trail to Papasay Ridge. This is waypoint 19.

Take the spur trail to the diabase overlook from which we have a spectacular view to the northeast of a grassy-sided creek and the eye stretching and beautiful hilly terrain beyond. The hills to the far north all dip (are tilted) toward Lake Superior, and these form what are referred to as the *Sawtooth*

Mountains. The Sawtooth Mountains are a rather generic name for hills that have long, gentle slopes in the direction of the lake and steep cliff-like or blunt nose shapes on the opposite side (due to *glacial plucking*). This gives the hills the profile of teeth on a wood saw. The hills that make up the Sawtooth Mountains are composed of either basalt or, further up the North Shore, an intrusive rock we refer to as Star Wars Porphyry.

Twenty: Trail Junction

Return to the main trail, and from here walk downhill over and by diabase outcrops and boulders through–what else–a maple-birch forest. We get a partial view of Nipissiquit Lake to the right just before a major trail junction, which is waypoint 20.

Twenty-One: Nipisiquit Lake and the Perfect Lunch Spot

Unanimous decision-it's lunch time! So we take the Nipisquit Lake Trail for the short walk to the lakeshore and a picnic table.

From the picnic table there is a nice view of the lakeshore and of the high hill of anorthosite that rises steeply above it. From where we sit the dark deer browse line in the cedar trees on the opposite side of the lake is clearly visible.

After refreshments or just "restments" we walk back to the trail junction and take the wide, grassy trail marked D. Walk downhill to a bridge across a boulder-filled creek that drains Nipisiquit Lake. This is waypoint 21. Lady and *ostrich ferns* can be found here as well as tall meadow *rue* and *goldenrod*.

Twenty-Two: Ups and Downs and Trail Wash

After the bridge the trail is flat with a low, swampy area to the left as it goes through a different kind of forest, one not seen for a while. This is a second or third-growth forest composed of spruce, alder, and paper birch.

It is then uphill over a trail composed of glacial till and back into the maple-birch forest with cedar. Walk down a small hill into a swampy area passing a basalt boulder that is all scratched up from being smacked by snowmobiles. This is followed by a series of gentle downhills and uphills through the nice, open woods before crossing a small drainage ditch (plastic piping), which is waypoint 22. This is a wet area, and it is obvious where water has run down the trail washing away the clay and silt-size material from the till and leaving the larger rocks behind.

Twenty-Three: Superior Hiking Trail

The trail, composed of glacial till, is relatively flat and dry as it winds through the beautiful maple, yellow birch, spruce, cedar, and paper birch forest. Some of the spruce and yellow birch are large old trees and easy to

130

admire as we walk through a planked section over a wet, muddy area.

To reach waypoint 23 there is a short uphill stretch over a rocky till trail. The waypoint is at the junction with the Superior Hiking Trail, at which point there is a bench to rest on.

Twenty-Four: Yellow, Yellow Birch

Take the right branch of the Superior Hiking Trail (toward Raven Rock) and go generally uphill over a rocky trail with boulders and *cobbles* derived from the glacial till. These are of many lithologies with diabase, basalt, and pink monzonite the most common. The forest is colorful and grand with maple, yellow birch (that is truly yellow), paper birch, and basswood. The junction with the spur trail to Raven Rock is waypoint 24.

Twenty-Five: Raven's Rock

We take the spur trail and walk past numerous boulders and outcrops of anorthosite to the top of Raven Rock. The view from the top of this anorthosite knob is to the northwest and is of another anorthosite hill, one which looks like it splits Mic Mac and Nipisiquit lakes and is the same tall hill seen from waypoint 21. Return to the Superior Hiking Trail and take the left branch toward Mt. Trudee.

Twenty-Six: Hardwood Forest

Continue to walk through the beautiful hardwood forest over a trail composed of glacial till with planked sections across low, wet spots.

This is followed by a gentle uphill section before coming to the junction between the Superior Hiking Trail that goes to Mt. Trudee (to the left) and the park trail we follow that goes to Mic Mac Lake (to the right). This is waypoint 26.

Twenty-Seven: White Pines

Head uphill on the park trail passing an anorthosite outcrop to the right. The boulders and cobbles on the trail vary in composition from *pegmatite* and pink monzonite to basalt and diabase. The forest remains as before, and we are certain it is just as gorgeous as ever. But by now we are so used to the colors and variety of colors it just doesn't look quite as impressive or eye-catching as it did at the start of the walk.

Following a short, flat section the trail heads downhill, after which it flattens out as it goes by an anorthosite outcrop to the left which is immediately followed by an outcrop of diabase with diabase boulders to the left of the trail. The forest is really dense along this trail section and we keep losing GPS reception.

Another gentle downhill takes us past a Bowling Ball Anorthosite outcrop to the left and through a forest that now has more birch than maple to waypoint

131

27, the junction with the spur trail that goes to the Conservancy of the Pines overlook. There are some nice white pines to the left of the spur trail.

Twenty-Eight: Conservancy of the Pines

Take the spur trail and walk over lumpy diabase to the Conservancy of the Pines overlook, which is waypoint 28. It's not much of an overlook, for the beautiful, tall red pines encircle the anorthosite outcrop and allow just the tiniest view of the lake. The pines are nice, and the wind in the tall pines sounds like water rushing through a rocky gorge. The Ojibwe actually have a name for this sound-Sissiquinod.

We are admiring the trees and imagining a whole valley full of them when a ruffed grouse explodes out of the undergrowth to our right and flaps its way downhill, causing both our hearts to beat faster and the imaginary valley of red pines to dissolve–obviously animal day continues.

Twenty-Nine: Mt. Trudee

Back at the trail junction go right and walk down a steep hill over wooden steps and diabase outcrops through maple, yellow birch, and paper birch woods with the occasional white pine to waypoint 29. This is a spot on the trail which affords a lovely view of Mt. Trudee, the prominent high hill of anorthosite to the south. There is a small anorthosite outcrop to the right of the trail.

Thirty: Spruce and Fir

The trail now heads uphill past an outcrop of Beaver River Diabase with birch trees growing on its top. Reaching the hilltop, walk along it a short distance before heading downhill. This is followed by another short, flat section then it's back up again over smooth weathering diabase to the top, with diabase outcrops on both sides of the trail.

Downhill (I'm beginning to feel like a yo-yo) over yet more diabase, and past a large *glacial erratic* of round anorthosite to a planked section in a low, swampy area with cedars and alders. Mic Mac Lake is now immediately to the right.

Continue on over a flat trail through a forest of small balsam fir and spruce trees with some cedar and birch and an occasional white pine. Waypoint 30 is at the junction with a spur trail that goes to an overlook of the Palisade Creek Valley; this intersection is labeled Junction I on a wooden post.

Thirty-One: Palisade Creek Overlook

Take the spur trail to the overlook, which is on an outcrop of anorthosite that is decorated with lingonberries (also called foxberry or cowberry) and sumac. The view from the overlook is of Mt. Trudee and *meandering* Palisade Creek whose banks are lined by red oak trees. There are multiple old beaver dams in the creek valley.

Thirty-Two: Old Road

Return to the trail junction and walk along the Mic Mac lakeshore toward Tettegouche Camp. The trail is relatively flat with lots of cobbles and boulders of basalt, diabase, and pink monzonite as it goes through a balsam fir and spruce forest with cedar and paper birch. Climb a gentle hill with a Bowling Ball Anorthosite outcrop to the left and anorthosite and diabase boulders on the trail, pass a diabase outcrop and a large glacial erratic of anorthosite before coming to a point where the trail becomes gravelly. The pebbles are all about the same size and, in places, the trail is lined by large boulders that look like they were placed there–in places the boulders have all been piled up. From all of this we assume this was once an old road, either for logging or for accessing a favorite fishing spot.

Continue down the road passing more glacial erratics of anorthosite and diabase to the junction with the trail that goes to the floating fen, and the one on to Tettegouche Camp. This is waypoint 32.

Thirty-Three: Access Road

It is just a short walk to waypoint 33, the junction with the park access road. To shorten the walk we could follow the access road back to the parking lot but we decide to continue on.

Thirty-Four: Fall Color Continues

The trail from Tettegouche camp toward Mt. Baldy heads uphill over glacial till through dense woods of cedar and spruce. The trail then flattens out, passing a large dead pine tree before entering a section of forest with balsam fir, spruce, nice yellow birch, and maple followed by a forest dominated by maple and paper birch with some white pine, spruce, and balsam fir. It's like green merging into green, red, and yellow followed by red and yellow with green polka dots. Waypoint 34 is at a lichen-covered outcrop of anorthosite that is exposed in the trail.

Thirty-Five: The Black Lagoon

The trail is relatively flat over anorthosite and diabase outcrops through a nice maple and basswood forest with some large white pine to a planked-over section across a wet, swampy area.

From this wet area the trail leads uphill, and then is level to the Black Lagoon (waypoint 35). This is a scummy, smelly pond full of dead trees, a place for mutant creatures and hideous monsters. There seems to be absolutely no life in or around this pond, which could be right out of Orc-land. This is the swamp that can be seen from Mt. Baldy.

Thirty-Six: Anorthosite Creek

From waypoint 35 it is a short distance to a small rocky creek that contains boulders of anorthosite. The rock exposed along the creek bottom is Beaver River Diabase that contains xenoliths of anorthosite. The anorthosite weathers white and the diabase is a reddish-tan color, so the sharp contact between the two is nicely illustrated. Again this is a place where it is possible to imagine the North Shore in miniature–diabase with blocks of anorthosite that could represent Split Rock, Carlton Peak, Day Hill, Raven Rock, or Mt. Trudee.

From Anorthosite Creek the trail goes downhill as it passes through a very pretty forest of maple, yellow birch, paper birch, red oak, and the odd basswood tree to a planked area across a low, muddy spot (waypoint 36). The roots from a fallen tree have managed to tip some of the planks high into the air.

Thirty-Seven: Closing the Loop

Walk through a forest of maple and birch with oak on a boulder-strewn trail. Pass a large exposure of diabase before coming to a trail junction, which is waypoint 37 (and also waypoint 7 from earlier in the walk). There is a steep hill of diabase to the left. Take the trail to the left and retrace the walk (waypoints 7 to 4) to the access road and park bench. Follow the road to the parking lot to end a long but pleasant walk.

Tettegouche State Park
Walk 6: Mic Mac Lake and the Drainpipe

Walk Logistics

Start and End: Trailhead at Tettegouche State Park

Getting There: The park entrance is just off Highway 61 about 4.5 miles northeast of the town of Silver Bay, or 0.5 miles southwest of the junction between Highway 61 and Highway 1. Take the road past the visitor's center toward the campground and Tettegouche Trailhead. Drive by the Baptism River parking lot, cross the Baptism River, and then follow the signs to the Tettegouche campground and trailhead parking.

Walk Distance: Just over 9 miles   **Difficulty:** Hiking Boots

Safety Concerns: Waypoints 15 and 28

Worth a Longer Look: Waypoints 7, 8, 9, 10, 12, 15, 16, 17, 20, 22, 25, 27

Waypoint-to-Waypoint

One: Trailhead and Fall Colors

We consider ourselves lucky for it is another bright, blue-sky, fall day with the temperature a perfect walking 55 degrees. The day has warmed up quickly for there was frost in the Tower area of Northern Minnesota, and it was only 40 degrees when we left Duluth this morning for the park.

Waypoint 1 is in the trailhead parking lot by the sign for the Superior Hiking Trail. Another sign informs us it is 3.5 miles to Tettegouche Camp on Tettegouche Lake which is where we are headed.

There are no other cars in the parking lot, which is a shame for it is such a lovely fall day and the colors are just about at their peak.

Two: Tree Zoos and Asters

Leave the parking lot and walk up a gentle slope over a wide gravel trail with a *tree zoo* for white pine to the left. The forest is birch with cedar and alder; large-leafed *aster*, blue fringed aster, and bush *honeysuckle*, along with *raspberries* and *thimbleberries* occur along the trail.

Waypoint 2 is at a junction with a ski trail that goes off to the left. This is junction A as inscribed on the wooden post where the trails meet.

Three: Palisade Head Rhyolite

Continue uphill over a trail composed of *glacial till* with the larger *boulders* having been moved to the side during trail construction. The boulders come from weathering and erosion of the till, with the clay and silt-size material,

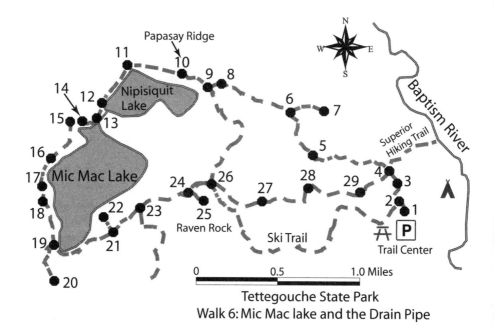

Papasay Ridge

11

14 12 Nipisiquit
Lake
15 13

16

17 Mic Mac Lake 24 26

18 22 23 25
Raven Rock

19 21

20

10

9 8

6

5

28 27 29

Baptism River

Superior
Hiking Trail

4
3
2
1

Ski Trail

Trail Center

P

0   0.5   1.0 Miles

Tettegouche State Park
Walk 6: Mic Mac lake and the Drain Pipe

along with a lot of the *pebbles*, having been washed away leaving the larger pieces behind.

At the hilltop walk through a nice stand of white pine into a forest dominated by spruce, aspen, and balsam poplar. Waypoint 3 is at an *outcrop* in the trail of pink rhyolite. This is the *Palisade Head Rhyolite*, which forms Palisade Head, Shovel Point, and High Falls. The rock contains small, square crystals of *potassium feldspar* (the mineral orthoclase) and gray glassy *quartz* and exhibits a hackly or rough weathering surface, which is characteristic of this rock.

The Palisade Head Rhyolite formed from an explosive (pyroclastic) volcanic eruption and was deposited from what geologists call a *pyroclastic flow*. See walk 1, the Shovel Point Walk, waypoint 2 for more information on the origin and distribution of this rock.

Four: Dead Birch and the Superior Hiking Trail

It is a short walk from the rhyolite outcrop up a rocky trail to the junction with the Superior Hiking Trail (labeled B on the wooden park post). To the left the Superior Hiking Trail goes to Mt. Trudee and eventually Silver Bay, and to the right it leads to High Falls and on to Highway 1.

For walk 6 continue straight ahead on the park trail in the direction of Tettegouche Camp. There are a lot of dead birch along this trail section. This seems to be the norm for the North Shore, and it is due to a combination of old age and disease.

Five: Sedges and Twig Eaters

Wide and grass-covered with some bouldery sections, the trail goes by a large white pine into a low, swampy area with cedar and birch along with aspen, alder, and mountain maple. Also called moose maple, these trees got this name because moose simply love their small branches. That may be why the Ojibwe gave the name "twig eaters" to moose.

The trail is lined with lady, interrupted, and *bracken ferns* along with large-leafed aster and thimbleberries. Sedges and rushes also occur mixed in with the tall grass, and I thought they were all the same–namely green grass. Not so, for as I am informed:

> The sedges have edges,
>
> The rushes are round,
>
> While grasses are jointed,
>
> And grow from the ground.

Feeling better with this knowledge, it's on through the low, wet grassy-sedgey section with planked areas over wetter spots to a bridge across a small, rocky creek lined by white cedars and young balsam fir. This is waypoint 5.

Six: Long Uphill

From the bridge head uphill over a wide, grassy trail (with sedges), which goes through a spruce, paper birch, balsam poplar, and cedar forest. It is a long uphill to the top and the junction (waypoint 6) with a spur trail that goes to an overlook of Lake Superior.

Seven: Palisade Head and Blueberries

Take the spur trail, which heads gently uphill with *sarsaparilla*, large leafed-aster, bracken ferns, bush honeysuckle, sumac, and *bunchberry* lining the sides of the trail. Mountain maple, small maple trees, and alder form the understory of the forest, which is dominantly birch and aspen.

Walking past and over outcrops of lumpy *Beaver River Diabase* (see *diabase weathering*) go up a steep hill to the overlook (waypoint 7). The *diabase* outcrop, with some kibbles and bits around it, provides a wonderful view of Palisade Head to the southeast, and of the hilly terrain of the North Shore to the south and east. Lake Superior is its blue self in the distance, and the Baptism River Valley opens up below us.

The spur trail continues on from the overlook but soon peters out, so it is not worth following. Besides, the *blueberries* all occur near the diabase outcrop, so in season there is no reason to travel further.

137

Eight: Beaver Pond

Return to the trail junction and continue to the right with the walking path passing through a grassy, wet area as it heads gently uphill in a forest of aspen, balsam poplar, and paper birch with some spruce. Alder and mountain maple form the understory. It is a short walk across the hilltop before the trail heads downhill to an ATV trail crossing.

Continue along the grassy trail with wet spots to a sign for the Nipisiquit Lake Trail (which we are on) followed by a pond with a large beaver lodge in it. The pond is full of dead balsam and alder, and an impressive beaver dam has a fairly significant drop down into a much smaller pond. The dead trees are the result of rising water levels due to the dam, and the tree roots have been flooded long enough for the trees to die. Just past the pond is a bridge across a small creek (waypoint 8), which had been nicely dammed by the beaver engineers. Park personnel apparently didn't like this, so they have breached the dam to let the water flow. The beaver had actually constructed a double dam, and have abandoned their one-story abode in the small pond for a three-story luxury house in the large, upper pond. Talk about upwardly mobile–the beaver are no exception to this idea!

Nine: Nice Forest and Trail Junction

It is now into a beautiful maple-birch forest as the trail heads gently uphill to reach a major trail intersection, which is waypoint 9. The path to the left goes up to the Superior Hiking Trail, the one straight ahead goes to Nipisiquit Lake and a wonderful lunch spot (and fishing spot?), while the trail to the right heads on toward Tettegouche Camp.

Ten: Papasay Ridge

Follow the Tettegouche Camp Trail as it heads gently uphill over and by diabase outcrops and boulders through a nice maple and yellow birch forest to the junction with the spur trail that goes to Papasay Ridge (waypoint 10).

Take the spur trail, and it is just a short walk to the diabase overlook from which there is a spectacular view to the northeast of a grassy-sided creek and the eye stretching and beautiful hilly terrain beyond. The hills to the far north are all dipping (tilted) toward Lake Superior, forming what are referred to as the *Sawtooth Mountains*. The Sawtooth Mountains are a generic name for hills that have long, gentle slopes in the direction of the lake (the way the lava flows dip), and steep cliff-like or blunt nose shapes on the opposite side, which are due to *glacial plucking*. This gives the hills the profile of teeth on a wood saw. The hills that make up the Sawtooth Mountains are composed of either *basalt* or, further up the North Shore, an intrusive rock we call the Star Wars Porphyry.

Eleven: Forest Change

From the junction walk downhill over diabase steps and on through the fiery blaze of fall colors passing a wide ski trail to the right. After the ski trail the forest changes with small balsam fir, spruce, and cedar becoming dominant, and the trail becomes bouldery with some planked sections. Growing along here are large-leafed aster, blue bead lily, bunchberry, bracken fern, and thimbleberry. Waypoint 11 is at a trail junction (E on the post) with the path to the left going along Nipisiquit and Mic Mac lakes to Tettegouche Camp, and the trail straight ahead going to Mt. Baldy and Nicado Lake.

Twelve: Spruce and Fir

Take the trail to the left, which narrows considerably as it goes through a maple and birch dominated forest. A dense stand of small balsam fir occurs to the left and separates the trail from the lake. Cedar makes an appearance as the trail turns toward the lake, and as it does we take in the nice views down the lake.

Moving away from the lakeshore the trail has planked sections over wetter areas as it enters a maple and paper birch dominated forest with some large yellow birch; again small balsam fir and spruce dominate between the trail and the lakeshore. Growing along the shore are blue-flag iris, one of the prettiest early summer flowers.

Waypoint 12 is at a spur trail that goes down to the lakeshore. The shore is rocky with most of the rocks composed of diabase boulders. There is a nice view down the lake.

Thirteen: Cattail Marsh

Continue down the main trail past a small outcrop of Beaver River Diabase to an open, grassy area with a small fen (see walk 4, waypoint 14 for the definition of a fen) that seems to connect Nipisiquit and Mic Mac Lakes. Cattails are common in this area with alder and bunchberries found along the trail. In some of the larger pockets of standing water cattails are abundant, possibly to the pleasure of two species of animals that make their homes here, namely red-winged blackbirds and muskrats.

Walk past a large boulder of diabase near the end of the open area and enter a grove of maple and birch with some spruce and one small basswood tree. Emerging on the other side it is once again into the open, with the trail now at the edge of Mic Mac Lake. This is waypoint 13.

Fourteen: Grassy Marsh

Follow the lakeside with cattails growing along the shore and white water lily further out; lichen, rock tripe, and moss-covered diabase outcrops to the right. There is a pile of *talus* composed of large boulders of diabase that come from the *frost wedging* of rocks exposed on the high hill to the right. Holes between the rock pieces may be inhabited by creatures like salamanders or snakes. To the left is a wide, grassy marsh with alder, *Labrador tea*, blueberries, *blue bead lily*, and *bog laurel*, and bunchberries.

Crossing over a planked trail section come to a tall, straight white pine that really stands out as it sits right at the edge of the wet, grassy area, and this is waypoint 14. There are also black spruce and tamarack trees here. The tamaracks are simply beautiful this time of the year, golden yellow in the bright sunshine.

Fifteen: Vulture Tree

Continuing over planked sections the trail becomes drier and more bouldery as it passes another pile of diabase talus before returning to its wet nature with more planked sections. The trail now follows the edge of a grassy fen that separates it from the lake. Labrador tea, blueberries, and alder may occur along the marsh.

Passing a red pine tree and more diabase boulders the overgrown trail cuts through the fen to a bridge that crosses a really wet spot. *Joe-Pye weed*, alders, and sedges grow here. Joe-Pye weed, a 3 to 5 foot tall member of the Daisy Family, has pinkish-purple flower heads in round-topped clusters. Narrow, short-stalked leaves give off a vanilla odor when bruised or crushed. Supposedly the plant is named for Joe Pye, a Native American doctor who treated early colonists for typhoid fever with the roots and leaves of this plant.

We come to a large, dead tree just past the bridge and, with its bare, gray branches and gnarled snags, it defiantly needs a vulture or two sitting atop it. The Vulture Tree is waypoint 15.

Sixteen: Flat-Topped Asters and Goldenrod

After the Vulture Tree the trail becomes drier and more dirt-packed as it heads uphill through a dense forest of small balsam fir with much larger birch and aspen. From the dense woods it is back into a maple and birch fall forest with some nice yellow birch and this continues to a sign for a hiking/ ski trail. This is near a bend in the trail where the forest opens up as the number of fir greatly decrease and maple and birch are joined by oak and large balsam poplars. Beyond the bend the trail follows an old road.

Going along the old road the trail is wider and the woods continue to be open and pretty with the red maples and yellow birch along with brownish-yellow oak. Coming to a wet, grassy area the trail narrows to wind through a sea of flat-topped white asters and *goldenrod*. This is waypoint 16.

Seventeen: Tettegouche Camp

Entering a dark balsam fir and spruce woods with some aspen, the trail is littered with boulders from the glacial till and some of the larger ones have been piled up along the trail during road construction.

The service road at Tettegouche Camp is waypoint 17. Take time to look around the camp or rest on the dock, which affords a nice view across Mic Mac Lake.

Eighteen: Mic Mac Lake

From the service road the walking path follows another old road that parallels the shore of Mic Mac Lake. It is just a short distance to waypoint 18, which is at the junction with a trail to the right that goes to a large *anorthosite glacial erratic* and the floating fen.

Nineteen: Glacial Erratics

Continue on the old road going by glacial erratics of anorthosite and diabase. The trail through here is gravelly and is lined by boulders placed there during road construction. The question we have is whether this is a logging road or a road that led to a favorite fishing hole?

Pass by a large glacial erratic of anorthosite, then small outcrops of diabase and anorthosite before going down a short slope and through a balsam fir and spruce forest with cedar and paper birch. The trail is level through this area with cobbles and boulders of basalt, diabase, and pink *monzonite* along it. Waypoint 19 is at the junction with a spur trail that goes to an overlook of the Palisade Creek Valley; this is labeled trail junction J.

Twenty: Palisade Creek Valley

Take the spur trail to the overlook, which is on an outcrop of anorthosite decorated with lingonberries (a type of cranberry, also called foxberry) and sumac (waypoint 20). There is a nice view of meandering Palisade Creek with red oaks along its sides and old beaver dams down the valley. Mt. Trudee and its steep cliff is the prominent landmark to the south.

Twenty-One: Bowling Ball Anorthosite

Return to the main trail (waypoint 19) which continues on through a forest of small balsam fir and spruce with cedar, paper birch, and the odd white pine. Mic Mac Lake is to the left. This is followed by a low, swampy area containing cedar and alder along with planked trail sections.

Drier now, the trail, composed of glacial till, heads uphill as it passes a glacial erratic of Bowling Ball Anorthosite and goes over diabase outcrops to the top. Head downhill over smooth weathering diabase, and from here the trail goes up and down passing a diabase outcrop with birch trees growing out of it. Rose-twisted stalk and blue bead lily grow along the trail.

141

Walk past a small outcrop of anorthosite (to the left) with a spectacular view of Mt. Trudee, the high hill of anorthosite to the right. After this it is up a steep hill over wooden steps and diabase outcrops through a lovely maple, yellow birch, and paper birch forest with the occasional white pine.

Near the top of the hill come to the junction with a spur trail to the left that goes to the Conservancy of the Pines overlook, and this is waypoint 21.

Twenty-Two: Conservancy of the Pines

Take the spur trail and walk over lumpy diabase to the overlook, which is waypoint 22. It's not much of an overlook, for the beautiful red pines encircle the anorthosite outcrop and allow just the tiniest view of the lake. The pines are very nice, and the wind in these tall pines sounds like water rushing through a rocky gorge. The Ojibwe thought the same thing and actually have a name for this sound–Sissiquinod.

Twenty-Three: Superior Hiking Trail

Return to the main trail and continue to the left going gently uphill past an outcrop of Bowling Ball Anorthosite through a forest that now has more birch than maple.

The trail flattens out as it crosses over a diabase outcrop with diabase boulders to the right. The diabase outcrop is immediately followed by one of anorthosite before the trail heads uphill through a dense forest of maples and yellow birch with basswood and balsam poplar.

At the top of the hill the trail becomes flat and bouldery (*pegmatite*, pink monzonite, basalt, and diabase) then descends and goes by an anorthosite outcrop to the left before coming to the junction with the Superior Hiking Trail (waypoint 23). The right branch of the Superior Hiking Trail goes to Mt. Trudee and then on to Silver Bay, whereas the left branch, the one we will follow, goes toward High Falls.

Twenty-Four: Raven Rock and Maple Forest

Following the Superior Hiking Trail, we walk through an open maple forest with some spruce trees. After passing a small swamp marked by wooden planks, it's a nice walk through open maple and birch woods to the spur trail leading up to Raven Rock (waypoint 24)

Twenty-Five: Overlook

Take the spur trail, which has boulders and outcrops of anorthosite along it to the top of Raven Rock. Raven Rock is an anorthosite knob and the view from the top is to the northwest and is of another anorthosite knob which looks like it divides Mic Mac and Nipisquit Lakes. From Raven Rock return to the Superior Hiking Trail.

Twenty-Six: A Place To Rest and Yellow Birch

It is now gently downhill to the junction with the park trail that goes to Nipisiquit Lake (to the left). To the right the wide, grassy park trail goes back to waypoint 2 of this walk and then on to the trailhead parking lot. The park trail is mostly wet and grassy, but to avoid the "drainpipe" (waypoint 28 of this walk) this is the only alternative. This junction, with its park bench, is waypoint 26.

Twenty-Seven: Giant White Pine

The Superior Hiking Trail continues on behind the wooden bench; the outcrop to the right of the trail is anorthosite. From the bench the hiking trail continues downhill through a yellow birch and cedar forest past another anorthosite outcrop, but one with a yellow birch growing on top of it. There is a small creek to the northeast.

The trail continues gently up and down through an open, rolling forest of yellow birch, paper birch, and maples. Passing a small swampy area with cedar trees, continue through the forest to the Paul Bunyan White Pine at waypoint 27. This tree must be 80-100 feet tall and at least 5 feet in diameter. This has to be the Empire State Building of the forest, for up it goes–straight, beautiful, and majestic–all the way to the nearest star.

Twenty-Eight: Drainpipe

It's a nice walk through open woods with yellow birch and paper birch, maple, cedar, and spruce before heading uphill to an outcrop of lumpy diabase that is weathering to kibbles and bits. Continue on past a small rock pile composed of basalt and diabase (exposed due to a tree tipping over) then along the edge of the hill before starting down into the Baptism River Valley. Passing outcrops of lumpy and crumbly diabase, and nice overlooks of the valley, come to a 150-foot-long descent through a steep rock crevice. A wooden railing and stone steps help in getting down part of the crevice, but otherwise we are on our own as we climb over large, angular boulders of diabase to the bottom. This crevice has been named the "drainpipe," and we decide this is a good name because, if we happen to be here in a rainstorm, we would be sucked like a spaghetti noodle straight down the steep rock face. Waypoint 28 is at the bottom of the drainpipe amongst large boulders of lumpy diabase that have been derived from the cliff by frost wedging. There is a nice grove of cedars at this point.

Twenty-Nine: Mighty Tree

The trail is level through cedar and yellow birch woods to a cutover area with second-growth aspen, birch, and mountain maple. Crossing an old road the trail passes through a cedar grove then back into a paper birch and

143

yellow birch forest.

The ridge to the right is composed of lumpy diabase. The tree growing from the diabase at waypoint 29 was there, we decide, before the boulder. The boulder rolled into it, and the tree split it apart!

Thirty: Trailhead Parking Lot

The hiking trail passes over outcrops of lumpy diabase as it goes through an older birch-balsam poplar forest to the Tettegouche State Park trail we started the walk on (waypoint 4). Tettegouche State Park Headquarters is 2.1 miles to the east, and High Falls, the highest waterfall entirely in Minnesota, is 0.5 miles to the northeast. This is waypoint 30. From here take the spur trail back to the trailhead parking lot. This is some walk, it is long but well worth the effort with a variety of rocks, plants, and landscapes to enjoy.

Crosby Manitou State Park

Introduction

George H. Crosby Manitou State Park is the only park along the North Shore that is not accessible directly from Highway 61. In terms of facilities this park is the most primitive and, in terms of development it is the most "wild" of all the parks included in this guidebook.

The park has two very different parts to its name, parts you would not consider compatible. George H. Crosby was a Duluth entrepreneur who was deeply involved in the development of both the Mesabi and Cuyuna Iron Ranges, places that have been extensively mined for iron ore since the late 1800s. Turns out he also appreciated the wilderness aspect of northern Minnesota and so donated 3,318 acres of wild, rugged land to the state with the stipulation that it was to be managed in a way that would ensure protection of its wild nature. The state has certainly lived up to its end of the bargain with the spacious, widely separated campsites accessible only by backpacking; there is no campground, flush toilets, or showers. The park is just what Crosby would have wanted it to be–a true wilderness experience with black bears, moose, and wolves included at no extra charge.

The second part of the name, Manitou, which is Ojibwe for Great Spirit, is the name of the energetic and noisy river that cuts through the park. The Great Spirit, for Native Americans, is the center of everything, and I would argue that this park has four great spirits.

The first great spirit is the river which, with its waterfalls, cascades, rocky gorges, steep canyons, and rough, tumbling water is the center of the park. The Manitou River is different from the rivers in the other seven state parks along the North Shore. It is spring fed, so even in late summer and through the dry fall, when the other rivers are often struggling to make a consistent gurgle, the Manitou flows free and strong.

The second great spirit is the old-growth forest of sugar maple, yellow birch, and white cedar. These are grand, big trees; true elders of the state with ages of more than 400 years for the yellow birch, 300 for white cedar, and 200 for the sugar maples. Four hundred years ago, Jamestown was not yet in existence and the Great Spirit really did rule the land.

If you are like me and are wondering just what the heck an old growth-forest is other than old, the Department of Natural Resources defines such a place as a natural forest that is at least 120 years old. A place where there has been no severe disturbances such as fire, wind storm, or logging. The old-growth forests in this park consist of tree species that have the ability to reproduce under a shady canopy and, because of this, they can seemingly persist indefinitely (until global warming gets them).

The third great spirit of the park is the Grandfather Rocks or what the Sioux people called Tunka Shila. For these Native Americans rocks were their first ancestors–in all this world they were here first. There was only rock, and life arose and flourished upon that rock, and therefore rocks should be treated with respect like an elder. They need to be recognized and honored, for they are the foundation for everything else, including this park. George H. Crosby Manitou State Park contains the greatest variety of Grandfather Rocks found in any of the parks along the North Shore. There are volcanic and sedimentary rocks along with a great number of igneous intrusive rocks. The intrusive rocks, which represent the cooled, hard remains of magma chambers that fed lava flows at the surface, belong to what geologists call the Beaver Bay Complex. In the park there are two different components of this complex–older and layered gabbroic to monzonitic rocks of the Blesner Lake Intrusion, and younger xenolith (inclusion)-rich rocks of the Beaver River Intrusion, which is diabase to gabbro in composition.

The volcanic rocks are basalt and rhyolite lava flows, which are part of the North Shore Volcanic Group and were happily flowing over the land some 1.1 billion years ago. The sedimentary rocks range from sandstones to debris flows, and each is derived from the weathering and erosion of the lava flows. The debris flows are spectacular to look at and best seen in the bed of the Caribou River close to where it flows under Highway 61 (Walk 13, Superior Hiking Trail Walking Guide).

The fourth great spirit of the park is the sum of the first three coupled with the environment they occur in. Parts of the park are much the same as when Native Americans walked through here hundreds of years ago, and the park captures just what George Crosby wanted–the spirit of the wilderness. So one park, two very different kinds of names, and three different spirits that come together to make Manitou the true center of everything a walker or hiker could want. The only thing missing are, well walks. So we have included four walks for this park, and each is devised with the idea of giving the walker the opportunity to explore, enjoy, and see all the different spirits of the park.

The trails themselves are some of the more challenging you will find described in this guidebook: narrow, lots of ups and downs, boulder-covered, and root-crossed. That said, they provide a real wilderness feel with wonderful scenery, inspiring views, great rocks, and they lead to some very nice campsites. To top it off they give a walker the true flavor of this very different and wonderful park.

146

George H. Crosby Manitou State Park

Walk 1: The Humpback and Manitou River Trail

Walk Logistics

Start and End: Parking lot in George H. Crosby Manitou State Park (state park sticker required to park here).

Getting There: Take Highway 61 to Highway 1. Follow Highway 1 for 7.4 miles to the junction with County Road 7 (Cramer Road). Turn northeast on to County Road 7, and go 7 miles (passing the Finland Recreation Center and the Sonju Lake Road) to the park entrance. Turn right, and the parking lot is 0.6 miles from County Road 7.

Walk Distance: 2.85 miles   **Difficulty:** Walking Shoes

Safety Concerns: Waypoint 5 and 13 (steep uphill climb)

Worth a Longer Look: Waypoints 3, 8, 11, 12, 14, 15, 16

Waypoint-to-Waypoint

One: Minnesota Biomes

It smells like rain and that pretty much sums up the summer weather except for the bit about it feeling like we are in a steam bath gone bad–all in all it is very not "northern Minnesota."

There is a sign in the parking area that shows an outline of Minnesota and depicts the state's three distinct biomes. Except for mountainous states, where plant communities change with elevation, it is unusual to have such a diversity of species and three distinct ecological communities in one state. Generally the western part of Minnesota is referred to as "prairie grasslands," the central part as "deciduous woods," and the northeast as "boreal forest." This latter area easily occupies two-fifths of the state.

Waypoint 1 is on the west side of the parking lot at the sign for the start of the Humpback Trail. We puzzle over the name for a few seconds before deciding it must mean the topography is camel-like, lots of ups and as many downs.

Two: Rotten Rock and Glacial Till

The trail begins in the true spirit of the park–it is bouldery, root-crossed, and heading uphill. The *boulders* and *cobbles* come from weathering and erosion

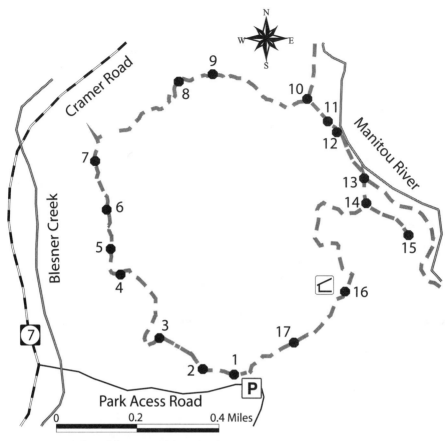

Crosby Manitou State Park
Walk 1: The Humpback and Manitou River Trail

of the *glacial till* that covers the park in deposits called *ground moraine*. The boulders are *basalt*, *gabbro*, *diabase*, and *monzonite* derived from the till due to frost heaving and the washing away of the finer clay and silt-size material they were once embedded in. The forest is dominantly sugar maple, paper birch, and spruce with a bit of white pine.

Waypoint 2 is at a deeply weathered and moss-covered outcrop of monzonite. The rock is rusty to reddish-brown with chalky white *plagioclase feldspar*, black, elongate or prismatic *pyroxene* crystals, and smaller and badly weathered crystals of pink *potassium feldspar*. This rock, unlike most "*granitic*" rocks on our planet, contains no *quartz* and, because of this, is called an "alkalic" rock, one rich in alkalis like potassium, calcium, and sodium. This particular alkalic rock, based on mineral composition, is called a pyroxene or iron-rich monzonite. The monzonite represents the uppermost and most "felsic" unit of the layered Blesner Lake intrusive body. Personally, I would call this stuff Rotten Rock and leave it at that.

148

Three: Kibbles and Bits and a Nice View

Continue uphill over crumbly brown Rotten Rock to the hilltop from which there is a partial view to the northeast of the Manitou River Valley. The forest is in full color mode with maple reds, browns, and oranges, birch yellows and yellowish browns, and the intense green of spruce.

Just past here come to a large, open outcrop area where the trail is covered in kibbles and bits (see *diabase weathering*). The exposed rock appears to be of a different composition than the Rotten Rock on the hillside as it lacks pink potassium feldspar or orthoclase crystals. Being composed dominantly of dark pyroxene (weathering rusty brown) and gray plagioclase (weathering chalky white in places) it makes a rock called gabbro, and this is another, more mafic part of the layered Blesner Lake Intrusion. The gabbro is covered in reindeer lichen and crumbly; the crumbly texture leads to the kibbles and bits seen on the trail.

Leaving the outcrop walk over more crumbly gabbro with kibbles and bits to waypoint 3, which is at the start of a short downhill section. There is another gabbro outcrop here along with a nice view to the west down the Cramer Road and Blesner Creek. The rolling hills are showing off their fall colors, and in the distance we see Wolf Ridge, the location of the environmental learning center.

Four: Chicken Tracks and Clubmoss

The view to the west continues as the trail heads downhill over crumbly gabbro with kibbles and bits. As we walk downhill we notice a change in the way the gabbro looks. In places the chalky white plagioclase feldspar crystals are oriented so they look like a chicken has walked randomly through the cooling magma leaving its "footprints" behind, much like a person does after walking through wet cement. This kind of feature in a rock is, naturally enough, called chicken track texture. In other places long dark crystals of pyroxene look like black streaks in finer, "speckled" cream to gray-colored plagioclase feldspar-rich rock.

Turning to follow the hillside, the trail flattens out and becomes bouldery (gabbro and pink monzonite) as it passes into an open maple and paper birch forest with lots and lots of red and yellow colors. Head gently uphill across a flat area before again going downhill. At the edge of the hill is a large outcrop of gabbro (waypoint 4), and around it we find three different kinds of *clubmoss*. Through this section balsam fir has become much more common. Interestingly enough the sky has now turned the same color as the paper birch trees, and there is an ominous darkness to the horizon.

Five: Poor Bridge

Walk downhill over a boulder and cobble littered trail to a small, dry creek (waypoint 5) with rotten wood planks across it. Coming down the hill the forest changes from maple, paper birch, and balsam fir into a younger forest (cutover) dominated by balsam poplar with some aspen.

Six: Spring Flowers and Gabbro

From the creek the bouldery trail goes uphill with the help of a few old log steps to an outcrop of smooth weathering *Beaver River Diabase,* which is finer-grained, fresher-looking, and contains more plagioclase feldspar than the Blesner Lake Gabbro. In places, however, the diabase does become coarser-grained and these varieties represent either the slower cooled-centers of large *dikes* and *sills,* or larger, sheet like intrusive masses. Within George H. Crosby Manitou State Park much of the Beaver River Diabase is this coarser-grained variety and is distinguished from the Blesner Lake Gabbro by its lack of layering, cross-cutting relationships, and the fact that it contains *xenoliths* of *anorthosite* and basalt.

Continue uphill with a nice view back to the hill (hump) just crossed and the high ridge behind it. Pass by a lichen-covered, rusty weathering outcrop of diabase to reach the hilltop. From here there is a view to the west of Blesner Creek, and the exposed rock is the same kind just passed with lichen included. In the spring woods look for *wood anemones*, Canadian mayflowers*, springbeauties*, *trilliums*, and coralroot *orchids*.

Seven: Ancient Stream

Now comes a long, relatively flat trail section before once again heading down slope over old wooden steps and a bouldery trail to the bottom where we find tons of boulders of basalt, gabbro, pink monzonite, and *rhyolite* all piled together in a low, wet area. These may represent an ancient stream deposit with the boulders coming from erosion of the glacial till. The stream removed the finer material in the till and, in some distant time, during a flood or spring runoff, managed to pile the boulders up in a suitable location (at the end of a gravel bar).

From the boulder pile it is uphill to another hilltop with a smooth weathering, lichen-covered, massive diabase outcrop (waypoint 7).

Eight: Beaver Pond and Spotted Rocks

Walk along the hilltop with gentle ups and downs over outcrops of Beaver River Diabase with partial views through the woods of the Blesner Creek Valley. The diabase varies from smooth-weathering to lumpy, and the woods are cedar, spruce, paper birch, aspen, and balsam fir.

Go downhill over a trail of glacial till with boulders and cobbles of gabbro, rhyolite, basalt, pink monzonite, and diabase. At the bottom walk through a cedar grove, over a flat diabase outcrop, and through a low, wet area before heading down the side of another hump. At the bottom the trail bends to the left as it passes a large cedar tree.

Just past the cedar tree come to a large, dried up beaver pond that looks like something out of a horror film. The pond contains a beaver lodge sitting high and dry, dozens and dozens of fallen, cross-piled trees, lots of dead standing cedar and ash, and small, isolated pools of scummy water with mucky areas between them. The dam at the end of the pond is really impressive, and we wonder what happened to the water and to the engineers who built the dam?

Continue along the edge of the pond over outcrops of diabase that have large dark blotches (pyroxene crystals) in a dark grey plagioclase feldspar matrix. Fresh surfaces of the rock look smooth, but on weathered faces the pyroxene blotches form raised lumps or bumps. This lumpy texture is called *ophitic;* the word comes from the Greek and means a stone spotted like a serpent. The pyroxene spots or blotches enclose much smaller crystals of plagioclase feldspar and are separated from each other by fine-grained areas of plagioclase feldspar with or without *olivine* and *magnetite*. The larger pyroxenes are more resistant to weathering than the intervening feldspar-rich areas and so end up as "raised lumps" throughout the mafic rock. It is this texture that gives the Beaver River Diabase its interesting weathering characteristics and leads to the kibbles and bits seen on the trail.

Pass by a large boulder of diabase to arrive at waypoint 8, a pile of diabase talus derived from the hillsides by frost wedging.

Nine: Nice View

The trail goes up and over lumpy diabase as it heads uphill through a paper birch, spruce, and balsam fir forest. At the top a large outcrop of lumpy or ophitic diabase (waypoint 9) occurs in a fairly open area with a nice view to the southeast of the Manitou River Valley. *Sarsaparilla* and *bearberry* may be found along the trail.

Ten: Manitou River Trail

It is now downhill over lumpy diabase into a low, wet area that is crammed full of boulders. The round to sub-round boulders are of mixed compositions with gabbro, diabase, and monzonite the most common. These are more than likely part of an old stream channel and could be related to the boulder pile seen at waypoint 7.

From the long-ago stream channel it is uphill over diabase outcrops, followed by a flat rocky section through a forest of paper birch, aspen, spruce, and balsam fir with some maple. It is then uphill again to a short level section before walking back downhill to come to the end of the Humpback Trail and the start of the Manitou River Trail (waypoint 10). The walking path through this section is lined by mountain maple, hazel, and alder.

The branch of the Manitou River Trail that goes to the left follows the Manitou River to campsite #1, which is located in a pretty grove of spruce and balsam fir. The campsite is isolated as it is located a long way from other campsites or any foot traffic. The river along this stretch of the trail is slow-moving and *meandering*, not at all like the river seen further downstream. There are numerous grass and marshy areas with alder and bush *honeysuckle* along the river, and the trail passes some nice, old, large spruce trees.

Eleven: Manitou Cascades

From the trail junction take the right branch of the Manitou River Trail passing campsite #2 before starting downhill through a balsam fir, spruce, and paper birch forest. In the distance we can hear the river as it flows over the Manitou Cascades, and it gets louder and louder as we walk down slope. Waypoint 11 is at the bottom of a set of old, cut log steps and the junction with a path that leads down to the river.

Take the river path, which ends above the Manitou Cascades. There is a nice view of the step-like cascades and the river beyond. The river flows over Beaver River Diabase that has been intruded by thin dikes of granitic rock. The cascades have formed here because 1) the dikes erode more easily than the diabase, and 2) there are *cooling joints* in the diabase. The steps are thus due to erosion along the joints coupled with removal of the granitic dikes.

Twelve: Base of Cascades and Monzonite Porphyry

Back at the junction continue downhill over a bouldery trail (gabbro, diabase, rhyolite, monzonite, and basalt) to a final steep descent via wood stairs to the base of the cascades. From this spot there is a great view of the very pretty, stair-stepped waterfall with turbulent, white water flowing over the nicely jointed diabase. At the bottom of the cascade the river widens to flow gently on.

There is a "neat" boulder here of what is called orthoclase monzonite porphyry (see *phenocryst*). This rock is made up of large crystals of *orthoclase feldspar* (phenocrysts) in a dark, fine-grained matrix of pyroxene, plagioclase, and orthoclase. A porphyritic rock is one which contains both large and small crystals, and this feature tells geologists something about the cooling history of the rock. To form the phenocrysts (large crystals) the magma has to cool slowly, but to form the smaller crystals the magma has to cool rapidly. One magma, two cooling events. In the case of this rock the orthoclase phenocrysts formed in a magma chamber situated well beneath the surface. The orthoclase was happily crystallizing, content with its surroundings, when something dreadful happened (a fault or crustal break) that caused the magma to rise rapidly toward the surface. As it did it took the large orthoclase crystals with it but, as it neared the surface the magma began to cool and crystallize very rapidly. No time here for large crystals to grow, so the resulting rock ended up with large orthoclase crystals (phenocrysts) in a much finer-grained material (the matrix). Geologists call such a rock a porphyry.

Thirteen: Long Climb

Continue to follow the river over a bouldery trail passing a boulder-filled creek to a long uphill section. Climb away from the river up numerous wooden steps to reach the point where the trail turns to once again follow the river but is now some 80 feet above the rushing water.

Pass an outcrop of Blesner Lake Gabbro on a root-crossed, rocky trail to waypoint 13, the junction of the Superior Hiking Trail (called Middle Trail in the park) and the Manitou River Trail.

Fourteen: Yew

Take the branch of the Superior Hiking Trial that goes straight ahead (uphill). Yew, a shrubby, low-growing evergreen, grows all along here. Yews are commonly found in forests that are cool, damp, and shaded, such as occur on north-facing slopes like this one. One warbler seen in this area, the black-throated blue, is known to nest in yew thickets.

The scientific name for *yew* is interesting. Its first name, Taxus, is a Greek word meaning bow, and apparently this North American species was used extensively by Native Americans for hunting bows. Taxol is a compound derived from yews that has shown beneficial effects in the fight against certain cancers. The second part of its name, Canadensis, is a bit more obvious; it means "of Canada" or in a more general sense "northern."

Waypoint 14 is at the junction between the Superior Hiking Trail and the Crosby Hill Trail.

Fifteen: Crosby Hill Overlook

Take the spur trail that heads gently uphill over and past outcrops of the Blesner Lake Gabbro through a mixed forest of cedar, balsam fir, paper birch, and spruce along with both red and white pine to a wooden bench, which is waypoint 15. From the bench we can hear the Manitou River, but we need to continue down the slope another 20 feet or so for a very nice river view. From this spot there is also a good view of the tall, anorthosite knob to the right and, in the distance, Lake Superior.

The red pines in front of the bench have grown up over the years to ruin the "bench" view. The outcrop at the bench is Beaver River Diabase with lots of kibbles and bits around the bench and on the trail. Kibbles and bits weathering is most common in ophitic rocks exposed on south-facing slopes because these slopes undergo many freeze-thaw cycles in the late fall and early spring, greatly enhancing the weathering of the rock.

Just down the trail toward the junction there is an outcrop of smooth-weathering, grey to tan Blesner Lake Gabbro.

Sixteen: Iron Formation and Picnic Shelter

Back at the trail junction continue to the left. The trail, bordered by young cedars, goes uphill, as it winds its way over and around piles of rock. These are *talus* deposits derived by *frost wedging* from the hillside to the right. Some of the rocks making up the talus are unusual and rare. They are composed of 50-75% *magnetite,* with green glassy apatite along with some plagioclase feldspar, pyroxene, and ilmenite (an iron-titanium oxide). This would be described as a type of *iron formation*, one formed by crystallization and settling of heavy minerals that accumulated at the bottom of a basaltic magma chamber, much like snow accumulates on a window sill. These heavy minerals ended up forming distinct layers in the magma chamber alternating with layers of lighter minerals like plagioclase feldspar. Other rocks found amongst the *talus* are gabbro and oxide-rich gabbro. These are part of the well-layered, dominantly gabbroic Blesner Lake Intrusion, which outcrops on the hillside above us. Also occurring on the trail are sub-round boulders of basalt and monzonite from the glacial till.

Continue uphill and walk just a short distance over a bouldery trail to waypoint 16, which is at a picnic shelter with a firepit. The rock outcropping by the shelter is Blesner Lake Gabbro. This intrusion is older than the Beaver River Diabase (cross-cuts it).

Seventeen: Large Cedars and Glacial Erratic

After a short rest it's on up the trail passing enormous standing and fallen cedars. A thick carpet of clubmoss and *bunchberry* clings to the ground everywhere we look, and this represents typical ground cover in a boreal forest. A large, moss-covered glacial erratic of anorthosite has a birch tree growing over and on it.

Continue up a gentle hill then down the opposite side over numerous boulders (basalt, gabbro, granite, and rhyolite to name a few), which come from the weathering of glacial till deposits. There are *thimbleberries* all through here and beneath these can be found an abundance of one-flowered *wintergreen.*

Waypoint 17 is at the junction between the Superior Hiking Trail and an unmarked park trail. The park trail leads to an outcrop of Blesner Lake

Gabbro from which there is a view to the northeast and east of the Manitou River Valley

Eighteen: Wide Trail and Parking Lot

From the junction continue on the Superior Hiking Trail passing two outcrops of Blesner Lake Gabbro (one in a dry creek bed) before coming to a large glacial erratic of Beaver River Diabase. The forest is dominantly maple and birch with some cedar, spruce, and balsam fir. There are lots of broad beech ferns and thimbleberries along this trail section.

From the glacial erratic it is not far to the parking lot and the end of the walk. And it was not a very pleasant end, for we were at the top of Crosby Hill Overlook when the rain began in earnest. By the time we reach the parking lot, thunder and lighting are in total control of the plum-colored sky. It simply pours for the next 40 minutes and the accompanying wind takes down numerous trees in the park.

Crosby Manitou State Park
Walk 2: Bensen Lake, Beaver Bog, and Matt Willis Trails

Walk Logistics

Start and End: Parking lot in George H. Crosby Manitou State Park (state park sticker required to park here).

Getting There: Take Highway 61 to Highway 1. Turn left and follow Highway 1 for 7.4 miles to the junction with County Road 7 (Cramer Road). Turn right on to County Road 7, and go 7 miles (passing the Finland Recreation Center and the Sonju Lake Road) to the park entrance. Turn right, and the parking lot is 0.6 miles up the dirt road.

Walk Distance: The Bensen Lake Loop is 0.8 miles; full loop is 3.75 miles.

Difficulty: Tennis Shoes (around Bensen Lake) to Walking Shoes (entire walk)

Safety Concerns: None

Worth a Longer Look: Waypoints 6, 8, 9, 10, 13, 14, 16, 23

Waypoint-to-Waypoint

One: Parking Lot

We are in the parking lot at George H. Crosby Manitou State Park, only today has turned out to be a most northern Minnesota day–it's fall in all its pre-Christmas color. Brilliant blue sky, no breeze, temperature about 55, and an old maple and birch forest to wander through. The only glitch to all this is that one of the trails we will be walking on is called Beaver Bog, and that is just a tiny bit worrisome.

Waypoint 1 is at the east end of the parking lot past the Superior Hiking Trail and Yellow Birch Trail signs at the junction between the park access road and the parking lot entrance.

Two: Bensen Lake Trail

Walk along the access road toward Bensen Lake with waypoint 2 at the sign for the Bensen Lake Trail (to the left).

Three: Planked Trail and Red Pines

The Bensen Lake Trail starts off in a grove of nice red pines (planted) then heads into a boardwalk section through a cedar grove with spruce and balsam fir trees. One of the best ways to identify these two tree types, as Steve tells me, is to shake hands with each. When I do I find the balsam fir

156

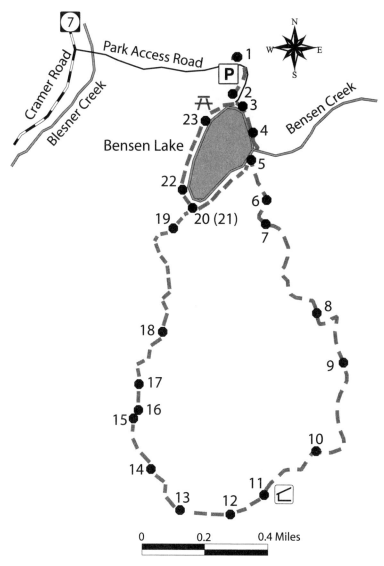

Crosby Manitou State Park
Walk 2: Bensen Lake, Beaver Bog, and Matt Willis Trails

has smooth, flat needles, which is why Native Americans used them for bed matts. The spruce has stiff needles all around, and in my mind that translates into a bad night's sleep if put beneath a sleeping bag. Another way to identify them is that balsam trees have small "bubbles" over their bark (hence bubbling balsam), whereas spruce has cracked or checkered bark.

Continue over a bouldery trail with Bensen Lake to the right. Pass a large *outcrop* of Blesner Lake *Gabbro* to the left with the *boulders* along the trail coming from this outcrop and others further up the hillside, all thanks to a process called *frost wedging*. The planked trail was completed around Bensen Lake in 2004 by the Minnesota Conservation Corp (MCC). This boardwalk helps protect white cedar roots from human foot traffic and also helps to keep people from tripping over the roots. Waypoint 3 is at the junction between the planked trail and the path up to campsite #20.

Four: Labrador Tea and the Blesner Lake Gabbro

Follow the boardwalk through a forest of cedar and black spruce trees with *Labrador tea, leatherleaf* and bog *Solomon's seal.* The adjacent hillside is made up of gabbro, which is part of the Blesner Lake Intrusion. This is a layered igneous body composed of *monzonite*, gabbro, oxide-rich gabbro, and igneous iron formation. Most of the intrusion is made up of the kind of rock seen here–gabbro.

The boardwalk follows the edge of the lake with a nice view across it and up the opposite hillside.

Walk past the path to campsite #21, and from there it is a short distance to waypoint 4, which is the path up to campsite #22.

Five: Large Birch and Trail Junction

The boardwalk continues through a cedar, balsam fir, and spruce forest to a bouldery creek that drains Bensen Lake. From the creek walk past some large, old birch trees to waypoint 5, the junction between the Bensen Lake Trail and (shudder) the Beaver Bog Trail which goes to the left.

If just doing the nice walk around Bensen Lake, proceed to waypoint 21 and continue the walk from there.

Six: Yellow Birch and an Enchanting Spot

Take the Beaver Bog Trail, which starts off rather nice by going past some old yellow birch and large spruce trees, but quickly becomes a narrow pathway.

Yellow birch gets its name from the bark on the young trees, which is silvery-yellowish in color. On older trees the smooth bark breaks open and curls back in thin plates. Yellow birch are long-lived trees and can reach over 70 feet in height and more than 3 feet in diameter. Deer, rabbits, and beaver feed on this tree, and Ruffed Grouse eat the buds during the winter. People eat it as well, though it is known to Native Americans as famine food. The inner bark, either cooked or dried, can be ground into a powder and used with cereals in making bread (a filler and used only when other forms of starch are not available).

After crossing a planked trail section over a small, dry creek come to a bog-like depression to the right. This is an ephemeral pond that only contains water in the spring or after an exceptional heavy rain storm. From here head

158

gently uphill through a fall forest of reds, browns, and yellows to a rocky stream that flows parallel to the trail. The stream will have a small, wonderful waterfall in the spring, but at the moment is just a trickle of water making its way downstream.

The exposed rock along and in the stream (including boulders) is the Beaver River Gabbro. This rock is medium-grained and composed of greenish gray *plagioclase feldspar* (some are stained pink by iron that is precipitating out of the water), black *pyroxene*, and, in the sunlight, a few sparkling green crystals of the mineral *olivine*. This intrusion, part of the *Beaver Bay Igneous Complex*, is younger than the Blesner Lake Gabbro and is distinguished from it by the fact that it contains numerous *xenoliths*, cross-cuts the Blesner Lake Gabbro, and lacks layering. This intrusion is the deeper, slower-cooled equivalent of the more common *Beaver River Diabase*.

This is waypoint 6 and it is a most enchanting spot in a beautiful forest. I kind of expect to see a unicorn on the opposite bank of the creek, or at the very least there should be a thatched roof cottage, peat smoke curling out the chimney, with flower gardens leading down to the stream. I love the barely gurgling rocky creek, the hypnotic way the sunshine drifts through the yellow and red leaves that stand in such marked contrast to the vibrant green of the spruce, and the deep blue of the sky.

Seven: Maple and Birch Woods

Continue uphill with the creek to the left and an outcrop of Beaver River Gabbro to the right. The woods remain dominantly maple and birch to waypoint 7, which is at a planked bridge over the creek.

Eight: Northern White Cedar and the Fall Forest

Leaving the creek walk uphill through a dominantly maple forest on a trail of *glacial till* with boulders of gabbro, *basalt*, and pink monzonite. The trail then levels out passing a *glacial erratic* of feldspar porphyry (see *phenocryst*) followed by a gentle uphill climb with yellow birch overhead.

Continue on the level trail as it goes through a beautiful fall forest of paper and yellow birch and maple with numerous mature, large trees–especially the yellow birch. The forest is nice and open with the ground hidden by a thick layer of maple leaves.

This is a nice enjoyable walk through the colorful old-growth forest. Come to a gentle and short downhill that ends in a wet area with a small stream and lots of cedar trees. This is waypoint 8, and in the spring it will be a very wet waypoint indeed.

A large and (we are sure) very old northern white cedar is to the right of the trail at the waypoint. The early name for this tree was Arborvitae which means "tree of life." Legend has it that Native Americans used a tea made from the bark and leaves of the tree to save explorer Jacques Cartier and his crew from scurvy–though some twenty sailors died before they tried it. This was at the present site of Quebec City in the winter of 1535-1536 and led to the northern white cedar being the first tree imported into Europe from North America.

Pilated woodpeckers love this tree and often excavate large, oval holes in the sides searching for carpenter ants. Porcupines eat the thin cedar stems as snack food, and deer and snowshoe hares use it for browse food.

Nine: Half-Way Stump

Just past waypoint 8 cross a planked section over a small creek as the trail goes through cedar, spruce, maple, paper birch, and yellow birch woods. Pass a birch tree that has grown up, out of a large white cedar stump and, in doing so, has split the stump in half.

From Half-Way Stump it is a pleasant walk through a dominantly maple and birch forest with cedar and spruce. In places the trail is bouldery (pink monzonite, gabbro, basalt, and *rhyolite*), but overall it is relatively smooth and flat to waypoint 9, a planked area over what must be a wet spot in the spring. Boulders from the trail have been used to anchor the planks, and there are nice yellow birch here.

Ten: Leaf Carpet and Beaver Dam

The pleasant forest walk continues over a red and yellow leaf-covered foot path that crunches, scrunches, and shuffles under our feet. Cross a low, wet area via planks to continue the nice walk all the way to waypoint 10, a small creek that trickles out of a beaver pond to the right. There is an old beaver dam here, and the pond is surrounded by tall grass. The boulders in the creek are basalt that weathers to a tan color.

Eleven: Spoff

After much heated discussion we decide the new word for the day should be Spoff, which stands for "same pretty old fall forest." So Spoff continues to the junction between the Beaver Bog, Matt Willis (to the right), and Cedar Ridge (to the left) trails. This is waypoint 11 and the end of the Beaver Bog Trail, which did not live up to its "should I really take this trail" name. There was one bog (dry) and no beaver. "False advertising," I say and vote to rename it the "Spoff Trail Walk." There is an old wooden shelter here (old as in falling apart) and a fire pit.

Twelve: Matt Willis Trail

Take the Matt Willis Trail to the right and continue through Spoff to a low area on an overgrown trail with the woods dominated by cedar trees. Cross a

160

small stream before coming to waypoint 12, an opening in the woods next to the beaver pond seen at waypoint 10. We have a nice view of the pond and grassy marsh around it, and the forest here is definitely not Spoff as it consists of cedar, balsam fir, and spruce with some brilliant red maples.

Thirteen: Boulder Creek

From the beaver pond it is but a short walk to return to Spoff. The trail, composed of glacial till, goes by a large white cedar stump with a small balsam fir growing out of it before coming to a small, boulder-filled creek (waypoint 13). The boulders represent a variety of rock types from rhyolite, pink monzonite, and granite to basalt, gabbro and diabase. These come from the glacial till and, over the years, the finer material (*silt*, clay, and *pebbles*) have been slowly removed by running water leaving only the large, immovable stuff behind.

Fourteen: Large Yellow Birch and Ruffed Grouse

Continue through a forest that remains simply incredible. Unfortunately our eyes are growing tired and our minds stuck on overload. Three hours of this spectacular color show amongst magnificent, tall trees and somehow it has become the norm. How soon our senses become dulled and begin to look at such a marvelous feat of nature as the same old thing-"A Spoff on us all!" says Steve.

Cross a seep via old, moss-covered and slippery planks then pass an ENORMOUS yellow birch (this has to be a member of the 400 club) to a sign that reads "State Game Refuge." I guess the forest creatures can also read, for just past the sign, on the correct side of it, we encounter three ruffed grouse, one very nice-looking white-tailed buck with quite a large rack, and a small, sleek, black furry creature Steve thinks might be a martin, though we only have a quick glance at it. The sign and the large cedar stump (uphill to the right) represent waypoint 14.

Fifteen: Blesner Lake Monzonite

Continue on through Spoff with cedar and some large spruce trees to a cedar grove in a low, wet area. From here it is back into Spoff as the trail crosses a boulder-filled creek before heading uphill to an outcrop of Blesner Lake Monzonite. This rock is medium-grained with pink orthoclase feldspar, lath-shaped plagioclase feldspar, and black pyroxene crystals. The rock is the "fresh" equivalent of what we called Rotten Rock at waypoints 2 to 3 on the Humpback Trail walk.

This rock is unlike most "*granitic*" rocks on our planet for it contains no *quartz* and, because of this, is called an "alkalic" rock, one rich in alkalis like potassium, calcium, and sodium. This particular alkalic rock, based on mineral composition, is called a pyroxene-rich or iron-rich monzonite. The monzonite represents the uppermost and most felsic (an igneous rock dominated by light colored, silicon and aluminum-rich minerals) unit of the layered Blesner Lake intrusive body.

Just above the monzonite outcrop there is an open, rocky area, and this is waypoint 15.

Sixteen: Big-Toothed Aspen

It is a short uphill walk from the outcrop to waypoint 16, which is at the junction with a spur trail that heads off to the left. Take the spur trail and walk a short distance to a moss-covered outcrop of monzonite surrounded by pine trees and big-toothed aspen. The view is obscured by small trees, but it looks down into the Blesner Creek Valley with the hillside covered in the reds and yellows of fall.

Seventeen: "Nice Change"

From the junction continue uphill with the trail going over more monzonite as it winds through a maple, paper birch, balsam fir, and white pine woods—we both shout "Nice Change!" Come to an outcrop of a fine-grained, grey rock (diabase) that has a rough, irregular surface. This turns out to be part of a *dike* or *sill* that is intrusive into the monzonite. To the left we get a nice view of the Blesner Creek Valley.

Eighteen: Gabbro Erratic

Monzonite again outcrops just up the hill from waypoint 17 thus confirming the intrusive nature of the gray rock. At the hilltop the forest seems younger and smaller with balsam poplar, paper birch, aspen, balsam fir, cedar, and some maple. This is a cutover area, and the trees that were logged were the relatives of the ones we have spent most of the day walking through.

The trail continues over and by monzonite outcrops before going downhill and returning to a maple and birch forest, but even here the trees are smaller. Suddenly we find ourselves wanting the big and the beautiful again.

Waypoint 18 is at a large, round moss-and-lichen-covered rock that, to me, just seems to rise up from the forest floor. Composed of pyroxene, plagioclase feldspar, and green, glassy olivine, the rock is a glacial erratic of gabbro.

Nineteen: Cedar Swamp and Mixed Woods

The trail remains flat through the "junior" forest before heading uphill, passing a monzonite outcrop before reaching the top. Now it is a short walk before heading downhill into a cedar swamp with the trail becoming bouldery and root-crossed.

From the swamp it is up a gentle slope over an outcrop of Beaver River Gabbro, which is intrusive into, and thus younger than, the monzonite.

162

Continue uphill to the top with the trail now closed in by mountain maple, hazel, and alder as it goes through mixed woods. Walk over a short, planked section after which there is a more open birch-dominated forest to waypoint 19, the junction with the path that goes to campsite #18

Twenty: Back at the Bensen Lake trail

From the junction it is a short walk downhill to the junction with the Bensen Lake Trail and the end of the Matt Willis Trail (waypoint 20).

Twenty-One: Fill-In and a Muskrat

This is the fill-in waypoint for those doing the walk around Bensen Lake.

From waypoint 7 walk along the boardwalk with tons of cedar trees and a number of Beaver River Gabbro outcrops in the hillside to the left. A nice surprise here for we get to watch a muskrat swim through the cotton-grass that lines the shore of the lake.

Waypoint 22 is at the junction with the Matt Willis Trail.

Twenty-Two: Old Beaver Lodge

Continue around Bensen Lake on the boardwalk, which soon ends. The wide, gravel trail that takes its place crosses an alder swamp (over a planked bridge) and passes by a collapsed beaver lodge. Part of the trail along this section has been routed over an old beaver dam.

After the swamp the boardwalk reappears, and we walk along the wooden path to waypoint 22 at the junction with the path to campsite #19.

Twenty-Three: Picnic Tables, Red Pines, and Lily of the Valley

Still on the boardwalk, we go through a mixed forest with lots of black spruce and cedar. Small outcrops of Beaver River Gabbro occur in the hillside to the left. Walk through a planted grove of red pines to waypoint 23, an open, grassy area with picnic tables.

There is a small outcrop of gabbro to the left when first entering the open area. Further on, still to the left, is a low, rock wall that has an old gate in it. Lily of the valley grows along the wall, so we assume this was once the site of a cabin or a house.

Large red pines grow all around the picnic site, and down by the lake there is a bench with a nice view. We walk down and sit on this awhile enjoying the blue water, the fall colors, and the vibrant blue sky. To add to the picture perfect atmosphere, fish are jumping out in the middle of the lake. Later we found out that brook, rainbow, and brown trout inhabit the lake along with splake, which is a hybrid of brook and lake trout.

Twenty-Four: Walk End

It's a short walk along a gravel path to the parking lot. This parking lot is for the picnic area, which also has a boat launching site (fishing must be good). From here walk back down the access road to the parking lot and the end of the very enjoyable, fall forest walk.

Crosby Manitou State Park
Walk 3: Beaver Bog, Cedar Ridge, and Yellow Birch Trails

Walk Logistics

Start and End: Parking lot in George H. Crosby Manitou State Park (state park sticker required to park here).

Getting There: Take Highway 61 to Highway 1. Follow Highway 1 for 7.4 miles to the junction with County Road 7 (Cramer Road). Turn right (northeast) on to County Road 7, and go 7 miles (passing the Finland Recreation Center and the Sonju Lake Road) to the park entrance. Turn right, and the parking lot is 0.6 miles from County Road 7.

Walk Distance: 4.9 miles   **Difficulty:** Hiking Boots

Safety Concerns: Waypoint 15 (no bridge)

Worth a Longer Look: Waypoints 6, 8, 9, 10 (from walk 2), 12, 13, 14, 15, 17, 20

Waypoint-to-Waypoint

Waypoints 1 to 11 are the same as those for Walk 2, The Bensen Lake, Beaver Bog, and Matt Willis Trail Walk.

Eleven: Trail Junction

Waypoint eleven is at the junction of the Beaver Bog and Cedar Ridge trails.

Twelve: Fall Forest and Glacial Till

Head to the left on the Cedar Ridge Trail,which is level, leaf-covered, and littered with cobbles of pink *rhyolite*, quartz porphyry (see *phenocryst*), *basalt, gabbro*, and *granite*. These cobbles are hard to see with all the leaves covering the trail. They come from the weathering and erosion of the *glacial till* which, in this part of the park, forms deposits called *ground moraine*. Over the decades the clay and silt-size material has been washed away leaving behind a whole caboodle of larger, immovable boulders and cobbles. The woods through this section are breathtaking with yellow birch and maple the dominant trees. We wonder how long it will be before we fall into the Spoff, (same pretty old fall forest) mode that we experienced on walk 2 .

Not quite yet–for the pleasant, relaxing, eye feast continues all the way to a cut yellow birch at which point the trail enters a low, wet area (cedar swamp). We head uphill into drier woods over a root-crossed trail to an area with lots of old, cut logs–there is a tree tip-up to the right, and this is waypoint 12.

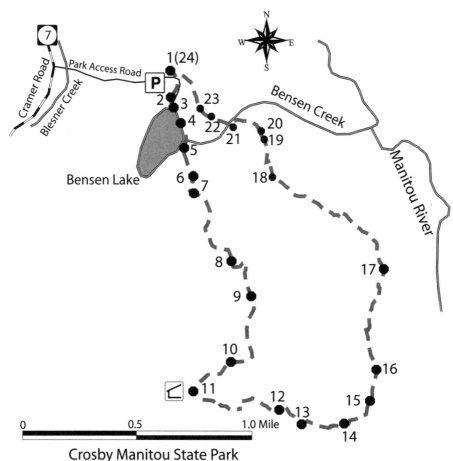

Crosby Manitou State Park
Walk 3: Beaver Bog, Cedar Ridge, and Yellow Birch Trails

Thirteen: Large Yellow Birch

The nice walk continues as the trail passes through open maple and yellow birch woods with some really large yellow birch trees (are these in the 400-year-old class?); cedar, spruce, and paper birch can also be found here. Waypoint 13 is where the trail takes a sharp turn to the left; and at this point there is an orange diamond sign. From the sign the trail follows an old logging road.

Fourteen: Kaleidoscope View and Frost Wedging

Walk along the old road through an open forest under a high canopy of red, orange, and yellow with a bit of green still hanging in there. With a gentle breeze it reminds me of a kaleidoscope, for no two views are the same. The trail is bouldery (same rock types as before) as it passes by a large, dead spruce tree to the start of a downhill section with a "caution steep slope" sign. We assume this was meant for skiers and not for us, but we are not certain of this.

So downhill we sprint into a gully occupied by a rock-filled, bubbling creek. The waypoint (14) is where a small stream joins the larger one just to the left of the trail. Lots of large boulders of medium-grained gabbro can be found here. The gabbro is composed of blocky, dark *pyroxene* that weathers a rusty color, grey *plagioclase feldspar* that weathers chalky white, a few green or brownish crystals of *olivine,* and metallic black crystals of *magnetite.*

The outcrop in the bank above the creek is composed of the same material as the boulders. This is part of the layered Blesner Lake Intrusion, which varies in composition from *monzonite* to gabbro, with zones of oxide-rich gabbro and igneous *iron formation.* It represents part of an old magma chamber that fed basaltic lavas that erupted out of the *Mid-Continent Rift* 1.1 billion years ago. The Blesner Lake Intrusion is older than the Beaver River Gabbro, which also outcrops in the park. The Blesner Lake Intrusion cooled and crystallized more than a mile below the earth's surface and, over the intervening 1 billion years, weathering and erosion have brought it to the surface. The boulders in the creek came from *frost wedging* of the outcrops that occur along the hillside.

Fifteen: Lost Bridge and the Estate Looking Hillside

Continue down the trail crossing the main branch of the creek using rocks as stepping stones. There is no bridge to help in the crossing so in the spring watch out or wear hip waders! The hillside to the left looks like an English estate with widely spaced maple and yellow birch trees along with some spruce; today it is nothing but a sea of reds and yellows–Wow!

The creek flows to the right as the trail, continuing downslope, turns away from the noisy water. Blesner Lake Gabbro is exposed in the hillside to the left. Waypoint 15 is at an old split log; in fact there are two of them placed end-to-end to help get across this low, wet spot.

Sixteen: Trail Junction

The level trail goes through a maple, yellow birch, spruce, and cedar forest though the trees here are definitely smaller and thus younger than those we have been admiring. These smaller trees give the woods a denser, more closed-in feeling, which stays with us to waypoint 16, a trail junction. At this point the Matt Willis Trail splits away from the Cedar Ridge Trail going off to the right and eventually joining the Manitou River Trail. We stay on the Cedar Ridge Trail (to the left).

Seventeen: Sawtooth Mountains

The bouldery trail, with planked sections, winds through a spruce, cedar, yellow birch, and maple forest with some big spruce. The boulders are round to sub round and of various compositions from rhyolite and monzonite to basalt, diabase, and gabbro with some exotic *gneiss* and *schist* thrown in by the glacier just for kicks. These two metamorphic rocks most likely came from the Voyageurs National Park area; the other rocks came from within or close to Crosby Manitou State Park.

The trail dips downhill crossing a small creek via a boardwalk (lots of cedar through here) before going gently uphill only to arrive at another swampy spot before again heading uphill. "Déjà vu," I say and hope there is not another repeat of this.

There isn't and waypoint 17 is just past the hilltop at a bench that provides a nice view to the east of Lake Superior and the fall forest. To see the reds and oranges from the hilltop is breathtaking, for the vast blueness of the lake provides the perfect backdrop for all this color. After a lot of Oh's and Ah's I realize the hill opposite this point is a *cuesta* and, according to my map, forms one of the teeth of the *Sawtooth Mountains*. A cuesta is an asymmetric ridge with a long, gentle slope on one side (this parallels the tilt or dip of the surrounding or underlying strata which, along the North Shore, is about 20 degrees toward the lake) and a steep cliff-like or blunt-nose-shaped face on the other side (the result of frost-wedging and *glacial plucking*). The resultant hill ends up looking like one of the teeth on an old wood saw. There are several of these teeth along the North Shore of Lake Superior from about Tofte to Grand Marais and these, as a group, are called the Sawtooth Mountains. Cuestas are typically formed from weathering of the basalt lava flows or by an intrusive rock we call the Star Wars Porphyry.

The outcrop we are standing on is Blesner Lake Gabbro (alas no cuesta), and the surrounding forest is dominantly large northern white cedar and large spruce with some maples.

Eighteen: "Chair" Stump and Maple-Yellow Birch Woods

From waypoint 17 it is gently up then downhill over and by gabbro outcrops and boulders (from the till) as the trail follows the hillside through a cedar, spruce, and maple forest to the "twin stump" cedar trees.

From here continue uphill and along the hilltop before heading down through a forest that now contains quite a bit more yellow birch and a lot less cedar. Some of the yellow birch trees are really big as well as magnificent and, of course, old.

The trail levels out as the woods become dominated by maple and yellow birch. This is how it remains to waypoint 18, which is the start of a gentle downhill. To the right is a stump cut to look like a chair, and to the left a large yellow birch tree. Along the hillside it seems like the woods are denser, and the maple are younger than what our eyes are accustomed to.

168

Nineteen: Meandering Stream and Trail Junction

It's downhill and across a planked section in a cedar swamp, then over a small stream that seems to *meander* over the entire area the planking covers. Numerous old cedar stumps are seen through here.

Walk downhill and back into a pretty nice maple and yellow birch forest with some cedar and spruce. Cross another planked section before coming to waypoint 19, the junction between the Cedar Ridge and Yellow Birch Trails. I think it is fitting that at the start of the Yellow Birch Trail there is a large yellow birch tree.

The trail that goes to the right is now called the Misquah Trail; it goes downhill to the Manitou River Trail (walk 4). Follow the Yellow Birch Trail (the Cedar Ridge trail ends here).

Twenty: Great White Pine and Clubmoss City

It is a short walk from the junction to what Steve calls *clubmoss* city, a place where clubmoss runs in all directions. From "clubmoss city" the trail is level as it goes by some large spruce and paper and yellow birch trees before heading downhill over a boulder and tree root-crossed trail to the bottom and waypoint 20, a large, beautiful, straight-as-an-arrow white pine that goes up and up and up. This great old tree must be 100 feet tall, a true cloud catcher that we estimate to be upwards of 200 years old. If so, it was a seedling about the time the British were burning Washington during the war of 1812! There is also a large white pine stump here and this makes us wonder why one survived and one did not.

Twenty-One: Boulder Creek

From the cloud catcher white pine it is on to a small creek that flows through a cedar swamp. Walk along the creek to waypoint 21, which is where the trail crosses the creek. The creek drains Benson Lake and is packed full of boulders that have a wide variety of compositions, but are all locally derived. Unfortunately for them, they will remain in this spot for the next little while (geologically speaking) as the current creek has not a chance of moving them the length of a frog's hair (unless Bensen Lake suddenly decides to empty itself in one big rush down the creek).

Twenty-Two: More Fall Color

It is now uphill over a *boulder* and *cobble* strewn trail with lots of tree roots across it. The forest is dominantly maple red and brown with very yellow, yellow birch and green spruce and cedar. Waypoint 22 is at the junction with a spur trail to the left that goes to the Bensen Lake Trail and an outhouse.

Twenty-Three: Red Pines and the Beaver River Gabbro

From the junction the trail remains rocky and root-crossed as it passes some large red pines though the woods are dominantly maple and birch. Waypoint 23 is at the start of an uphill section with an outcrop of gabbro to the right. This is the Beaver River Gabbro, although it looks much like the Blesner Lake Gabbro unless you take the geological time to map it out (it contains xenoliths to the northeast of here and cross-cuts the Blesner Lake Intrusion).

Twenty-Four: Parking Lot

Continue uphill over the rocky, root-crossed trail and across one last planked section before entering the parking lot (where the walk began) and bringing an end to a true northeastern Minnesota fall walk.

Crosby Manitou State Park
Walk 4: Manitou River Walk

Walk Logistics

Start and End: Parking lot in George H. Crosby Manitou State Park (state park sticker required to park here).

Getting There: Take Highway 61 to Highway 1. Follow Highway 1 for 7.4 miles to the junction with County Road 7 (Cramer Road). Turn right (northeast) on to County Road 7, and go 7 miles (passing the Finland Recreation Center and the Sonju Lake Road) to the park entrance. Turn right, and the parking lot is 0.6 miles from County Road 7.

Walk Distance: about 6 miles   **Difficulty:** Hiking Boots

Safety Concerns: Waypoints 18, 30, and 31

Worth a Longer Look: Waypoints 4, 5, 6, 12, 13, 17, 18, 20, 21, 24, 26, 30, 31

Waypoint-to-Waypoint

One: Parking Lot

Once again we are in the parking lot at George H. Crosby Manitou State Park on yet another glorious fall day. There is a definite nip to the air, but otherwise it's a perfect blue, blue sky day with just the lightest of breezes and a great, old forest waiting to show off its warm colors.

Two: Glacial Erratic and the Beaver Bay Igneous Complex

The trail we start out on is called Middle Trail and is part of the Superior Hiking Trail. Middle Trail leads to the Manitou River Trail, and starts out by going slightly uphill on a wide footpath that is more akin to a four-lane highway. The trail has been constructed this way because this is a popular section with many walkers coming here to view the cascades of the Manitou River.

Pass a large *glacial erratic* of the *Beaver River Diabase* (also see *diabase*) along with numerous smaller *boulders* of *gabbro* and one gabbro *outcrop* in a dry creek bed. The forest is dominantly maple and birch, with cedar, spruce, and balsam poplar. There are lots of tiny broad beech ferns and *thimbleberries* along this section.

After going by another outcrop of gabbro come to the junction with an unmarked park trail (to the right), which is waypoint 2. The gabbro outcrop here is medium-grained, smooth-weathering, and forms part of the Blesner Lake Intrusion. This is a layered igneous body composed of *monzonite,*

171

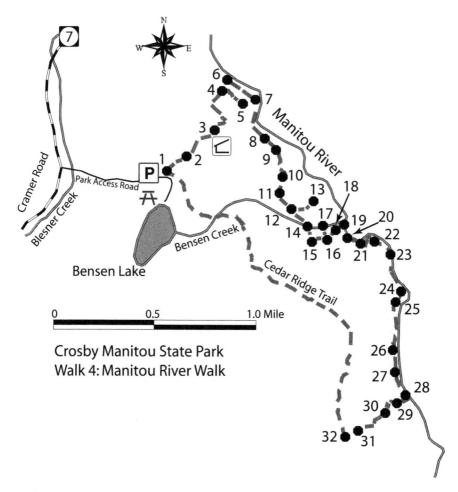

Crosby Manitou State Park
Walk 4: Manitou River Walk

gabbro, oxide-rich gabbro (lots of *magnetite* in it), and igneous *iron formation*. Most of it is made up of the kind of rock seen here–gabbro. The Blesner Lake Intrusion forms part of what is called the *Beaver Bay Igneous Complex*, a series of distinct igneous intrusions that are all about the same age and were feeders for *basalt* lava flows at the surface. The Beaver Bay Igneous Complex extends from just south of the town of Beaver Bay north to Grand Marais; the most abundant part of it is called the Beaver River Diabase and Gabbro. This particular intrusion outcrops here in the park and in its gabbroic form is difficult to tell from the Blesner Lake Gabbro. In fact, to distinguish them the rocks have to be geologically mapped. When this is done it can be shown that the Beaver River cross-cuts the Blesner Lake, has *anorthosite xenoliths*, and is not layered.

Take the spur trail to an outcrop of Blesner Lake Gabbro from which there is a view to the northeast and east of the Manitou River Valley.

Three: Huge Cedars, White Flower of the Day, Clubmoss, and Anorthosite

Return to the main trail, which slopes gently upward to the top of a small hill as it crosses over numerous boulders (basalt, gabbro, *granite,* and *rhyolite* to name a few). These come from the *glacial till* deposits. Thimbleberry is everywhere, but in looking beneath these bigger plants there is an abundance of one-flowered *wintergreen.*

A short downhill section takes us past a moss-covered glacial erratic of anorthosite. The anorthosite has a birch tree growing over and on it, and my thought is here we have life clinging to a poor bare rock, as it probably did billions of years ago. The life form I'm referring to is stromatolites (blue-green algae) that grew in large colonies along rocky shorelines billions of years ago, right in this area.

Continuing downhill the trail passes enormous standing and fallen cedars. There is a thick carpet of *clubmoss, bunchberry*, and *blue bead lily* that cling to the ground everywhere we look. This, according to Steve, represents typical ground cover in boreal forests.

The trail levels out but remains bouldery with anorthosite glacial erratics to waypoint 3, a picnic shelter with fire pit. The rock outcropping by the shelter is Blesner Lake Gabbro. From this spot we can hear the constant sound of water crashing over rocks in the river, which is not far below.

The cedar trees are northern white cedar whose early name was Arborvitae, which means "tree of life." Legend has it that Native Americans used a tea made from the bark and leaves of the tree to save explorer Jacques Cartier and his crew from scurvy–though some twenty sailors died before they tried it. This was at the present site of Quebec City in the winter of 1535-1536 and led to the northern white cedar being the first tree imported into Europe from North America.

Piliated woodpeckers love this tree and will excavate large, oval holes in the sides searching for carpenter ants. Porcupines eat the thin cedar stems as snack food, and deer and snowshoe hares use it for browse.

Four: Magnetic Rocks and Crosby Overlook

The trail, bordered by young cedars, goes downhill, as it winds its way over and around piles of rock. These are *talus* deposits derived by *frost wedging* from the hillside to the left. Some of the rocks making up the talus are unusual and rare. They are composed of 50-75% magnetite, with green glassy apatite and silver-colored arsenopyrite along with some *plagioclase feldspar*, *pyroxene,* and ilmenite (an iron-titanium oxide). This would be described as a type of iron formation, one formed by crystallization and settling of heavy minerals that accumulated at the bottom of a basaltic magma chamber, much like snow accumulates on a window sill. These heavy minerals formed distinct layers in the magma chamber alternating with layers of lighter minerals like plagioclase feldspar. Other rocks found amongst the talus are gabbro and oxide-rich gabbro. These are all part of the well-layered Blesner Lake Intrusion, which outcrops on the hillside above us. Also occurring on the trail are sub-round boulders of basalt and *monzonite* from the glacial till.

Waypoint 4 is at the junction of the Superior Hiking Trail and the Crosby Hill Trail.

Five: Crosby Hill Overlook

Take the spur trail, which goes gently uphill over outcrops of the Blesner Lake Gabbro through a mixed forest of cedar, balsam fir, paper birch, and spruce along with both red and white pine to a wooden bench, which is waypoint 5. From the bench we can hear the Manitou River, but we have to continue down the slope another 20 feet or so for a nice river view. From this spot we also get a good view of the tall, anorthosite knob to the right, and in the distance Lake Superior.

The red pines in front of the bench have grown up over the years to ruin the "bench" view. The outcrop at the bench is Beaver River Diabase with lots of kibbles and bits around the bench and on the trail. Kibbles and bits weathering (see *diabase weathering*) is most common in *ophitic* rocks exposed on south-facing slopes because these slopes undergo more freeze-thaw cycles in the late fall and early spring, greatly enhancing the weathering of the rock.

Down the trail toward the junction is an outcrop of smooth weathering, grey to tan Blesner Lake Gabbro.

Six: Trail Junction and Yew

Return to the trail junction and proceed downhill to another trail junction– this is the junction between the Superior Hiking Trail and the Manitou River Trail (waypoint 6). One branch of the River Trail heads upstream (to the left), and it's only a short distance to a great view of the Manitou River Cascades (see waypoints 11 and 12 from Walk 1 for a description of the cascades). The other branch of the Manitou River Trail follows the Superior Hiking Trail to the right and downstream.

The shrubby, low-growing evergreen called yew is abundant all along this section. Yews are commonly found in forests that are cool, damp, and shaded, such as occur on north-facing slopes like this one. One warbler seen in this area, the black-throated blue, is known to nest in yew thickets.

The scientific name for yew is interesting. Its first name, Taxus, is a Greek word meaning bow, and apparently this North American species was used extensively by Native Americans for hunting bows. Taxol is a compound derived from yews that has shown beneficial effects in the fight against certain cancers. The second part of its name, Canadensis, is a bit more obvious; it means "of Canada" or, in a more general sense, "northern."

Seven: Campsites and the Manitou River

Take the trail to the right and walk downstream over a rocky path that follows the hillside with nice views of the river to campsite #3, a nice open site.

The trail heads downhill to the river's edge over more rock talus. Waypoint 7 is at campsite #4, another nice spot with large rocks that provide a place to sit and contemplate the moody river as it flows by. The water is the color of root beer–root beer with a big head of foam–for there is a large amount of frothy stuff slowly circling on eddies in the stream. This is truly hypnotic, the foam going around and around and around.

Shaking off the spell I begin to look at the boulders that jam-pack the river. Steve is investigating bolita mushrooms and the green stains of the fungus Chlorociboria, which is attacking stumps and logs: it feeds on the decaying wood. The green color staining the wood is actually the mycelium. Mushrooms are the fruiting bodies (spores) of fungus emerging from the mycelia. In a wet, warm summer and fall the green stains of the tiny turquoise and seldom seen mushrooms can be found on the underside of sticks.

Eight: More Large Cedars and Spring Peepers

Continue along the river over a small creek through a thick boreal forest of aspen, birch, cedar, spruce, balsam fir, and balsam poplar. Outcrops along the trail are gabbro; boulders from the glacial till include pieces of an intrusive rock with numerous large plagioclase feldspar crystals. This particular intrusion outcrops further along the Superior Hiking Trail and is called the Star Wars Porphyry.

The trail heads uphill to a small pond surrounded by large cedar trees. Today the pond is dry, and Steve thinks it is only really full and/or wet soon after snowmelt, or after a heavy rainfall. This environment would be the perfect place for spring peepers, little tree frogs, to hatch their eggs in early spring.

Continue uphill over a knob of gabbro then walk down to waypoint 8, a cedar grove with large trees.

Nine: Rock Contact and Trail Junction

The trail crosses outcrops of smooth-weathering Beaver River Diabase to a junction (waypoint 9) where the Superior Hiking Trail goes to the left to cross the new bridge over the river, and the Manitou River Trail continues straight on.

At this spot you are close to the contact between the Blesner Lake and Beaver River Intrusions. The diabase, on a regional basis, is the most common kind of rock in the Beaver River Intrusion and here it represents the more rapidly cooled, finer-grained phase of the gabbro that outcrops just up the hill.

Ten: Beaver River Gabbro

The trail heads uphill to an outcrop of Beaver River Gabbro. The forest is made up of spruce and balsam fir with paper birch and cedar. Continuing uphill the trail passes an outcrop of gabbro in the hillside to the left. After a sharp turn the trail heads up and over more gabbro to waypoint 10, an outcrop of Beaver River Gabbro from which we have a partial view of Lake Superior and the Manitou River Valley. The valley is proudly showing off its red and orange colors.

Eleven: Thick Firs and Trail Junction

Continue along the edge of the hillside over numerous small gabbro outcrops with the balsam fir and spruce trees becoming quite thick to waypoint 11, the junction between the Manitou River Trail, which goes straight ahead, and a trail that goes down to the river and campsite #5. This trail eventually meets up with the Manitou River Trail at waypoint 19.

Twelve: Open Woods

Go straight ahead and downhill through more open woods with lots of maple trees (nice red and brown colors), some spruce, balsam fir, and cedar to waypoint 12, which is at the junction with the spur trail to Misquah Overlook and campsite #6.

Thirteen: Anorthosite and a Great View

Take the spur trail uphill over an outcrop of anorthosite to the Misquah overlook, which is on a large anorthosite outcrop (13). There is a wonderful view of the hilly landscape with all the reds, browns, oranges, yellows, and greens spread out below us, a magic carpet that takes us all the way to the icy blueness of Lake Superior sparkling in the distance much like the feldspar crystals sparkling in the anorthosite at this overlook.

Anorthosites are rare, coarse-grained igneous rocks composed of more than 85% plagioclase feldspar; other minor constituents are apatite, magnetite, ilmenite, *olivine*, and pyroxene. The anorthosites found along the North Shore occur as inclusions or xenoliths in the Beaver River Diabase. In fact, the round hill to the right is another anorthosite inclusion, and the shape of the hill is typical for anorthosite. We have come to call this "bowling ball" weathering. It is due to a combination of two geological processes: frost wedging and *exfoliation*.

The anorthosite outcrop has plagioclase crystals over an inch long that are greenish-grey to grey in color, though it is hard to tell this without sunglasses. The rock is criss-crossed by small fractures, some of which contain pink orthoclase feldspar as well as cream-colored plagioclase feldspar. At the overlook there is a "renegade" campsite in a grove of red pines, a nice spot to camp even if it is unofficial.

Fourteen: Anorthosite Creek

Return to the main trail and head downhill past a lichen and moss-covered outcrop of anorthosite and some nice-sized spruce trees to what we call Anorthosite Creek (it is actually Bensen Creek) because of all the anorthosite boulders in and along it. The large boulder close to the trail has parallel lines through it that make the rock look layered, but these are actually fractures that have been emphasized by weathering.

Cross the creek and come to an outcrop of anorthosite (waypoint 14) with spruce and cedar trees growing on it.

Fifteen: Trail Junction

Continue on up a set of wooden steps and past a large spruce tree to the junction between the Manitou River Trail and the Yellow Birch Trail. This is waypoint 15.

Sixteen: Scarlet Red Mountain Maple

The Manitou River Trail goes to the left and downhill through a yellow birch and cedar forest with some spruce, paper birch, and the moose's favorite food, mountain maple, which is absolutely scarlet red. Waypoint 15 is at the junction with a spur trail that goes to the left.

Seventeen: Waterfall and Grotto

Take the spur trail down a steep set of steps and across a planked section to arrive at a bench by a very pretty little waterfall in a nice grotto. This is a really secluded idyllic spot–all that's needed are unicorns and little people! The creek is Anorthosite Creek, and the water is falling over a resistant outcrop of Beaver River Gabbro. Immediately to the left of the bench is an outcrop of anorthosite. The contact between the gabbro and anorthosite is knife-sharp and follows a fracture in the rock.

A large block of anorthosite sits just below the moss-covered falls, and this is either a glacial erratic or was frost-wedged from an exposure somewhere up the creek and rolled and/or bounced to this spot. Either way the boulder has probably been here a long, long time. Waypoint 16 is at the bench (nice spot for lunch or a snack).

Eighteen: Rhyolite Pieces

Return to the trail junction and from there continue downhill through a nice yellow birch and cedar forest with the token spruce, balsam fir, and paper birch. Some sections are pretty steep, but there are wooden stairs in places to ease the strain on your knees. The hill bottom is at Anorthosite Creek, which is crossed by a split log bridge (waypoint 18). The Manitou River is immediately ahead.

Anorthosite Creek needs a name change, for the stream bottom is covered by hundreds of pieces of rhyolite. The rhyolite is a lava flow and has 3-15 % clear, square *quartz* crystals and about the same percentage of tabular pink *orthoclase feldspar* crystals within a very fine-grained pink matrix. The rock also contains 2-3% elongate to irregularly shaped *amygdules* that are lined by quartz and feldspar. Some of the rhyolite pieces have red to grey *flow bands* that, in places, look swirly.

There are so many pieces of rock and they are so angular that bedrock must be just beneath the surface. This broken rock represents frost-heaved material. As far as we can tell this particular flow has no name, and we have no idea of its lateral extent. However, it does belong to the *North Shore Volcanic Group* and is about 1.1 billion years old.

Nineteen: Flow Top Breccia and the Manitou River

Just a few feet from the bridge is the junction with the trail that goes to campsite #7 and, from there, follows the river upstream to eventually head back uphill and join the Manitou River Trail at waypoint 11. Just before the campsite there is a nice little cascade and waterfall.

Angular rhyolite pieces litter the creek bottom all the way to the river. Some pieces represent flow top breccias with fragments of massive-looking and quartz-feldspar crystal rhyolite cemented together by *jasper* (red quartz) and clear quartz. Rhyolite lavas are very viscous (have a great resistance to flowing), and the top part of the flow will cool more rapidly than the central portions. These two characteristics lead to the hotter, more plastic interior pulling and dragging the harder, cooler upper part and breaking it into angular pieces of all different sizes. The broken material is then cemented together by the quartz and jasper, which probably precipitated out of warm waters flowing through the lava after it was buried. This same material fills amygdules in basalt, in which case the jasper can form nice, red *agates*.

Twenty: River Cascade and White Pines

The trail follows the boulder-filled river through a cedar, paper birch, and spruce woods across Anorthosite Creek (here we rename it Rhyolite Creek). Then it is over boulders of the Beaver River Diabase to campsite #8, which is guarded by two large white pines that sit right at the river's edge. There is a small cascade here with nice steps formed in the red-colored rhyolite outcrop in the river. The steps may have formed from weathering along *cooling joints*. The campsite is waypoint 20.

Twenty-One: Clinging Cedar and Pebble Beach

Continue downstream with rhyolite exposed along both sides of the river. Pass by more white pine trees before coming to an old, split log bridge over a small creek. Rhyolite outcrops on the opposite side of the creek, and down at the river is a nice beach composed of *pebbles* and *cobbles* of rhyolite. This is waypoint 21.

From the beach we have a nice view both upriver and downriver where a U-shaped cedar tree grows out of a rhyolite cliff to dangle over the water. Talk about life taking hold and clinging to the strangest of places!

Twenty-Two: Campsite #9

Paralleling the creek the trail passes a rhyolite outcrop to the left before heading uphill via old log steps to waypoint 21, which is campsite #9. Large cedar and spruce trees are abundant here.

Twenty-Three: Split Rock and Large Trees

Heading back toward the river, the trail passes a giant white pine with a pink rhyolite outcrop visible in the river below. Just past the large white pine is another "renegade" campsite.

From the campsite it is downhill over wooden steps past more nice, large white pine and some large paper birch, which are now true giants, for they occur in a forest of much smaller balsam fir, spruce, and cedar. The trail continues downhill to the river and a large rhyolite outcrop. There is a small pile of talus on the opposite side of the river. Walk along the river to an opening in the cedar trees and a beach of boulders and cobbles of rhyolite and diabase; directly opposite the beach is a wall of pink rhyolite. The rhyolite has narrowly spaced, horizontal fractures through it that remind me of "split rock," the rhyolite at Split Rock State Park. The fractures most likely formed by a process called unloading or exfoliation. The beach is waypoint 23.

Twenty-Four: Forest Glade

Continuing along the river, the trail becomes closed in by small balsam fir and spruce with larger cedar and white pine scattered through the dense woods. The root-crossed trail then passes through numerous small cedar groves before coming to a beautiful open cedar grove beside a rocky tributary to the Manitou River (waypoint 24).

At this waypoint the forest floor is open and spacious making it a pleasant place with large yellow birch and cedar. This is a nice forest glade with a beutifull river happily bubbling along about 150 feet away.

Twenty-Five: River Terrace

Follow the tributary (which is more likely an overflow channel) to where the trail crosses it to get to campsite #10 and waypoint 25. The campsite is above yet another cedar grove, which is located on an old *flood plain* or terrace of the river. There is a glacial erratic here composed of granite.

Twenty-Six: OxBow and Rhyolite Beach

Just past the campsite the trail heads back down to the river and a nice cobble-boulder beach that has formed on the inside part of a *meander* bend. Upstream, just past the bend, is a river *oxbow*. The beach cobbles are composed mostly of rhyolite, with some basalt and diabase.

From the beach it is a short walk to a small creek beyond which the narrow, root-crossed trail continues through a dense balsam fir and spruce forest with large cedars and birch.

Head uphill, walking around a fallen pine tree, before going back downhill to cross a small boulder-filled creek (boulders weathering out of the till). The trail then follows the river through a yellow birch, balsam fir, and spruce forest with the hillside to the right composed of rhyolite. In this section the trail has lots of cedar roots across it.

Walk a short ways uphill before the trail returns to the river and waypoint 26, a cedar grove at the water's edge with a beautiful *river terrace* immediately to the right.

Twenty-Seven: Murmuring River

The river is straight and full of gabbro, diabase, basalt, and rhyolite boulders that come from erosion of the river banks and *slumping* of this glacial material into the water. The river is noisy through here as it murmurs and chatters its way around the numerous rocks. Waypoint 27 is at campsite #11.

Twenty-Eight: Rapids and White Pine

The root-crossed trail continues through a cedar forest with large cedar and spruce trees. Cross two small creeks (now dry) before walking up and over a diabase outcrop with the dark pyroxene crystals oxidized to the reddish-brown iron mineral *hematite*. After the outcrop walk back down to the river and waypoint 28, a small rapids created over step-like ledges of smooth-weathering Beaver River Diabase. The diabase has a reddish, hematite-rich look with white spots that are weathered plagioclase feldspar crystals. Nice size white pines can be seen across the river, and the waypoint is in yet another cedar grove.

180

Twenty-Nine: Dead-End Trail

A short uphill walk to a dead end! The trail is gone, vanished, slumped away into the river. The "new" trail makes a right angle turn and it is just a short walk along it to the junction with the Matt Willis Trail (waypoint 29)

Thirty: Steep Steps and Fall Colors

Take the Matt Willis Trail (unless going to campsites #13 to 16) and walk uphill over steep, wooden steps that have rounded tops that make them difficult to walk on-imagine what they would be like if wet! The trail then flattens out a bit but remains root-crossed as it goes through a yellow birch, maple, cedar, paper birch, and white pine forest. Through this section the bright fall colors overwhelm the greens of the cedars and pine; with the bright afternoon sunshine, this is the north woods at their very best. Waypoint 29 is at campsite #12.

Thirty-One: Still Steep But No Steps

It is all uphill as we walk by a beautiful white pine tree and cross numerous small, planked, dry creeks to the edge of a ravine, a steep creek valley, which the trail now parallels.

Cross another small, planked stream that empties into the ravine. After this the trail turns away from the steep creek valley but continues uphill over more planked sections. The trail is also bouldery with the gabbro, diabase, monzonite, rhyolite, granite, and basalt boulders coming from the erosion of the glacial till on the hillside.

Still steeply uphill (essentially the trail is crossing elevation contours at a right angle so we are glad it is dry) over a rocky trail through a yellow birch and cedar forest with some red maple, yellow birch, green white pine, and a few large cedar trees. Near the hilltop (thank goodness) maple and birch become more abundant and cedar less so; the colors seem to explode, overwhelming everything but the blue sky.

Waypoint 30 is at the junction between the Matt Willis Trail and the Cedar Ridge Trail.

Thirty-Two: Parking Lot Via Walk 3

Take the Cedar Ridge Trail (to the right) and from here refer to walk 3, starting at waypoint 19 for we now follow the Cedar Ridge and Yellow Birch Trails back to the parking lot.

Temperance River State Park

Introduction

Water, rocks, and the results of the interaction between the two are the major focus at Temperance River State Park. The park is located just northeast of Schroeder, Minnesota, and its centerpiece is the dynamic Temperance River, which has created a world of its own–a river gorge complete with waterfalls, chutes, rapids, and cauldrons.

Upstream from the gorge, like so many other North Shore rivers, the Temperance is like Dr. Jeckyll looking to become Mr. Hyde. Up here it is a gently flowing, wide body of water dotted with large and small boulders that come from the erosion of the glacial till making up its banks. Today the water chatters and laughs its way around these reminders that even in this milder world the river has the power to shape and reshape the landscape. Another reminder of the river's power is the sand and gravel deposits which, in places, make up parts of the hiking trail between the river and Carlton Peak.

These sandy deposits are the remains of an old delta, a small version of the ones found at the mouths of the Nile and Mississippi rivers. The Temperance River Delta was once a wide, fan-shaped deposit that formed where the river flowed into Glacial Lake Duluth. Several sand and gravel pits are located in what remains of the delta deposit between here and the road to Carlton Peak.

The Temperance River Delta formed about 10,000 years ago as the river rapidly eroded through the glacial deposits (till). The flowing water sorted the till particles by size into a) clay and silt, which were carried out into the glacial lake, and b) sand and gravel which were deposited as a delta where the river flowed into the lake. This deposition was due to a dramatic decrease in the velocity of the flowing water as it entered the deeper and much larger glacial lake. Over time, as water levels in Glacial Lake Duluth fell (because the Laurentide Ice Sheet kept uncovering lower and lower outlets as it melted off the land) the river's gradient increased, and it quickly cut down through the delta, largely removing it before setting to work on carving up the basalt lava flows to form the present gorge.

The name for the river dates back to the mid-1800s. According to local legend it was called the Temperance because it was one of the few rivers along the North Shore without a bar at its mouth–a gravel bar, that is. But the odd thing is walk 3 leads to a nice pebble and sand "bar" at the mouth of the river! So we have to wonder whether this bar formed in the last 150

182

years, or was the name of the river but a figment of a teetotaler's imagination?

What role the gravel bar played I don't know, but the Temperance is a fine trout stream and a poplar fishing spot. Brook, brown, and rainbow trout have been stocked in the river over the years with the brown and brook trout having established natural populations. Chinook salmon and steelhead trout may also be found near the mouth of the river.

Rocks are also a major feature of the park, and they are all basalt lava flows and/or diabase with one big exception—the anorthosite mass that forms Carlton Peak. The basalt lava flows are 1.1 billion years old. They are part of what is called the North Shore Volcanic Group, formed by lava that erupted from the Mid-Continent Rift and flowed over the barren landscape to cool and harden as a thick pile of what are called plateau lavas.

Even without the wild river gorge the lava flows are rather special because in them are preserved textures and structures that are usually associated with flows in Hawaii, Iceland, and the Galapagos Islands. There are beautiful and well-preserved billowy and ropey pahoehoe flow tops, vesicle cylinders, pipe vesicles, cooling joints, lizard skin weathering, and sheet structures. The Temperance River took full advantage of these primary features, along with the consistent 20-degree tilt toward the lake, to create the spectacular rock gorge.

Carlton Peak is the dominant topographic feature in this neck of the woods and a "must visit" for those who come to walk in this park. The open tops of Carlton Peak and nearby Ted Tofte Overlook provide two of the best views available from anywhere along the North Shore of Lake Superior. And in the fall, oh my goodness what a treat! Laid out below the visitor is a feast fit for 10 kings, a quilt of many different colors that goes on and on with sparkling blue Lake Superior as the perfect background.

Carlton Peak and Ted Tofte Overlook are composed of a relatively rare rock type called anorthosite (also called moon rock because astronauts brought back samples of similar material from the moon). This high, resistant knob of rock occurs as a xenolith in a large, igneous intrusive body called the Beaver River Diabase. Underlying an area from Beaver Bay to Grand Marais the diabase is the same age as the basalt lava flows and represents a magma chamber for, and feeders to, the basalt lavas.

Anorthosite is a resistant, durable rock, and because of this it tends to form round or knob-like landforms that are topographic highs. This weathering feature has been called "bowling ball" weathering and is due to a combination of running water, frost-wedging, and exfoliation.

Finally, when along the North Shore, Lake Superior can never be forgotten. Temperance River State Park is bordered by the great lake which has attacked and eroded the rocky shore and in doing so provided the visitor with beaches, coves, views, and a desire to sit for long periods of time and watch the rolling waves come and go.

In this section of the book we have put together three walks that we believe truly allow the visitor to see and experience the heart (Temperance River) and soul (Carlton Peak) of this park. So welcome to Temperance River State Park, a place where water and rocks have interacted over 10,000 years to create the wonderful landscape and features you are about to experience.

Temperance River State Park
Walk 1: Temperance River, Carlton Peak, and Ted Tofte Overlook

Walk Logistics

Start: Temperance River State Wayside on Highway 61

Getting There: Take Highway 61 to the Temperance River, about 1 mile northeast of Schroeder. The wayside is on the northeast side of the river; parking is available on both sides of the highway.

End: There are three differnt choices for this walk depending on the number and type of vehicles at your disposal. The choices are:

1) Starting point at the Temperance River State Wayside.

2) Britton Peak parking lot on Cook County Road 2 (Sawbill Trail).

3) Quarry off the Carlton Peak Road.

Getting There:

1) Same as above.

2) Take Highway 61 to Tofte. Just northeast of the Blue Fin Resort turn onto the Sawbill Trail (Cook County Road 2). Go 2.7 miles on the Sawbill Trail to the Britton Peak parking lot, which is on the right.

3) The Carlton Peak Road is a minimal maintance road, so there are numerous cracks in the pavement and the upper part is gravel and rocky. A pick-up truck or SUV is recommended (I had no problem in my Ford Explorer). From the Temperance River Wayside go northeast on Highway 61, passing the campground and park headquarters. The Carlton Peak Road is just before a "Superior National Forest sign" (0.5 miles from the park headquarters). Turn left and follow the road up to the quarry area, which has plenty of parking, picnic tables, and an outhouse. The parking area is just below Ted Tofte Overlook.

Walk Distance: 6.5 miles round trip from the wayside, 4.7 miles to the Britton Peak parking lot, 3.25 miles if you park at the quarry.

Difficulty: Hiking Boots   **Safety Concerns:** Waypoints 5, 12

Worth a Longer Look: Waypoints 2, 3, 4, 9, 11, 12, 14, 17

Waypoint-to-Waypoint

Parts of this walk are taken from the book "A Walking Guide to the Superior Hiking Trail: Natural History, Scenery, and Other Trail Features."

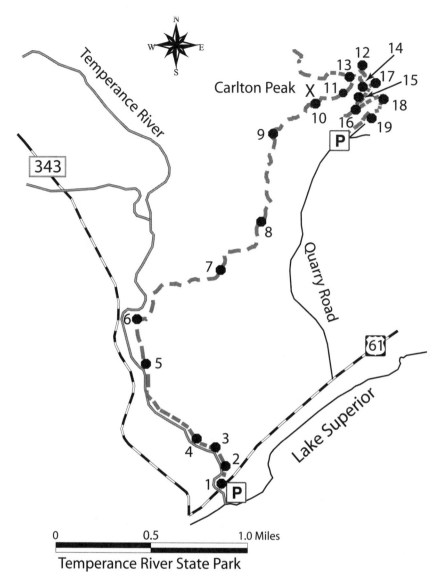

Temperance River State Park
Walk 1: Temperance River, Carlton Peak, and Ted Tofte Overlook

One: Temperance River Wayside

It's a gorgeous summer afternoon at the wayside; a gentle breeze wafts in from the lake, the sun is high and bright, and the sound of the rushing water not only gives us a good feeling, but draws us to it like bears to honey.

Waypoint 1 is in the wayside parking lot, which is part of Temperance River State Park.

Two: Froth Rock and Potholes

It's a short walk up the east side of the river to a park sign for the Cauldron

Trail. This is waypoint 2.

Amygdaloidal basalt outcrops here, but we could also call this outcrop "froth" rock. Round *amygdules*, or gas holes, make up 30 to 45% of the lava flow. These vary from pinhead to dime-size and are filled by *chert, calcite,* and/or a cream-colored *zeolite*. This "froth" rock represents the top of a *pahoehoe lava* flow.

Small *potholes* in the rock indicate the river once flowed over this outcrop, probably forming a small waterfall; the river has since cut down through the basalt to form a narrower but deeper channel.

Three: Eroded Potholes and the River Gorge

From the park sign the trail goes up and over basalt lava flows and basalt steps to a large outcrop from which you can watch the river race through a narrow gorge (Hidden Falls Gorge) that has been cut into an amygdaloidal basalt lava flow. The gorge owes its existence to 1) a fracture or crack in the rock that the river has slowly widened over time, and 2) the formation of large potholes in the fractured rock and the erosion of the downstream side of each pothole. This process is like the cascading fall of a row of dominos; the erosion of the uppermost pothole leads to the erosion of the next one and so on.

Waypoint 3 is at the bridge across the Temperance River and the Gitchi-Gumi State Trail.

Four: Water Chutes, White Water, and Billowy Flow Tops

Continue upriver over amygdaloidal lava flows with great views of the river gorge, water chutes, rushing white water, and more potholes to an overlook at a small waterfall (waypoint 4). The waterfall has formed here because the amygdaloidal top of the basalt lava was more easily eroded then the massive lower part; this led to a "terraced" or "stepped" effect in the flow and the creation of the waterfall. On the opposite side of the river the exposed rock ledge has a nice billowy pahoehoe flow top.

The forest is spruce, balsam fir, birch, and aspen, along with a smattering of big-toothed aspen, willow, and cedar, some of which cling to the sides of the rock ledge. The trail at this point is fairly flat and follows an old *river terrace*.

Five: River Change, Boulder, and Dying Birch

Walking upstream it is interesting to note that the river, above the falls and its vigorous lower reaches, becomes a gentler, wider, straighter body of water. Up here the river is dotted with large *boulders* that come from the erosion of *glacial till* deposits that covered the land after the glacial ice melted away. As the river cut down through this material it carried away the finer clay, sand, silt, and *pebble*-size material leaving the heavier *cobbles* and boulders behind.

Passing an area where the river bank is being undercut by the river (there is a green erosion control fence here) we walk through a forest filled with dead and dying birch. *Fireweed,* with its pretty purple flowers, is prolific through here. The wide, well-used trail follows along, then above the river to waypoint 5, a well-worn path down to the river where there is a basalt *outcrop* and a view of a small waterfall.

There are many informal trails where people have attempted to get down to the waterfall. Be careful to stay on the main hiking trail as some of the side trails are well-worn and dangerous.

Six: River Delta

The trail turns away from the river, passing a junction with a state park ski trail. In this section not only are the birch dying but so are the aspen. A sharp bend in the trail represents waypoint 6, and this spot provides a nice view of a river *meander*.

Along this section the walking path is composed of sand instead of the usual glacial till, cobbles, tree roots, gravel, clay, rock outcrop, and/or kibbles and bits. The sand is part of what used to be a large river *delta,* which is discussed in the introduction for this park.

Seven: Honeysuckle, Doll's Eyes, and a Canadian Carpet

The trail, now well above the river, follows the meander to a sign that informs us we are 2 miles from Carlton Peak. From here the pathway turns east, for a long walk (0.4 miles) over a flat, well-packed trail (gravel part of the delta) through a mixed forest with a pretty typical *Canadian carpet*, to a small creek, which is waypoint 7. Ferns are abundant along the creek as are numerous other wetland plants giving this area a soft, deep green and full-of-life feeling. *Baneberry* (with red and white berries that look like doll's eyes) is common along this trail section.

Eight: Beaver River Diabase and Dead Trees

After leaving the creek the trail becomes rocky with cobbles of basalt and *diabase*, as well as a few larger granitic *glacial erratics*. Following the bottom of a hill, which has outcrops of *Beaver River Diabase* along it, the trail passes over and past diabase boulders that have, through a process called *frost wedging*, broken free of the hillside and rolled to this position. After passing an outcrop of diabase, it's a short walk to a small rocky creek that is waypoint 8.

Nine: Heinz 57, Rose Hips, and Chokecherries

From the creek we head uphill over a rocky trail with the glacial till

188

providing a Heinz 57 variety of cobbles: *pegmatite, schist, granite, monzonite*, basalt, and diabase. Waypoint 9 is at a spur trail that leads to an outcrop of Beaver River Diabase and a nice view of the Temperance River Valley and Taconite Harbor.

Along this section the rose hips are big and red and fireweed is thick and purple. The chokecherries are falling off the bushes and are incredibly sour– they make my mouth pucker, it is like eating a lemon, lime, and grapefruit all at the same time! Lots of climbing false *buckwheat* can be found along the side of the trail.

Ten: Ash Swamp and the Shadow of Carlton Peak

The relatively flat trail continues over and past numerous small diabase outcrops, through more stands of dead or dying birch with a mountain maple understory. Then it's through an ash swamp with boardwalked sections to waypoint 10, a small clearing with a picnic table and the junction with a state park ski trail/road. At this waypoint we are literally in the shadows of Carlton Peak, with the smooth rock wall rising steeply in front of us.

Eleven: Anorthosite and Jack Pines

The trail heads steeply uphill over *anorthosite* boulders, rocky crevices, and rocky steps as it follows the side of Carlton Peak to the spur trail (here called summit trail) that leads to the top of this large anorthosite *xenolith*. In places large chunks of anorthosite have broken off (frost wedging and *exfoliation*) from the main mass to form pieces that are now essentially wedged into, or leaning against, the anorthosite outcrop. Many look like "leaners" in the game of horseshoes.

The anorthosite varies from pinkish-gray to greenish-gray. The large *plagioclase feldspar* crystals are glassy, and the prominent crystal faces reflect the sunlight in a sparkling array of colors and patterns.

The summit spur trail, which is waypoint 11, heads to the top of Carlton Peak with the hiking trail continuing straight ahead. At the spur trail junction there is a Superior Hiking Trail Association "happy" book–a place to record thoughts or impressions of this hike. It is called a "happy" book because most of the entries are just that. Today one person wrote, "climbed here in 1970, nice to see how little it has changed." Carlton Peak is a favorite place for local rock climbers. Lots of pin cherry trees in this area and they all have large fruits.

Spur Trail to the Summit: Views, More Views, Frost Wedging, and More Views

Take the spur trail to the top of Carlton Peak. In doing so we pay close attention to the footpath that leads to the top, for there are all kinds of trails that lead down off the bare summit. In fact one of the entries in the "happy" book said "Happy ending–was lost at the top for half an hour, started down the wrong side!"

The top of Carlton Peak is at 1526 feet (waypoint 11 is at 1400 feet), so the views to the east, south, and west are fantastic. Most of the hills visible to the south and west are composed of diabase while the knob-like features are related to Carlton Peak–they are formed by the bowling ball weathering (exfoliation) of anorthosite xenoliths.

The anorthosite is chock-full of weathering pits. Rainwater or snow melt gets into cracks or small depressions in the rock and then undergoes numerous freeze and thaw cycles. Slowly these depressions widen and deepen until, eventually, they become joined to form long, irregular channels.

There are a lot of jack pine at the summit along with some red pine; the footings from a fire tower that closed in the 1950s can still be seen.

Twelve: Ted Tofte Overlook

After descending back to the "happy" book the trail continues gently downhill along the edge of this massive block of anorthosite to waypoint 12, the spur trail to the Ted Tofte Overlook. It's a short walk over a rocky anorthosite trail to the overlook, which is simply spectacular for it provides a 360-degree view. Imposing Carlton Peak, with its jack pine-covered top, is immediately behind us, a sheer drop into an anorthosite quarry is straight ahead, and all around are the rolling hills of the North Shore. On a blue sky fall day, it is red, orange, brown, yellow, green, and blue from north to south and from east to west. This and Carlton Peak are two of the very best overlooks along the entire North Shore.

The anorthosite is pinkish-grey with large, shiny plagioclase feldspar crystals up to two inches long. Also found here are radiating pink and white zeolite minerals that appear to be filling in small holes in the anorthosite as well as occurring as a coating along fractures. These are very pretty and unusual, for it is extremely rare for such minerals to occur in the anorthosites found along the North Shore. Their origin still needs to be sorted out.

Thirteen: Choices

From the overlook walk back over the anorthosite, which is pitted, grooved, and worn smooth by running water helped along by the freezing and thawing of water in fractures and depressions. Waypoint 13 is at the junction with the spur trail that goes uphill to the main branch of the Superior Hiking Trail (to the right) and downhill to the quarry (to the left).

If returning to the parking lot at the Temperance River Wayside, follow the spur trail back to the main branch of the Superior Hiking Trail (right), turn left at the junction, and retrace this walk back to the starting point.

If going on to the Britton Peak parking lot follow the spur trail back to the main branch of the Superior Hiking Trail (right), turn right at the junction, and follow the Superior Hiking Trail to the parking lot (waypoints 13-16 from Walk 16: Carlton Peak in "A Walking Guide to the Superior Hiking Trail: Natural History, Scenery, and Other Trail Features").

Finally, if you have parked in the quarry area, take the spur trail to the left.

Fourteen: Anorthosite Wall

Follow the spur trail down to an old, rocky road with outcrops, boulders, and cobbles of anorthosite and Beaver River Diabase. The diabase exhibits lumpy weathering. This road was once the access road to the fire tower that was at the top of Carlton Peak.

Waypoint 14 is on an old mining bench of the quarry which provides a great view of the tall and straight anorthosite wall; the Ted Tofte overlook is at the top of the wall. The long, straight, vertical lines along the wall represent the trace of drill holes which were used for blasting the anorthosite. The blasted anorthosite was trucked to Taconite Harbor where it was used as rip rap in the building of the safe harbor.

Fifteen: Spur "Road" and Junction

Continue on down the rocky road through a birch and aspen forest with large boulders of anorthosite to either side. Waypoint 15 is at the junction with a road that goes off to the right.

This side road leads to an outhouse and a series of picnic tables that are widely spaced along both the road and the gravel "bench" found on the other side of a small pine forest.

Sixteen: Another Junction

Stay on the main road (to the left) and it is just a short walk to waypoint 16, which is at a triple road junction.

Seventeen: Anorthosite "Dome" and the Quarry Wall

Take the upper road (to the left), which goes to the quarry wall seen from waypoint 14. There is a large, open area to park in, and this is waypoint 17. From this waypoint we not only have a great view towards the lake but can also see several quarry benches, which were the flat areas used to blast the anorthosite into large chunks.

The quarry wall is awesome and has a distinct "dome" outline due to exfoliation and frost wedging. The massive, greenish to pinkish walls simply sparkle in the sunlight, and fractures through the rock are sealed by green *epidote* and the red quartz mineral *jasper*. The anorthosite forming the wall is spotted in places, and these spots have a distinct greenish color to them. When examined more closely the spots represent fine aggregates of plagioclase feldspar with minor amounts of the minerals sphene and apatite.

Eighteen: Main Parking Area

Return to waypoint 16 and walk down the road to the lower left, which is directly below the road followed to get to waypoint 17. This leads out onto an old quarry bench (lots of spots in the anorthosite here). Continue down the road (past an outcrop to the right with diabase and anorthosite) to waypoint 18, which is the main parking area with an outhouse.

Nineteen: Xenoliths and the Carlton Peak Road

From waypoint 18 look back up the road for a fantastic view of an outcrop with a light-colored anorthosite xenolith in the dark-colored Beaver River Diabase. In the other direction is a small round pond, more quarry terraces, and Lake Superior.

From this point return to your parked vehicle and drive back down the Carlton Peak Road to the junction with Highway 61.

Temperance River State Park

Walk 2: Temperance River and Forestry Road Overlook

Walk Logistics

Start and End: Superior Hiking Trail parking lot on Forest Road 343.

Getting There: Take Highway 61 to Forest Road 343 about 1 mile northeast of Schroeder (just southeast of the Temperance River). Follow Forest Road 343 0.9 miles to the parking lot on the left.

Distance: 2.2 Miles   **Difficulty:** Tennis Shoes

Safety Concerns: Outcrops by the river can be slippery when wet.

Worth a Longer Look: Waypoints 1, 3, 5, 6, 7, 10, 11, 12

Waypoint-to-Waypoint

Note: A shorter version of this walk could begin at the Temperance River State Wayside on Highway 61. Follow waypoints 10 through 12 on the east side of the river, then cross the bridge over the Temperance River and walk back downstream on the west side from waypoint 6 to waypoint 9.

Waypoint One: Overlook

Waypoint 1 for this walk is located on Forest Road 342, 1.3 miles from the junction with Highway 61. Drive about 0.3 miles beyond the parking lot to a scenic overlook, which is waypoint 1 for the walk. Enjoy a great view of the river and Carlton Peak. The river has a spectacular *slump* on the outside bend of a *meander*. The open, bare hill above the meander is slumping into the river and, based on the trees scattered down its length, it is taking the forest with it. Carlton Peak dominates the skyline, and the jack pines at its top contrast nicely with the dominantly paper birch forest.

From the overlook drive to the Superior Hiking Trail parking lot.

Two: Parking Lot

The small parking lot alongside Forestry Road 343 is waypoint 2.

Three: Swiss Cheese Basalt and Vesicle Cylinders

Follow the Superior Hiking Trail across the road and down to the river. Exposed here are large outcrops of *amygdaloidal* to *massive basalt* (flow tops and bottoms) that are chock-a-block full of *potholes*. The potholes vary from 4 feet in diameter down to donut-size and give the surface of the outcrop a "Swiss cheese" look. The waterfalls are formed by: 1) the erosion

193

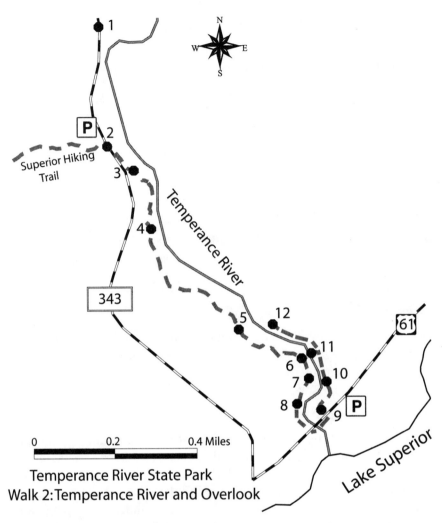

Temperance River State Park
Walk 2: Temperance River and Overlook

of the sides of potholes resulting in connections between them, and 2) deepening of the downstream potholes more than the upstream ones.

Continue along the hiking trail and about 300 feet down the river there are *vesicle cylinders* in the basalt; these are small round areas crammed full of *amygdules* surrounded by massive basalt. These features form due to the concentration of gas rising up through the cooling lava flow along cylindrical-shaped pathways. Potholes seem to form preferentially in these amygdaloidal zones. The area of vesicle cylinders is waypoint 3.

Four: Froth Lava and Basalt Steps

Walk down river passing more "Swiss cheese" rock (hollowed out vesicle cylinders) to waypoint 4, an outcrop of "frothy" basalt. This is the amygdaloidal top of a *pahoehoe lava flow* with amygdules from pinhead-size to more than 2 inches in diameter. *Quartz, calcite,* and *zeolites*

194

(laumantite) fill the amygdules. Just above this *outcrop* is a rock wall that provides nice views both up and down the river.

Five: Arches, Flow Contacts, and Pipe Amygdules

A long walk (0.4 miles) downriver to a basalt outcrop and waterfall. Here there are two lava flows exposed in the outcrop on the opposite side of the river. These are identified by amygdaloidal tops and massive bottoms. "Arch-like" features have formed in the amygdaloidal part of the flows due to erosion by fast-flowing water.

Just below the trail, on the river side, *pipe amygdules* near the top of a flow are overlain by the massive base of the next flow. The pipe amygdules are filled by quartz and zeolites; one large amygdule is filled by radiating crystals.

Pipe amygdules are elongate, cylindrical zones that extend vertically up through a lava flow ending in a vesicle cylinder. These reflect the rise of gas through a cooling lava, most commonly basalt. They may be caused by the flow of lava over wet ground with the water flashing to steam and rising up through the flow, or they may simply represent easy conduits through the lava for the upward-streaming gas. The gas moves upward along these features leaving behind an empty, elongate space in the cooling and hardening basalt. These open spaces are then filled in by the precipitation of minerals out of the warm groundwater (in theory, then, one could find pipe *agates*).

Six: Pothole Gorge and Bridge Across River

Continue downriver with a nice view into a large fracture in a basalt flow that has been widened by fast-flowing water. Within the fracture zone are excellent examples of how potholes erode and become connected to form falls and narrow, steep-walled gorges. The view down into Pothole Gorge continues to waypoint 6, the bridge across the river at the Gitchi-Gami State Trail. There is a trail junction here with the Superior Hiking Trail continuing northwest to Carlton Peak, and two park trails, one on either side of the river, leading down to the wayside parking lot. Stay on the spur trail that follows the west side of the river.

From the bridge we have a great view of a beautiful water chute with steep walls and lots and lots of potholes. The rock outcropping here is amygdaloidal basalt.

Seven: Abandoned Pothole

The trail goes over amygdaloidal basalt with amygdules filled by quartz (milky-colored chert and jasper) and a fibrous zeolite mineral (laumantite or thomsonite) to waypoint 7, a large pothole that has been left high and dry by the river. The pothole looks like a small cave whose top has collapsed; it must be 10-12 feet across. This would be a great den for a family of bears.

Eight: Small Creek

It's a short walk over a rough, rocky trail of amygdaloidal basalt that parallels the river to waypoint 8, a bridge over a small creek. From here we can see the parking lot on Highway 61.

Nine: Bridge Across River and Wayside

From the creek continue along the river to a reddish basalt outcrop in the river bank with a ropey pahoehoe flow top. From here it is on to Highway 61 and across the bridge over the river to arrive at the parking lot and waypoint 9.

Ten: Froth Rock and Potholes

From the parking lot take the Cauldron Trail. It is a short walk along the east side of the river to a sign for the Cauldron Trail. Waypoint 10 is located at the sign.

The amygdaloidal basalt seen here, could easily be called "froth" rock. Round amygdules, or gas holes, make up 30 to 45% of the lava flow. These vary from pinhead to dime-size and are filled by *chert*, calcite, and/or a cream-colored zeolite. This "froth" rock represents the top of a pahoehoe lava flow. Also along here nice columnar *cooling joints* are exposed.

Small potholes in the rock indicate the river once flowed over this outcrop, probably forming a small waterfall; the river has since cut down through the basalt to form a narrower but deeper channel.

Eleven: Eroded Potholes and the River Gorge

The trail continues up and over basalt lava flows and basalt steps to a large outcrop from which we have a great view of the river racing through a narrow gorge (Hidden Falls Gorge) which has been cut into an amygdaloidal basalt lava flow. The gorge owes its existence to 1) a fracture or crack in the rock that the river has slowly widened over time, and 2) the formation of large potholes in the fractured rock and the erosion of the downstream side of each pothole. This process is like the cascading fall of a row of dominos; the erosion of the uppermost pothole leads to the erosion of the next one and so on.

Walk under a power line to Waypoint 11, which is at the bridge across the Temperance River.

Twelve: Water Chutes, White Water, and Billowy Flow Tops

Continue upriver, past a hiking club sign, over amygdaloidal lava flows with great views of the river gorge, water chutes, rushing white water, and more potholes to an overlook at a small waterfall (waypoint 12). The waterfall has formed here because the amygdaloidal top of the basalt lava was more easily eroded then the massive lower part; this led to a "terraced" or "stepped" effect in the flow and the creation of the waterfall. On the opposite side of the river the exposed rock ledge has a nice billowy pahoehoe flow top.

The forest is spruce, balsam fir, birch, and aspen, along with a smattering of bigtooth aspen, willow, and cedar, some of which cling to the sides of the rock ledge. The trail at this point is fairly flat and follows an old *river terrace*.

Walk back to the bridge and cross to the opposite side; this is the same as waypoint 6 of this walk. When walking back up the trail to the parking lot take time to notice the changes in the river. It becomes gentler, wider, and straighter, and is dotted with *boulders* eroded from the *glacial till*.

Walk 3: Temperance River and Lake Superior

Walk Logistics

Start and End: Temperance River State Wayside on Highway 61

Getting There: Take Highway 61 to the Temperance River, about 1 mile northeast of Schroeder. The wayside is on the northeast side of the river; parking is available on both sides of the highway.

Walk Distance: About 1 mile   **Difficulty:** Tennis Shoes

Safety Concerns: None

Worth a Longer Look: Waypoints 2, 3, 4, 5, 7, 8, 9, 10

Waypoint-to-Waypoint

One: Parking Lot

Waypoint 1 is at the Temperance River State Wayside parking lot on the south (or lake) side of Highway 61 at the beginning of the trail that goes down the west side of the river to the lake.

Two: Ropey Pahoehoe and Half-Potholes

A short walk down the trail takes us to the footbridge across the Temperance River (waypoint 2). The rock exposed on both sides of the river gorge is *amygdaloidal basalt*. In the gorge there are large half-*potholes*, half because the downstream side has been eroded away by the busy river. On the west side of the river, just below the bridge, there is a rock wall built around a large pothole. The pothole demonstrates not only the power of the river but also how high the river once was. It flowed over the rocks exposed here, and in doing so drilled out this great pothole before it cut down through the basalt lavas to its present position some 20 feet below us. At an erosion rate of 0.25 inches per year (pure guess work) it would have taken the Temperance over 1000 years to form the gorge seen here.

Just below the "walled" pothole and below the bridge on the opposite side of the river are beautiful, almost perfectly preserved ropey tops to a 1.1 billion year old lava flow. These features are characteristic of recent *pahoehoe* basalt lavas found in Hawaii, Iceland, and on the Galapagos Islands; to find these here, at the Temperance River, and in incredibly old rocks is positively amazing! The flow tops are reddish-brown in color due to the oxidation of the iron minerals in the basalt, but the twisted, entrail-like flow pattern is well-preserved. This pattern results from a combination of temperature and

198

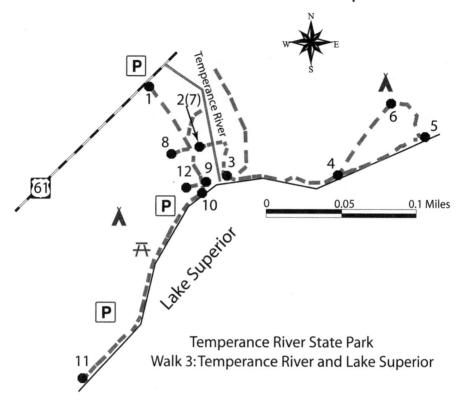

Temperance River State Park
Walk 3: Temperance River and Lake Superior

viscosity (resistance to flow) of the lava when it was erupted. As the lava began to flow over the ground, the top was cooled by the atmosphere and the bottom by the ground. The lava in between became insulated and remained as hot as the day it was erupted. This hot lava flowed away and, as it did, it dragged the crust, which was cool but yet somewhat plastic, into the ropey and billowy shapes seen here and other places in the park. Locally these flow tops exhibit what we call "dinosaur skin" weathering where the cooled and glassy top breaks into squares or rectangular-shaped pieces that together look like the skin on a Tyrannosaurus Rex. The flow top below the "walled" pothole may not be visible during spring run-off.

The flow tops are amygdaloidal and the *amygdules* (gas cavities) are filled by white *calcite*, *quartz*, and cream to pinkish-colored *zeolite* minerals. The ropey and amygdaloidal flow tops grade down into more massive centers and bottoms, and this can be seen on the left-hand side of the bridge. The massive lava flow that overlays the ropey pahoehoe has *pipe amygdules*.

Looking down river we can see the end of a rather prominent sand and pebble "bar" sticking its nose into the river's mouth. Later in the walk we will visit a rock outcrop at the edge of the "bar" and walk along it in a southeast direction.

Three: River Views

Walk across the bridge and up the wooden stairs and take the trail down river toward the lake. In the spring of 2007 this part of the trail was closed due to slumping. To get around this take the trail to the left and walk up a steep set of stairs. At the top turn right and follow the trail down to the waypoint at a viewing platform. There are are nice views into the river gorge and of the area where the river widens before its final exit into the lake. Waypoint 3 is at a viewing platform that overlooks the river. Directly across from the platform is a pile of large boulders (*talus*) that have been *frost-wedged* off the steep cliff.

Four: Separated Basalt

From the viewing platform the gravel trail goes over basalt outcrops and down to a nice gravel beach located on the east side of the river; on the opposite side of the river is a half-moon-shaped gravel bar that extends part way out across the river mouth.

The exposed rock is amygdaloidal basalt; many of the minerals filling the amygdules (gas cavities) have been weathered out.

From the beach walk up the wooden steps to the left that lead to a large *outcrop* that occurs between the lake and the walking path. This is another amygdaloidal basalt, and it has been nearly cut in half along a large fracture that has been continually widened by wave action over the years. Looking into the fissure we can see veins of quartz and calcite that cut through the basalt. The outcrop provides a nice view of the rocky shoreline.

The trail continues along and above the lakeshore with continuous basalt outcrop to waypoint 4, which is at the junction with a small path that goes to the left.

Five: Froth Rock and Taconite Harbor

Continue straight ahead to a large outcrop of basalt on the lakeshore from which there is a good view down the lake (southeast) of Taconite Harbor and the Minnesota Power coal-fired electricity plant. The rip-rap for the safe harbor came from a quarry on Carlton Peak.

The basalt exposed on the lakeshore is tan to dark grey in color and full of pinhead-size amygdules that are round to irregular in shape and filled by calcite, quartz, and zeolites–many have been weathered out. This kind of basalt is what we refer to as "froth" rock, and represents the top or near top of a pahoehoe lava flow. From the outcrop we have a fantastic view down the lakeshore. The basalt is a speckled blue color from all the *bird's-eye primrose* growing in the fractures in the basalt, later in the summer there will be *harebell* and *butterwort*. At the end of the outcrop area we come to a set of wooden steps that lead up to waypoint 5. This is at the junction with a trail that heads off to the left and represents the loop trail to follow back to the river; the path straight ahead leads to a very amygdaloidal outcrop on the lakeshore. The outcrop represents two different lava flows. The top of an amygdaloidal flow that is overlain by the more massive base of another flow. The reddish flow top has preserved ropey flow structures.

All of the basalt lavas exposed in the river and along the lakeshore are about 1.1 billion years old and belong to what geologists call the *North Shore Volcanic Group*. They were all erupted out of the *Mid-Continent Rift* to form plateau lavas, and today the flows are tilted about 20 degrees toward the lake.

Six: Campground Road

Take the trail to the left and walk past a sign with information on "Superiors Rock Garden" and up wooden steps to the campground road with camping sites all along it. The junction of the road and the trail is waypoint 6.

Seven: Overlook and Potholes

The trail continues to the left and downhill looping back to waypoint 4. From this waypoint return to the bridge and cross it to return to waypoint 2, which is also waypoint 7.

For a short side trip, head right on the trail and follow the short path that leads to an overlook of the river. There is a steep drop down into the gorge and on either side are solid basalt walls. Nicely shaped potholes can be seen in the basalt and, again, this is an indication not only of the river's power, but also the higher elevation it once flowed at. The basalt outcrop directly below the overlook is dotted with white amygdules.

Eight: Polygonal Cooling Joints

Return to the bridge. Take the trail to the right (when facing downriver) passing over a basalt outcrop that has beautifully outlined polygonal *cooling joints* (waypoint 8).

Nine: Collapsed River Bank and Happy Fish

Continue up the wooden steps and take the trail to the left that goes downriver. This section of the trail is bounded by a fence because of the steep drop into the river and the instability of the riverbank. Waypoint 9 is at a large viewing platform with a bench and a nice overlook down to the river. The trail to the right goes down a set of stairs to the road that leads to the picnic ground and the beach.

From the platform the river looks more like a wide pool of water after it exits the narrow canyon, and I guess this makes the fish happy. The basalt exposed below the platform has a very nice polygonal cooling joint.

Ten: Beach Flow

It's a short walk down the path with wooden steps to an overlook of an outcrop of amygdaloidal basalt on the beach that looks like a pin cushion (more froth rock).

There are two ways to get down onto the beach and the outcrop. We take the "unofficial" way and follow the worn path straight ahead and down onto the outcrop. The other way is to go back to the viewing platform and take the trail to the left that goes down wooden stairs to the picnic ground road. At the road turn left, and once on the beach turn left again and walk down the beach to the outcrop (waypoint10).

The amygdules in the lava flow are dominantly filled with calcite and zeolites. There is a nice flow contact here with the froth rock (flow top) overlain by the base of a more massive lava flow. In places veins and stringers of the red mineral hematite, along with white calcite, cut across the flow and this material locally replaces the basalt matrix to produce white amygdules in a red rock.

When viewed from above the basalt outcrop has a ropey looking surface and is reddish in color, which is typical for the oxidized top of a pahoehoe lava flow.

Eleven: Humpty Dumpty

The beach has been extended by longshore currents part way across the mouth of the river to create a river bar. The longshore currents, created by Lake Superior's breaking waves, move sand and pebbles parallel to the beach. They then carry this material beyond the end of the bar and deposit it in the calmer waters of the river.

Walk southeast (right) along the beach to a large, polished *glacial erratic* that sits directly in front of the picnic area. This rock is *monzonite* in composition, and to me it looks like Humpty Dumpty after he fell off the wall! Here is yet another example of a large rock left behind by the melting ice more than 10,000 years ago. Too big and heavy to go anywhere, this erratic must have spent a long time on the bottom of Glacial Lake Duluth. Then, as water levels fell, it was left high and dry a hundred or so feet above the water. As present day Lake Superior rose (due in part to glacial rebound) the monzonite boulder found itself right on the beach, and here it has remained for over a thousand years, getting smoother and shinier with each passing storm. Speaking of which, this boulder would be a front row seat for watching great storm waves. Humpty Dumpty is surrounded by fine sand with larger *pebbles* and *cobbles* found closer to the water.

From Humpty Dumpty continue down the beach to an amygdaloidal basalt

202

outcrop that looks hummocky in places and has "lake" potholes carved into it. These form from wave action combined with depressions in the rock (easily eroded billowy parts of the flow tops?) and the abrasion of the rock by sand and pebbles carried in, and swirled around by, the storm waves and backwash. There are also nicely preserved reddish-colored pahoehoe flow tops indicating there is more than one flow exposed here.

Waypoint 11 is at the end of the beach at the edge of a basalt outcrop.

Twelve: Beach Stroll

Walk back toward the river either strolling down the beach or walking along the paved road, to the wooden steps at the end of the picnic area, which is waypoint 12. From here go up the stairs to the viewing platform (waypoint 9) and then return to the parking lot.

Cascade River State Park

Introduction

Cascade River State Park features not only a spirited river that has carved out a spectacular rocky gorge but also a wide variety of geological features that are the result of the interaction of the ancient volcanic rocks with glacial ice, running water, and crashing waves. And it is moving water, in the form of the Cascade River, Cascade Creek, Indian Camp Creek, Spruce Creek, Cut Face Creek, and Lake Superior, that continues to shape the park's landscape.

A prominent basalt lava flow, called the Terrace Point, is responsible for many of the geological features in the park. This flow, which is over 160 feet thick, extends across the entire 10-mile length of the park, forming Lookout Mountain, Moose Mountain, and a good portion of the lower gorge of the Cascade River. Both Lookout and Moose mountains are nice examples of a topographic feature called a cuesta, which is an asymmetric ridge with a long gentle slope on one side and a steep cliff on the other side. The gentle slope parallels the tilt of the underlying strata, which here is between 10 and 20 degrees. The steep cliff is formed by glacial plucking and frost wedging. The resultant hill ends up looking like one of the teeth on an old wood saw. There are several of these cuestas, formed from different basalt lava flows and intrusive rocks, along the North Shore between Tofte and Grand Marais; together these are known as the Sawtooth Mountains.

The Terrace Point Lava Flow is 1.1 billion years old and is part of a succession of lava flows referred to as the North Shore Volcanic Group. These lavas were erupted from the Mid-Continent Rift and flowed out over a barren landscape, one flow after another, to form a thick, pancake-like stack of lava flows which, together, are called plateau lavas.

The other notable rocks in the park are red-colored, thinly bedded or layered volcanic sandstones and siltstones, which locally exhibit ripple marks and mud cracks. They can be traced across the entire length of the park, are up to 40 feet thick, and directly overlie the Terrace Point Lava Flow. These sedimentary rocks are made up of material that was eroded from basalt lavas during a lull in volcanic activity. Composed of sand to silt-size grains of plagioclase feldspar, pyroxene, and magnetite that were transported by streams and rivers, the rocks are red in color because they also contain small amounts of the red iron oxide mineral hematite.

The Cascade River has eroded down through the sedimentary rocks and the Terrace Point Lava Flow to create the lower gorge. In doing so the river took

204

advantage of bedding planes and the general softness of the sedimentary rocks, as well as amygdaloidal zones, columnar cooling joints, and the billowy flow tops of the lava flows to form the many potholes, waterfalls, chutes, and cascades seen in the gorge.

Sections of the walking trails, in the lower part of the park, are composed of sand and/or gravel that represents part of what was once a large river delta. This formed several thousand years ago as water levels in Glacial Lake Duluth fell. The gravel deposits are made up of rounded pebbles of varying rock compositions, as well as some cobbles and sand. These were derived from the erosion and size-sorting of the glacial till by a much younger and more vigorous Cascade River shortly after the ice melted off the land. The gravel is found in thin deposits on top of the lava flows from an elevation of about 600 feet (the current level of Lake Superior) up to an elevation of 900 feet (the shoreline of old Glacial Lake Duluth). As the Cascade River flowed into this ancient lake the velocity of the river water decreased rapidly, and the sand to pebble-size material dropped out, creating the delta. Lense-like deposits of sand in the delta represent local working of the delta by wave action as water levels in the glacial lake fell below the elevation of the delta.

Another interesting aspect of the park's geological past can be seen at the long road cut opposite the car pullout at Good Harbor Bay on Highway 61 just above the Cut Face Creek wayside. The rock exposure consists of thinly bedded volcanic sandstones and siltstones (the same volcanic sedimentary rocks that can be seen along the Cascade River) that are overlain by a basalt lava flow. Toward the west end of the outcrop, the lava flow becomes fragmental. The fragments are really neat because they are composed of cinder (lumps of scoria), volcanic bombs, and massive lava fragments. The best way to explain these features is that the hot lava flowed over a sandy beach into shallow water. The interaction of the hot lava and the much cooler water led to steam explosions that blew the cooled top and bottom parts of the lava flow to smithereens (creating the basalt fragments). The hot molten interior of the flow was blown into the air where it was cooled quickly and hardened by air and steam to form scoria and volcanic bombs. When they hit the ground, some of the bombs were still hot, and the water rapidly cooled them to produce the very fine-grained, massive outer edge seen on some of the fragments. If stopping at the Cut Face Creek wayside take the time to walk out onto the rocky beach and have a look at the scoria pieces, small volcanic bombs, and pieces of red sandstone that can be found there.

The park has over 10 miles of shoreline that is composed mostly of a sparsely amygdaloidal lava flow that immediately underlies the Terrace Point Lava Flow. The lake has extensively polished and eroded this flow which now provides the setting for magnificent views up and down the North Shore as well as some nice picnic areas.

The park itself is the site of an old CCC camp (Civilian Conservation Corps), which dates back to the 1930s, and the trails near the river as well as most of the stonework in the park are from that time. It was here that members of the Corps cut the large pine logs for the buildings at Gooseberry Falls State Park. Cascade River officially became a state park in 1957.

The park is part of what is called the Jonvik Deeryard. This represents the state's most extensive winter gathering place for white-tailed deer (anyone tell the wolves this?). In the 1950s it was reported that as many as 525 deer per square mile could be found along an eight-mile stretch of Highway 61 in the Jonvik Deeryard. Today the winter count is substantially lower at 125 per square mile. The deer converge on this area from the interior forest because it is a south-facing slope and thus temperatures are warmer, the snow is not as deep, it is more sheltered from the wind, and the many conifers provide food and shelter. The effect of all these deer has been to browse back favorite species like mountain maple and cedar.

The four walks we have chosen for this park were designed to show off the rocky gorge of the Cascade River, the long, beautiful shoreline of Lake Superior, and the most-fascinating aspects of the park's geology.

Cascade River State Park
Walk 1: Lakeshore and Lower Gorge

Walk Logistics

Start and End: Cascade River Wayside on Highway 61

Getting There: Take Highway 61 to the Cascade River, which is about 8 miles northeast of Lutsen or 9 miles southwest of Grand Marais. Park in the wayside parking lot on either side of the highway.

Walk Distance: 3.85 miles   **Difficulty:** Walking Shoes

Safety Concerns: Watch for wet rocks along the lakeshore

Worth a Longer Lake: Waypoints 2, 3, 4, 5, 6, 8, 9, 11, 13, 22, 23, 24

Waypoint-to-Waypoint

One: Wild White Horses

We are standing in the wayside parking lot on the lake side of Highway 61, busy putting on wind jackets and gloves. When we stepped out of my Explorer we found the winds of change blow strong as late summer slips into early fall. There is a devilish cool breeze, and it is coming straight off the agitated lake to push ragged white clouds away from us at a rapid gallop. Upset at being stirred by the brisk wind, the lake is taking it out on the shore by sending a never-ending line of tall waves to break against the dark rocks in great booming crashes that send frothy white water in all directions. It is said Lake Superior is more like an ocean than a lake, and at the moment I am inclined to believe it. As I watch the breaking waves all I can think of is Wordsworth's "wild white horses" and how they "play, chomp, chafe, and toss wildly in the spray." What we are watching is a small part of the constant battle between the land and water, a battle water always wins.

Waypoint 1 is in the parking lot on the south side of the highway close to the bridge across the Cascade River.

Two: Ophitic Lavas and a Symphony By the Lake

Cross the bridge over the river and take the trail just past the guardrail that heads down toward the noisy lake. Waypoint 2 is at the second trail junction where a short path leads to the lakeshore.

The wet and slippery rock exposed along the shoreline is a massive *basalt* lava flow that exhibits lumpy weathering with some kibbles and bits on the *outcrop* (see *diabase weathering*). These two characteristics indicate this lava flow has what is referred to as *ophitic* texture. Ophitic is a Greek word meaning a stone spotted like a serpent. The spots are large *pyroxene* crystals

207

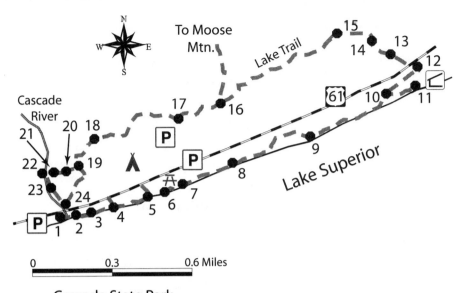

Cascade State Park
Walk 1: Lakeshore and Lower Gorge Trail

0   0.3   0.6 Miles

Cascade State Park
Walk 1: Lakeshore and Lower Gorge Trail

(augite) that enclose much smaller crystals of *plagioclase feldspar*. The large pyroxene crystals are separated from each other by fine-grained areas of plagioclase feldspar with some *olivine* and *magnetite*. The larger pyroxenes are more resistant to weathering than the intervening feldspar-rich areas and so end up as "raised lumps" throughout the rock. These lumps, upon further weathering, crumble apart to what we call kibbles and bits. Be sure to check out the wave sculpted potholes down by the lakeshore.

The lake is an awesome sight with great white rollers coming ashore, and the sound is like drums, cymbals, and horns all playing at once and all playing way too loudly.

Three: Rock Plants and a Cobble Beach

Return to the main trail and continue along the lakeshore passing through a grassy area with mountain ash, paper birch, and spruce trees to waypoint 3, which is at a trail down to the lake and a *pebble* and *cobble* beach. The basalt exposed here has well defined "spots" that are composed of dark crystals of pyroxene (the mineral augite). The rock has a pitted look to it (weathering of spots?) and contains numerous stringers and veins of either *quartz* and feldspar (pink and cream-colored) or *calcite* (in places stained red by the iron mineral *hematite*); some fractures are coated by hematite.

All along this bare, rocky shoreline keep an eye out for truly hardy plants, ones that like fog, cold air, and stiff breezes. Plants we have seen include *cinquefoil* (shrubby and three-toothed), *harebells, butterwort, bird's-eye primrose*, and upland *goldenrod*.

208

Four: Vesicle Cylinders

Continue along the main trail, which is grassy with one swampy spot in an area of cedar, spruce and birch trees. This is followed by a junction with a well-used trail (waypoint 4) that crosses the trail we are following. To the left it goes up to Highway 61 and on to the Cascade River Campground. To the right it goes to the lakeshore.

Take the trail to the right, which ends on a large outcrop of basalt. From the outcrop there are spectacular views up and down the lakeshore which, at the moment, is white spray from horizon to horizon. Wow, what a sight and what a great place to be on a day like this!

The basalt outcrop is dark grey and contains *vesicle cylinders* (these are best seen on the wet rock) with most of the mineral-filled vesicles (*amygdules*) weathered out. Vesicle cylinders are round to irregular-shaped areas in the tops of lava flows that contain abundant amygdules; they are separated by sparsely *amygdaloidal* or *massive* rock. These features form from concentrations of gas rising up through a cooling lava along cylindrical-shaped pathways. The basalt is cut by three different kinds of veins–red hematite, white to pink calcite, and quartz plus plagioclase feldspar.

Five: Diabase Dike and Shetland Ponies

Back at the main trail we continue along the lakeshore over a planked, wet area as we walk through cedar, spruce, and paper birch woods past a small stand of cedar trees at the edge of a large, open outcrop to yet another trail to the left that goes up to the highway and then onto the campground road. The trail also goes to the lakeshore and we follow it to waypoint 5. This is out on the outcrop where a *diabase dike* has intruded the basalt lava flow. The dike can be followed down the outcrop to the lake.

The dike has a beautiful chilled margin (easier to see when dry), which indicates the basalt lava flow was hard and cold when it was intruded by the diabase. The margins of the hot diabase magma were rapidly cooled against the cold, hard basalt (fine-grained chilled margin) while the magma in the center of the dike cooled more slowly and thus has a larger grain size.

The great view continues though the lake is definitely calming down with the white wild horses now more like Shetland ponies.

Six: Mystery Rock

Continue on with spotted basalt forming outcrops along the walking path (the trail goes around one), and these have undergone rather intense weathering creating a crumbly rock. The forest through here is spruce, cedar, and paper birch with mountain ash; along the trail can be found, in early summer, *blue bead lily*, *bunchberry*, *starflower*, and *Canadian mayflower*. In September large-leafed *aster* is in bloom. The traffic noise from Highway 61 is quite loud here.

Passing some large cedar trees come to a picnic table and fire pit on the lakeshore (waypoint 6). The Spotted Basalt that is exposed here has what looks like "splat" marks all over it (to the left and down the lakeshore). These are round to irregular pinkish areas composed of pink *orthoclase feldspar*, cream-colored plagioclase feldspar, and dark pyroxene. These minerals together form a rock called *monzonite,* which is a relatively rare igneous rock because it contains no *quartz*. These patches are one to two feet across, and Steve thinks they look like pink water from a water balloon hitting the outcrop. Their origin is not known. I mean, how do you get a coarse-grained, slowly cooled igneous rock to form patches within a rapidly cooled lava flow? Three-toothed and shrubby cinquefoil along with harebells grow on the exposed rocks.

That mystery unsolved, we turn our attention to the picnic area, which is a really pleasant place. It is in a cedar grove with a view out over what appears to be an endless expanse of advancing waves. Lunch here with a nice glass of Chardonnay, contemplating the lake and the "mystery" of the spotted pink rock, would be nice way to spend a couple of hours.

Seven: Picnic Tables and Monzonite "blob"

From the mystery rock it is a short walk to a wide, well-used trail that heads off to the left. We find another picnic table here in yet another cedar grove, which is just beyond the trail junction. The wide trail to the left leads up to a parking area adjacent to Highway 61.

We now notice picnic tables scattered about all through here, and waypoint 7 is at a junction of a second trail that goes down to the lakeshore from the opposite end of the parking area. The outcrop at this waypoint is weathered Spotted Basalt with a beautiful monzonite blob in it. The monzonite has a coarse-grained center and a finer-grained margin (chilled?), so the mystery deepens! Canadian mayflower, strawberry, large-leafed aster, and sarsperilla can be found along here.

Eight: Glacial Erratic

Staying on the main trail, which is now composed of gravel that represents part of the Cascade River *delta*, we pass another picnic table from which it is a short stroll to the junction with a path up to an outhouse.

Continue on the wide gravel trail past a cement foundation through a cedar forest with spruce and paper birch. Spotted Basalt is exposed along the lakeshore and in the high bank immediately to the left of the trail. Walk through a stand of spruce to an open grassy area with a large *glacial erratic* of Spotted Basalt, and this is waypoint 8.

In this open area we find *ox-eye daisies, buttercups, brown-eyed Susan, yarrow, yellow sweet clover*, and yellow and orange *hawkweed*. Hawkweed is a member of the Composite Family, and orange hawkweed is also called "devil's paintbrush." The name for this plant comes from the belief that hawks ate the flowers to improve their vision. Yarrow contains a chemical called achilleine that speeds the formation of blood clots and gives the plant its other name–bloodwort. In the spring blue bead lily, Canadian mayflower, sarsaparilla, *rose-twisted stalk*, wood anemones, raspberries, and Mertensia can be found along this trail section.

Nine: Weathered Basalt and an Open Hillside

The grassy trail heads up toward a series of outcrops of lumpy and crumbly Spotted Basalt. These are nice examples of how spots weather to lumps, which then disintegrate to crumbles and kibbles and bits. .

Walking on, over a grassy and/or kibbles and bits-covered trail, come to an open hillside dotted with paper birch, glacial erratics, basalt outcrops, and a whole bunch of yellow and white flowers. This open area extends from just below the highway to the lakeshore and is very pretty with all the yellow-leaved birch trees, golden grass, and the various colors of the flowers.

The trail bends away from the lake, turning toward Highway 61 before taking another sharp turn to parallel the road. It then makes a right turn to head back to the lake and waypoint 9, the junction with a path that leads down to a rocky outcrop on the lakeshore, which is Spotted Basalt with lumps and crumbles.

Ten: Backpack #1

The wide grassy trail continues along the lakeshore through birch woods with some mountain ash and aspen. There are boulders of basalt as well as kibbles and bits on the trail, which eventually bends away from the lake going gently uphill. Passing a Spotted Basalt outcrop come to waypoint 10, a sign that reads "Backpack #1," and a trail junction with backpacking campsite #1 somewhere down the trail to the right.

Eleven: Beach Pavement

Take the time to walk the short distance down to the campsite, which has a shelter, a bear-proof food locker, an outhouse, and a picnic table (no order of importance here). The campsite is waypoint 11. Below the campsite is an absolutely gorgeous *boulder* and cobble beach that looks as if someone from the park service spent a whole lot of time fitting all the rock pieces together to provide the cobblestone pavement effect. "Beach pavement" is the lake's equivalent of the wind's desert pavement. Desert pavement is found in places like Death Valley and the Kalahari Desert and is composed of a layer of cobbles, boulders, and pebbles that are too large to be moved by the wind. The desert wind blows away the finer material, the silt and sand, and, as it does so, the boulders, cobbles, and pebbles become more and more concentrated until they eventually form an almost uniform surface cover. The lake's version is to use its wave power to carry away the finer material, and to sort and jostle the larger stones into place rounding off the corners of those that refuse to fit. The end result is this nice boulder and cobblestone beach.

This would be a great place to camp (the sound of the breaking waves beneath a moonless, starlit sky would be exceptional). It is also a good lunch spot, and the private beach is kind of neat.

Twelve: Highway 61

After spending some time exploring this spot and sitting at the picnic table watching the waves come and go, we walk back to the trail junction and continue on a wide, grassy trail, which now follows the highway. The trail makes a sharp turn to the left, heading up to Highway 61 with waypoint 12 just below the road.

Thirteen: Sawtooth Mountains

Walk across the highway and over a beautiful kibble and bit weathered outcrop, then uphill to a power line from which we have a great view to the south of the *Sawtooth Mountains*. This is waypoint 13.

Fourteen: Birch and the Birch Forest

Walk under the power line and through a birch forest with some spruce and aspen to waypoint 14, a sign that explains a 1908 forest fire that burned through this area. Blackened pine stumps are the relics of that fire. This was once part of a great forest of white and red pines. A map of Minnesota's pre-settlement vegetation is available online from the Minnesota Department of Natural Resources "Data Deli."

After the white pine forest was cut in the early part of the twentieth century, a series of huge fires swept through the cutover areas, feeding on slash piles and brush. Some of these fires resulted in the loss of many lives in Minnesota and Wisconsin. After the fires, a birch forest grew up. Most of the dead and dying birch trees that are seen in the state parks are remnants of this "second-growth" forest.

Birch is a "pioneer" species under certain circumstances because it produces a lot of seeds that are easily and widely distributed by the wind. If a birch seed lands on nutrient-rich soil, and if it gets enough moisture and sunlight, it will grow quickly. The "ifs" are important. A hot fire that burns away the forest duff and exposes the nutrient-rich soil favors the growth of birch. Birch seedlings, like all plants, need some water, but they also need a fair amount of sunlight. They will not do well under a canopy of other trees. This means a birch forest does not generally replace itself when the trees age and

212

die. In hiking along the trails along the North Shore there are a lot of areas where the birch forest is dying. The cause is often the bronze birch borer, but in another sense the cause is "old age." The average time for a birch tree to live is 75 to 100 years, so the big old birches that got their start in the early part of the twentieth century are not going to last much longer.

Fifteen: Glacial Till and Boundary Junction

The trail continues gently uphill over *glacial till* to a long, really straight section that follows the park boundary to waypoint 15, the junction with a trail that goes straight ahead along the boundary, and the walking path that goes to the left toward Trail Center and the park campground.

Sixteen: Moose Mountain Trail

From "boundary junction" walk downhill past a lichen-covered glacial erratic. The trail then levels out and is wide and grassy with boulders of lumpy and crumbly basalt as it goes through a birch forest with cedar, spruce, and balsam poplar.

Go over a wet, grassy area as the trail heads downhill for a short distance before once again leveling out to waypoint 16. This waypoint is at the junction with a trail to the right that goes to Moose Mountain (part of walk 2). We continue ahead toward Trail Center and the campground.

Seventeen: Trail Junctions

Walk past the parking area for group campsites, and along the road to a hiking trail sign and a walking path to the right. Take the walking path and continue along it to waypoint 17, another trail junction. We continue on the trail to the left.

Eighteen: Glacial Lake Duluth

From the trail junction the level, grassy trail goes over cobbles, boulders, and pebbles of basalt and diabase. This material represents part of the delta built by the Cascade River when *Glacial Lake Duluth* occupied the Lake Superior Basin. Walk through a cedar forest with one lonely white pine zoo (a wire enclosure around small trees to stop the deer and moose from eating the terminal buds). The trail runs parallel to the campground road before the road curves away to the left. Waypoint 18 is at the junction with a trail that goes off to the right. Continue on the trail that goes straight ahead.

Nineteen: Trail Junction

It is a short walk downhill over the gravel trail with boulders and cobbles from the delta along with one small basalt outcrop of the Terrace Point Lava Flow (see introduction to the park) to waypoint 19. This is a junction with a trail to the left that goes to Trail Center and one to the right that leads to the Cascade River and the Cascade River Loop Walk along the Superior Hiking

Trail (walk 4). Follow the trail to the right.

Twenty: A Maze of Trails

The trail heads toward the Cascade River passing a large glacial erratic of coarse-grained, white granite to waypoint 20, which is yet another trail junction (it is like an English garden maze through here). The trail to the right goes to the river and meets the Superior Hiking Trail above the river bridge; the trail to the left goes to the river and meets the Superior Hiking Trail at the river bridge.

Twenty-One: Another Junction

Take the wide, grassy trail to the left and it is just a short walk downhill on a gravel trail to a hiking club sign and yet another trail junction. Here the trail to the left goes to Trail Center parking lot and the one to the right continues on to the river and bridge.

Twenty-Two: Cascade River

Take the trail to the right, and it is another short walk, first up a set of stone steps then down some wooden ones, to the river and bridge across it.

Today the river water is frothy and full of tannins that give it the look of root beer, foam included. From this vantage point, which is 50 or 60 feet above the river, we can see three small step-like falls and a water chute through the narrow basalt gorge cut into the Terrace Point Lava Flow. On the opposite side of the bridge is an old stone staircase that leads to the top of the cascades. Even though this is a bit off the regular trail it is well worth the short side trip! Along this section are white pine zoos and lots of informal overlooks (that is, no human-made structures). *Bunchberry* lines the walking path.

Twenty-Three: Potholes and River Gorge

From the bridge walk down the Superior Hiking Trail to another overlook of the river and the continuation of the spectacular gorge (waypoint 23). Downstream is a nice waterfall. The Terrace Point Basalt, a *pahoehoe* lava flow, has small, round amygdules filled by pink to white thomsonite (a semi-precious *zeolite* mineral), white calcite, and clear quartz. Good examples of *potholes* can be seen in the rock, and dark pools of calm water seem to reflect the quiet of the forest.

Twenty-Four: Overlook and Parking Lot

Continue downhill on a gravel trail and downstream to another rocky, noisy overlook of the basalt gorge. From this spot it is a short walk to a spur trail to the right that leads to a bench with a nice view of the lake and the highway. From here cross a small creek and pass a trail to the left before reaching Highway 61 and the parking lot.

Cascade River State Park
Walk 2; Moose Mountain and the Cascade River

Walk Logistics

Start and End: Cascade River Wayside on Highway 61

Getting There: Take Highway 61 to the Cascade River, which is about 8 miles northeast of Lutsen or 9 miles southwest of Grand Marais. Park in the wayside parking lot on either side of the highway.

Walk Distance: about 3.8 miles   **Difficulty:** Walking Shoes

Safety Concerns: None

Worth a Longer Look: Waypoints 2, 3, 5, 15, 16, 27, 28

Waypoint-to-Waypoint

One: Cascade River Wayside

We are at the Cascade River wayside, and the afternoon lake is but a shadow of the lake we walked along in the morning (see walk 1). The wind has dropped to a light breeze, and the long, crashing waves with their breaking "wild horses" have turned into large ripples that meekly beg the land for permission to come ashore. The temperature has climbed to 60 degrees, and with no biting insects to harass us, this should be a nice afternoon for a walk up to Moose Mountain. Waypoint 1 is at the Cascade River wayside.

Two: Deltas and Waterfalls

Leaving the parking lot walk down a set of wooden stairs on the west side of the river and follow the park trail along the river to a nice gravel beach close to the bridge. The gravel that composes the beach represents part of a *delta* that formed several thousand years ago as the water level of *Glacial Lake Duluth* fell. The gravel deposits are made up of rounded *pebbles* of varying rock compositions, as well as some *cobbles* and sand. These were derived from the erosion and size-sorting of the *glacial till* by a much younger and more vigorous Cascade River shortly after the ice melted off the land (see introduction or glossary for further information).

There is an outcrop of reddish weathering, *amygdaloidal basalt* here with *quartz* and thomsonite (pink *zeolite* mineral)-filled amygdules. The *outcrop* on the opposite side of the river looks like the Spotted Basalt of walk 1.

From the gravel beach walk up wooden stairs on a gravel trail past a reddish-colored basalt outcrop that overlooks a wide, gently flowing river with a

215

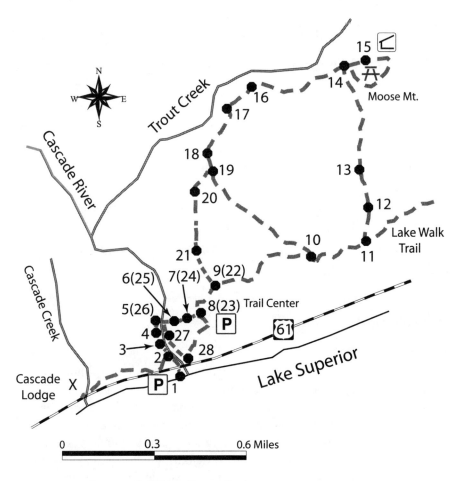

Casacade River State Park
Walk 2: Moose Mountain and the Cascade River

dark basalt wall on the opposite side. Waypoint 2 is at the junction of the park trail and the Superior Hiking Trail. The junction affords a great view upriver of a small waterfall with the water flowing over, into, and through a large eroded *pothole*. After exiting the pothole the water flows over reddish basalt that it has polished smooth as satin. The waterfall and pothole represent the flow contact between the Spotted Basalt and the Terrace Point Lava Flow, which forms most of the lower river gorge and overlies the Spotted Basalt. The trail to Cascade Lodge is to the left and up the stairs.

Follow the Superior Hiking Trail upstream.

Three: Thomsonite, Potholes, and Rock Trees

After walking up a set of wooden steps it's a short distance to waypoint 3, a junction with a path that leads to a rail-enclosed viewing platform overlooking Cascade Falls. To the left is an outcrop of amygdaloidal Terrace Point Lava Flow that weathers a reddish-brown color. The round *amygdules* of this *pahoehoe* lava flow are small, and filled by pink to white thomsonite (a semi-precious zeolite mineral), white *calcite,* and clear quartz. Good examples of potholes can be found in the basalt, and dark pools of water seem to reflect the quiet of the forest.

Standing at the edge of the outcrop is a lone warrior in the form of a cedar tree. Looking like it grew right out of the rock, it reminds me of the Little Spirit Cedar tree at Grand Portage. Steve tells me cedars always seem to find crazy places to wind their roots. They can survive using nutrients from the meager soil trapped in cracks in the bedrock as long as they have access to moisture. More cedars line the gorge, and because it is close to the fall season, their needles are turning orange.

Four: Cascades and White Pine

Continuing up the river via a series of wooden steps, cross under a power line, which is waypoint 4. Along the gravel trail and in the river are outcrops of basalt; the river forms a series of steps or cascades over these rocks. There are large white pine through here along with a lot of mountain ash laden with berries.

Five: Root Beer Water

Just beyond the power line pass a park trail to the left, which is just before the bridge across the Cascade River, and this is waypoint 5. The water is frothy and full of tannins that give it the look of root beer, foam included. From this vantage point, which is 50 or 60 feet above the river, there is a view of a small step-like falls and a water chute through a narrow basalt gorge. An old stone staircase leads to the top of these cascades. Even though this is a bit off the regular trail, it is well worth the short side trip! Along this section are white pine zoos (fenced enclosures to protect the pines from deer) and lots of informal overlooks (that is, no human-made structures). *Bunchberry* lines the walking path.

Six: Maze of Trails

Cross the bridge and take the park trail that goes straight ahead with the Superior Hiking Trail and Cascade River Loop trail going to the left and right to follow the river. From the bridge it is a short walk first up wooden steps then down stone steps to waypoint 6. This is a trail junction (there will be a lot of junctions on this walk, for this area is a maze of trails). The trail to the right goes to Trail Center and a parking lot whereas the trail for our walk continues to the left. A hiking club sign can be seen here.

Seven: Maze Continues

Follow the wide, grassy trail uphill to another junction (waypoint 7). The trail to the left goes upriver to eventually join the Superior Hiking Trail and the Cascade River Loop. The trail to the right is the one to stay on for the Moose Mountain walk.

Eight: Glacial Erratic

A short walk takes us past a large *glacial erratic* of coarse-grained, white granite to waypoint 8, another trail junction. The trail to the right goes down to Trail Center, and the one to the left continues on to Moose Mountain.

Nine: Terrace Point Lava Flow

From the junction the trail heads gently uphill and is composed of pebbles and cobbles from the old river delta. Walk past a small outcrop of Terrace Point Lava Flow to waypoint 9. Of course the waypoint is another trail junction. The trail to the left is part of the return loop for this walk; for now, follow the trail that goes slightly to the right and ahead.

Ten: Tree Zoos and Moose

The trail follows the road to the campground as we walk through a cedar forest passing one lonely white pine *tree zoo*. Such "zoos" are small wire enclosures around young trees to protect them from deer and moose. These two animals love the terminal buds at the top of these trees and will happily snip them off; thus they ensure the tree doesn't grow any taller or take any part in the reseeding process. Moose also love the small, supple branches of mountain maple, which is also known as moose maple. Possibly that's why the Ojibwe refer to moose as twig eaters.

The trail along this section is composed of cobbles, *boulders*, and *pebbles* of basalt and diabase. This material represents part of the old delta built by the Cascade River.

Waypoint 10 is at the junction with a spur trail that heads off to the left and will eventually rejoin this trail. To continue on our walk to Moose Mountain, we take the trail straight ahead.

Eleven: Group Camping

Walk past yet another spur trail to the right and along the road past the parking area for group campsites to another trail junction (waypoint 11). The trail to the left goes up to Moose Mountain. The pathway straight ahead is a continuation of the Lake Walk Trail (walk 1).

Twelve: Basalt and Road Flowers

Taking the wide, grassy trail to the left (an old logging road) walk gently uphill through a forest of spruce, cedar, paper birch, and balsam fir to the exposed top of a reddish-weathering basalt lava flow (Terrace Point Lava Flow) and this is waypoint 12.

Yellow and orange *hawkweed*, *tansy*, clover, *yarrow*, *mullein*, and *goldenrod* can be found along this old road.

Thirteen: Old Mountains and Ophitic Rocks

From the lava flow continue uphill with the trail now composed of rocks that have been eroded from the glacial till. Over the years the finer clay and silt-size material has been removed by running water leaving the larger rock pieces behind. Frost heaving continues to add to the growing collection of rock debris. The cobbles and boulders seen here include grey and pink *gneiss*, black *schist*, reddish and gray basalt, and dark *diabase*; there is also lots of kibbles and bits on the trail (see *diabase weathering*).

The kibbles and bits come from the weathering of either basalt or diabase that has what is referred to as an *ophitic* texture. Ophitic is a Greek word meaning a stone spotted like a serpent. The spots are large *pyroxene* crystals (augite) that enclose much smaller crystals of *plagioclase feldspar*. These large pyroxenes are more resistant to weathering than the intervening feldspar-rich areas and so end up as "raised lumps" throughout the rock. These lumps, upon further weathering, crumble apart to form kibbles and bits.

The gneiss (banded) and schist (subparallel alignment of dark minerals) are metamorphic rocks that formed under conditions of high pressure and temperature. They are similar to rocks seen in Voyagers National Park or Quetico Park in Ontario. If derived from either of these areas, then the boulders once formed part of the roots of a 2.5 billion-year-old mountain range that was mostly eroded away over two billion years ago. These ancient, alp-like mountains formed from a continental collision, and the rocks seen here are a result of that plate tectonic process. Similar rocks are forming today beneath the Himalaya Mountains.

Waypoint 13 is at a "4 corner" post (# 4 on the post), which is a state park boundary marker. There is a trail junction at this point with the trail to the right following the park boundary and the trail for this walk continuing uphill.

Fourteen: Spur Trail

The trail continues over glacial till with some kibbles and bits from the weathering of ophitic basalt and/or diabase boulders. The till deposits are called *ground moraine,* and this is a broad, thick blanket of sediment and rock left behind when the ice melted away. Ground moraine tends to smooth out the topography by filling in valleys or depressions. The forest is mostly composed of nice paper birch with cedar, spruce and balsam poplar.

At the top of the hill balsam poplar becomes more abundant, and waypoint 14 is at the junction with the Moose Mountain spur trail. The trail we have

219

been following continues straight ahead going downhill to cross Trout Creek. A sign warns us that the bridge over Trout Creek is out and that we should not go any further on this trail. But since we are headed to Moose Mountain we needn't worry about it.

Fifteen: Moose Mountain

Take the spur trail uphill toward Moose Mountain. The trail is wide and grassy with some kibbles and bits as it passes over the top of partly exposed outcrops of Terrace Bay Lava Flow. Waypoint 15 is at the top where we find a picnic table, shelter, fire pit and great view to the west. Lookout Mountain is the most prominent feature and, like Moose Mountain, it is a *cuesta*. Both of these mountains form part of what are called the *Sawtooth Mountains*.

Between Moose Mountain and Lake Superior, which sparkles blue in the distance, is a fall forest of yellows and browns of birch, poplar, and aspens mixed in with the green of the spruce, cedar, and fir–along with a few maple reds.

The rock outcrop here is sparsely amygdaloidal Terrace Point Lava Flow.

Sixteen: Trout Creek and a Nice Camping Spot

Return to the trail junction and take the walking path that goes straight ahead. This trail parallels Trout Creek, which is a tributary of the Cascade River. The creek has cut a deep and steep valley into the volcanic sandstones and siltstones that overlay the Terrace Point Lava Flow. These sedimentary rocks are also well exposed where Trout Creek enters the Cascade River, and in the road cut at Good Harbor Bay on Highway 61. The valley is steep and deep because of the power of the creek to erode the soft sandstones and siltstones which are bounded by basalt lava flows to the south and north.

The trail is wide and grassy with boulders of glacial till as it goes through a birch forest with spruce and cedar. Waypoint 16 is at the entrance to backpack campsite #3, which has a shelter, picnic table, and outhouse. This is a really nice camping spot set in amongst white pine and would be a quiet, scenic place to spend a summer or fall evening

Seventeen: Pleasant Walk

The trail continues downhill with the steep valley of Trout Creek to the right. It is an easy, pleasant walk from waypoint 16 to waypoint 17 which is at the junction with a trail to the right, which goes down to Trout Creek where the "bridge is out," and a trail to the left, which is the continuation of this walk.

Eighteen: Small Creek

From the junction it is a short downhill walk to a small creek. Cross the creek and head uphill after which the trail levels out through a pretty stand of cedar trees with some balsam poplars. This is followed by a wet grassy section to waypoint 18, which is at the junction with a trail to the left that goes to Trail Center, and one to the right, which leads to the Cascade River. Take the trail to the left toward Trail Center.

Nineteen: More Trail Junctions

It is a short walk to the junction between a trail that continues downhill toward Trail Center and a park trail that goes both to the left and the right (park boundary trail?). Take the trail to the right.

Twenty: Start of a Delta and a Glacial Erratic

Start out on a grassy to gravelly trail with small cedar trees. The exposed bank along the edge of the trail contains basalt boulders set in a finer-grained, gravelly matrix. At this point we are just below the 930-foot elevation contour, which marks the start of the Cascade River Delta. There is a large glacial erratic of Spotted Basalt to the left after which we walk over the top of a basalt outcrop to waypoint 20, the start of a gentle downhill. The forest along here is open, providing partial views of Lake Superior.

Twenty-One: Fifty Yard Sign

Continue downhill on a wide, grassy trail with larger pieces of *massive* basalt scattered along it. Walk by a pretty glacial erratic of banded pink and white gneiss that is cut by a pink vein of *potassium feldspar*. The top of a basalt outcrop (lichen-covered) occurs opposite the glacial erratic and just before the "fifty yard" sign. The purpose of this sign is to warn people that they are fifty yards from a trail junction (21) and, if a cross-country skier, to please slow down.

Twenty-Two: Cascade River Both Ways

At the trail junction the walking path to the right goes to the Cascade River, joining the Superior Hiking Trail above the river bridge. The trail straight ahead also goes to the Cascade River and joins the Superior Hiking Trail at the bridge. Continue straight ahead and walk gently downhill over a wide, grassy trail with pebbles and cobbles derived from the Cascade River Delta. The forest is spruce, paper birch, and cedar to waypoint 22, which is the same as waypoint 9 from earlier in the walk. Take the trail to the right which heads toward the Cascade River.

Twenty-Three: Another Trail Junction

It is a short walk downhill over a gravel trail with boulders and cobbles from the delta deposit, along with one small outcrop of the Terrace Point Lava Flow, to waypoint 23. This is a junction with a trail to the left that goes to Trail Center and one to the right that leads to the Cascade River.

Twenty-Four: Granite Erratic and a Garden Maze

Take the trail to the right (toward the Cascade River) passing a large glacial erratic of coarse-grained, white granite to waypoint 24, which is yet another trail junction (it is like an English garden maze through here). The trail to the right goes to the river, meeting the Superior Hiking Trail above the river bridge; the trail to the left also goes to the river, meeting the Superior Hiking Trail at the river bridge.

Twenty-Five: Hiking Club Sign

Take the wide, grassy trail to the left, and it is just a short walk downhill to a hiking club sign and yet another trail junction. The trail to the left goes to the Trail Center parking lot, and the one to the right continues on to the river and the bridge.

Twenty-Six: River Bridge

Take the trail to the right, and it is another short walk, first up a set of stone steps then down some wooden ones, to the river and the bridge across it (same as waypoint 5).

Twenty-Seven: River Gorge

From the bridge, walk down the east side of the Cascade River along the Superior Hiking Trail to an overlook of the river and its spectacular gorge (waypoint 27). This waypoint is across the river from waypoint 4.

Twenty-Eight: Overlooks and Parking Lot

Continue downhill and downstream on a gravel trail to another rocky, noisy overlook of the basalt gorge. From here it is a short walk to a spur trail to the right that leads to a bench with a nice view of the lake and highway. Return to the Superior Hiking Trail, cross a small creek and a path to the left that leads up to the campground before reaching Highway 61 and the wayside parking lot.

Cascade River State Park
Walk Three: Cascade River and Cascade Creek

Walk Logistics

Start and End: Cascade River Wayside on Highway 61

Getting There: Take Highway 61 to the Cascade River, which is about 8 miles northeast of Lutsen or 9 miles southwest of Grand Marais. Park in the wayside parking lot on either side of the highway.

Walk Distance: 1.8-1.9 miles   **Difficulty:** Tennis Shoes

Safety Concerns: Possibly wet, grassy trails

Worth a Longer Look: Waypoints 2, 3, 5, 8, 14, 18

Waypoint-to-Waypoint

One: Nicest Time of Year

It's a lovely fall day in northern Minnesota with the bright sunshine turning the rippled waters of Lake Superior into a sparkling, multifaceted, bluish-green gemstone. All this verifies the claim that this is the state's nicest time of year.

Waypoint 1 is at the Cascade River wayside.

Waypoints 2 through 5 are the same as those for walk 2, the Moose Mountain Walk

Six: Trail Junction

Walk a very short distance downstream to the park trail located just below the bridge and then walk along it a short distance to another trail junction (waypoint 6). The trail to the right heads upriver and parallels the Superior Hiking Trail, whereas the walking path for this hike continues straight ahead and goes toward Cascade Creek.

Seven: Cascade Delta and Rabbit Warrens

Composed of sand and gravel with *boulders* of *basalt, granite, monzonite,* and *banded gneiss* (part of the delta deposit) the trail starts out level before going down a short slope and crossing a planked area that is wet in the spring. It's then uphill, paralleling a power line, with the trail becoming wide and grassy. Cross a small creek which, in the spring, will have lots of *marsh marigolds* to waypoint 7, another trail junction. In many instances the walks through this park seem to be nothing but trail junctions; this whole place is the "rabbit warren" of state park trails. Along this trail section, in the spring,

223

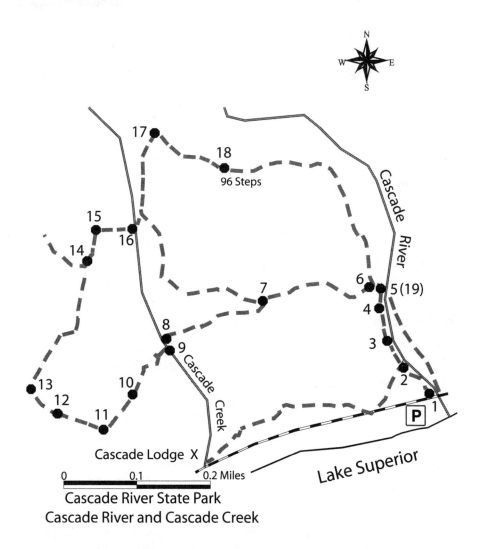

Cascade River State Park
Cascade River and Cascade Creek

there will be *Canadian mayflowers*, *honeysuckle*, *violets*, tall lungwort, *blue bead lily*, and *sarsaparilla*. A yellow, red-gilled polypore fungi grows on the spruce trees.

The trail to the right goes uphill toward waypoint 16 of this walk, whereas the walking path for the hike continues straight ahead toward Cascade Creek.

Eight: Cascade Creek and a Glacial Erratic

Walk under than along the power line over a planked, wet area on a wide and, once again, gravel-covered trail. The trail recrosses under the power line to a V junction. Take the trail to the right that goes downhill, crossing a small creek before heading uphill over reddish-colored, Terrace Point Lava Flow, which is weathering to kibbles and bits.

The kibbles and bits come from the weathering of basalt lava that has what geologists call a *ophitic* texture. Ophitic is a Greek word meaning a stone spotted like a serpent. The spots turn out to be large *pyroxene* crystals (augite) that enclose much smaller crystals of *plagioclase feldspar*. The large pyroxene crystals are separated from each other by fine-grained areas of plagioclase feldspar with some *olivine* and *magnetite*. This gives the rock a mottled black and gray look. The larger pyroxenes are more resistant to weathering than the intervening feldspar-rich areas and so end up as "raised lumps" throughout the rock. These lumps, upon further weathering, crumble apart to form kibbles and bits. In the spring there are hanging yellow buckets along this section which we think are for feeding the deer.

At the hilltop the trail levels out, and the sand bank at the edge of the trail contains large boulders of basalt and banded gneiss that represent part of the Cascade River Delta. The delta deposits continue to waypoint 8, which is at a lovely spot on Cascade Creek. Looking upstream we see a nice waterfall with ribbons of white water cascading over water-polished basalt. Downstream is like wow! Once over the first falls, the water cascades in long, lacy fingers and silk-like sheets down a whole series of small, step-like falls to a larger waterfall. After flowing over this, the water tumbles under a bridge into a quiet pool before resuming its noisy journey to the lake.

The bridge crosses the creek just downstream from waypoint 8. There are two benches on the bridge from which one can watch this lovely precession of water. This is the perfect spot for a snack, for lunch, to read a book, or simply to sit and contemplate the joy of being able to experience something like this in such a peaceful, harmonious spot.

At the edge of the creek, on the opposite side, sits a large *glacial erratic*, which may have come from the Giants Range. No, the Giants Range is not a mythical land. This rock is a 2.5-billion-year-old piece of *granite* that formed part of a large intrusive igneous complex referred to as the Giants Range. The Giants Range is located immediately north of the Mesabi Iron Range and the rock was thus transported by the glaciers over 60 miles. The ice melted away over 10,000 years ago and that is how long this lone warrior has occupied this spot. Imagine all the comings and goings it must have seen. It was once covered by the delta of the Cascade River, then it sat on a warm, sandy beach above the receding waters of Glacial Lake Duluth, where it was walked around by wooly mammoths, giant beavers, and dire wolves. It watched the white pine forest grow up around it, saw the same forest logged, and, most recently, witnessed the establishment of a state park and all the different footprints this brought with it.

Just before the creek there is a trail junction with what is called the Cascade Creek Trail (parallels the creek) and the path we have been following, which continues across the creek. But in order to follow our path, the water must be low, or a pair of hip waders must be handy. Given those two conditions it is best to take the Cascade Creek Trail downstream to the bridge and cross the creek there.

For a bit of exploration one can take the Cascade Creek Trail upstream to the waterfall. The rocks exposed along the stream banks and within the stream are sparsely *amygdaloidal*, reddish-brown Terrace Point Lava Flow with fractures filled by the red iron mineral *hematite* and white *calcite*. Angular pieces of amygdaloidal basalt occur all along the banks of the creek and represent the top of the Terrace Bay Lava Flow. This part of the lava flow is actually located upstream, meaning these pieces have been eroded by *frost wedging* and carried downstream by the high, fast-moving waters of spring. After crashing over the waterfall the velocity of the water decreases and the rock pieces are left behind. The very amygdaloidal *outcrops* seen in the banks of the creek behind Cascade Lodge represent the top of the so-called Spotted Basalt that underlies the Terrace Point Lava Flow and is exposed along the lakeshore (see walk 1).

Nine: A Splendid Place

Take the trail downstream to the bridge. From the bridge there is an even better view of Cascade Creek as it does just that, cascades away over rocky ledge after rocky ledge as it flows toward the lake. The benches on the bridge are at waypoint 9 and what a splendid place this is. Just below the bridge is an old cement dam which is now filled up by rocks and gravel.

Ten: Wildflower Trail

From waypoint 9 we cross the bridge and follow a Cascade Lodge Trail called "wildflower" trail. This path crosses the trial we were walking on to reach the creek. Stay on the lodge trail and head uphill passing a narrow trail to the left that goes to the lodge and cabins. The narrow walking path continues to the right passing a sign for *rose-twisted stalk* (lots of it here), sarsaparilla and *dewberries* also occur along here. Waypoint 10 is at another junction, this one with a wide ski trail/road and the narrow path we have been following. Take the wide, straight road to the right.

Eleven: Birch Forest

The road parallels the power line as it passes by a nice birch forest and *raspberry* bushes to reach waypoint 11. This is the junction between the lodge/park trail to Lookout Mountain and a snowmobile trail that goes off to the left. Take the trail to Lookout Mountain.

Twelve: Gneiss Erratic

Walk uphill on a trail composed of sand and gravel to a small creek and a glacial erratic of gray-and-pink-banded gneiss by a large cedar tree (waypoint 12). The gneiss may have come from Voyager's National Park and

226

thus traveled about 75 miles in glacial ice to get here. Rose-twisted stalk and Canadian mayflowers are abundant in the spring.

Thirteen: Up the Delta

As we continue to walk uphill we are walking up the Cascade River Delta. Mixed in with the sand and gravel of the delta are *cobbles* and boulders that continue to the next trail junction, which is waypoint 13. The trail to the left continues on to Lookout Mountain, and the one to the right heads uphill toward the Superior Hiking Trail. Take the trail to the right, now called the Pioneer Trail, and continue uphill.

Fourteen: Hilltop and Old Delta

The trail continues on the delta with the sandy bank to the left full of rounded cobbles that are all about the same size. This is characteristic of sorting and rounding by the type of stream that formed the delta.

At the hilltop the trail levels out as it enters an open area about the size of a soccer field. This is good place to see and examine the deposits of the old delta. The gravel here is dominantly composed of cobbles and sand, and is representative of the material mined from this area for road building and other construction projects.

The trail through this area is actually an old road, one that was used in the past for mining these sand and gravel deposits.

Waypoint 14 is in this open area. The trail at the far side of the open area (to the right) goes to Cascade Lodge; the walking path continues straight ahead on the wide, gravel road. The trail to the left leads to the Superior Hiking Trail.

Fifteen: Road Walk

Continue along the wide, gravel road past a sign for the Pioneer Trail before coming to a junction with the Superior Hiking Trail. This is waypoint 15. There is a dense stand of small balsam fir trees just up the road from the waypoint.

Sixteen: Top of the Delta

Cascade Creek is just past waypoint 15. The bridge across it is waypoint 16. Upstream from the bridge are tons of cobbles and boulders, and the outcrop in the creek is sparsely amygdaloidal basalt. There are white cedars, birch, and young balsam fir here along with bristly *clubmoss*, running clubmoss, blue-bead lily and rose-twisted stalk. On the downstream side of the bridge there are *horsetails* and ferns.

At this spot we are at about 830 feet above sea level and close to the top of the delta. The boulder deposits seen here represent the weathering of boulders and cobbles out of the glacial till just to the north and east. This material may then have been carried to this spot by fast flowing streams. These streams entered the delta and their velocities decreased. This would cause all of the heavy material carried by the stream to be deposited.

Seventeen: Deer Yard Lake Trail

From waypoint 16 it is uphill to a trail junction. Take the Superior Hiking Trail to the left and walk along then above the creek, to yet another junction. This is with a wide cross-country ski trail called Deer Yard Lake Trail, part of the Cascade River interconnected ski trail system with 32 miles of trail. Waypoint 17 is at the "you are here sign."

Eighteen: 96 steps and a Canadian Carpet

Follow the Superior Hiking Trail down river (to the right) to what some folks call the "infamous 96 steps." At this junction you can look down into the Cascade River Valley to the infamous 96 wooden steps that lead down to the river. This is part of the Cascade River Loop (which is walk 4 in this section of the book). We follow the spur trail to the left (sign says to campground). Mosses and *Canadian carpet* are thick through here (in fact Steve calls this clubmoss heaven with running, bristly, and ground cedar all very abundant), and there are large-leafed *aster, brown-eyed Susans, yarrow,* rose-twisted stalk and horsetails along the trail. Blooming in the spring will be blue bead lily, Canadian mayflower, *bunchberry, starflower, wood anemone,* and *pyrola.*

Nineteen: Sandstone and cooling Joints

The trail heads downhill, parallel to the river over gravel and boulders passing outcrops of amygdaloidal basalt and stands of large white pine. As we walk along there are nice views down into the river. On the far bank can be seen exposures of red *sandstone.* Formation of this sandstone began, when exposed lava flows were eroded during lulls in eruptive activity. Ancient streams then carried this eroded material downstream and deposited it as sandbars and channel deposits that were later buried, compacted, and cemented together to form solid rock. *Cross-bedding* and *ripple marks* are well preserved in these ancient stream deposits. Because they resulted from erosion of basalt lavas, the sandstones are composed of grains of plagioclase feldspar, pyroxene, magnetite, and small fragments of basalt. Because the sandstones are more easily eroded than the basalt they tend to form valleys, coves, and to underlay low areas.

As we continue along we pass a large block of basalt, part of a *cooling joint,* that hangs over the river and will, in the not-too-distant future, fall spectacularly into the water. For now, the way it sits above the water, gives it the appearance of a lone sentinel guarding the river from unwanted intruders.

From here it is a short walk to the bridge across the Cascade River and waypoint 19. This is the same as waypoint 5 from the first part of this walk.

Once at the bridge we have two route choices. One is to cross the bridge and follow the trail on the east side of the river. The other option is for us to retrace our steps along the trail on this side of the river to the parking lot.

Cascade State Park
Walk 4: Cascade River Loop

Walk Logistics

Start and End: Cascade River Wayside on Highway 61.

Getting There: Take Highway 61 to the Cascade River, which is about 8 miles northeast of Lutsen or 9 miles southwest of Grand Marais. Park in the wayside parking lot on either side of the highway.

Hike Distance: 7.8 miles   **Difficulty:** Hiking Boots

Safety Concerns: Waypoints 7, 9, 10, 12, 14

Worth a Longer Look: Waypoints 2, 3, 4, 5, 6, 7, 8, 10, 11, 13, 16, 18, 20, 21, 25, 28

Waypoint-to-Waypoint

With a few changes, this walk has been taken from the "Walking Guide to the Superior Hiking Trail: Natural History, Scenery, and other Trail Features."

One: Fall Days and Superiors Waves

From the Cascade River wayside the sound of Superior's wild waves, thundering hard against the rocky shore, is a vivid and scary reminder of why this body of water is much more like an ocean than a lake. The constant pounding–a harsh cacophony of drums, cymbals, and horns–is part of the eternal battle between land and water: a battle water always wins.

This morning the wind is blowing steadily inland pushing the grey, patchy clouds away from us at warp speed. The slanting rain that had fallen most of the morning has stopped, and it looks like it is going to clear up and be a nice, early fall hiking day after all; about 60 degrees, breezy, and no bugs.

Waypoint 1 is at the Cascade River wayside.

Two: Deltas and Waterfalls

Leaving the parking lot we walk up a wide, gravel trail lined with *thimbleberry* plants to the Cascade River Loop Trail, which begins at a bridge across the river. From the bridge, which is waypoint 2, there is a view upstream of a small waterfall and, downstream, a gorge carved out of reddish-colored *basalt*.

Along this section of the walk the gravel that composes the trail represents

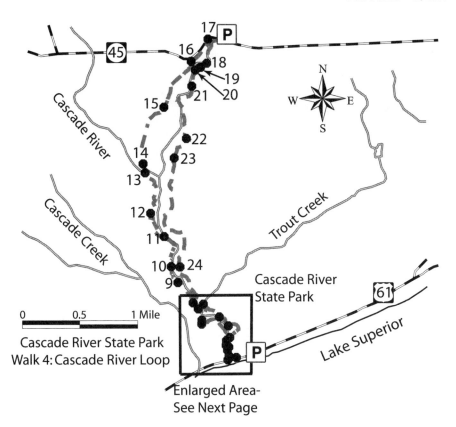

45

17 P
16
18
19
21 20
15
22
14 23
13
12
11
10 24
9

Cascade River

Cascade Creek

Trout Creek

N
W E
S

Cascade River
State Park

61

Lake Superior

0   0.5   1 Mile

Cascade River State Park
Walk 4: Cascade River Loop

P

Enlarged Area–
See Next Page

part of a *delta* that formed several thousand years ago as the water level of *Glacial Lake Duluth* fell. The gravel deposits are made up of rounded *pebbles* of varying rock compositions, as well as some *cobbles* and sand. These were derived from the erosion and size-sorting of the *glacial till* by a much younger and more vigorous Cascade River shortly after the ice melted off the land. The gravel forms thin deposits on top of the basalt lava flows from the current level of Lake Superior (about 600 feet) up to an elevation of 900 feet, which marks the shoreline of old Glacial Lake Duluth. As the Cascade River flowed into this ancient lake the velocity of the river water decreased rapidly, and the dominantly sand to pebble-size material dropped out and created the delta. Locally the gravel deposits are very sandy, and this represents beach deposits formed from the reworking of the delta by wave action as the water level in the glacial lake fell.

Take the branch of the trail on the west side of the river (left bank).

Three: Thomsonite, Potholes, and Rock Trees

After walking up a set of wooden steps we come to waypoint 3, a junction with a path that leads to a rail-enclosed viewing platform overlooking a waterfall. To the left is an outcrop of *amygdaloidal* basalt that weathers

231

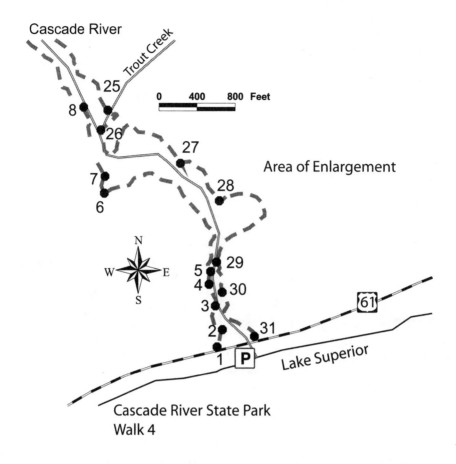

Cascade River

Trout Creek

25

8

26

27

Area of Enlargement

7

28

6

N

W — E

S

5

29

4

30

3

61

2

31

1 P

Lake Superior

Cascade River State Park
Walk 4

0   400   800 Feet

reddish-brown. The round *amygdules* of this *pahoehoe* flow are small and filled by pink to white thomsonite (a semi-precious *zeolite* mineral), white *calcite,* and clear *quartz*. Good examples of *potholes* can be found in the basalt, and dark pools of water seem to reflect the quiet of the forest.

Standing at the edge of the outcrop is a lone warrior in the form of a cedar tree. Looking like it grew right out of the rock, it reminds me of the Little Spirit Cedar tree at Grand Portage. Steve tells me cedars always seem to find crazy places to wind their roots. More cedars line the gorge, and because it is close to the fall season, their needles are turning orange.

Four: Cascades and White Pine

Continuing up the river via a series of wooden steps, we cross under a power line, which is waypoint 4. Along the gravel trail and in the river are outcrops of the Terrace Point Lava Flow; the river forms a series of steps or cascades over these rocks. There are large white pine through here along with a lot of mountain ash laden with berries.

Five: Root Beer Water

Just beyond the power line we come to a bridge across the river, and this is waypoint 5. The water is frothy and full of tannins that give it the look of root beer, foam included. From this vantage point, which is 50 or 60 feet above the river, we can see three small step-like falls and a water chute through a narrow basalt gorge. We take an old stone staircase up to the top of these cascades. Even though this is a bit off the regular trail, it is well worth the short side trip! Along this section are white pine zoos (fenced enclosures to protect the pines from deer) and lots of informal overlooks (that is, no human-made structures). *Bunchberry* lines the walking path.

Six: The Sentinel, Sandstones, and the 96 Steps

Continuing upriver and uphill there are nice views of the basalt gorge from three or four short side trails; the white pines are tall and stately and look like they are trying to touch the passing clouds. A large block of basalt, part of a *cooling joint*, hangs over the river and will, in the not-too-distant future, fall spectacularly into the water. For now, the way it sits above the water gives it the appearance of a lone sentinel guarding the river from unwanted intruders.

Sneaking past the sentinel we continue upriver over a wide gravel and bouldery trail with outcrops of amygdaloidal basalt and stands of large white pine. As we walk along we have nice views down into the river. On the far bank there are exposures of red *sandstone*. Formation of the sandstone began when exposed lava flows started to erode during lulls in eruptive activity. Ancient streams then carried this material and deposited it as sandbars and channel deposits that were later buried, compacted, and cemented together to form solid rock. *Cross-bedding* and *ripple marks* are well-preserved in these ancient stream deposits. Because they resulted from the erosion of basalt lavas, the sandstones are composed of grains of *plagioclase feldspar, pyroxene, magnetite*, and small fragments of basalt. Because the sandstones are more easily eroded than the basalt, most low areas and coves along the shoreline have formed in the sandstone.

Moving away from the river we continue uphill to waypoint 6, the junction where the Superior Hiking Trail goes west to Lookout Mountain, and east, down to the river by way of the 96 steps.

Seven: 96 Steps and the Flood Plain

Down we go, 96 steps to get to the river and a junction (waypoint 7) with a side trail that leads to the water's edge. The hiking trail heads upstream along the river's *flood plain*.

Eight: Red Sandstone

The trail climbs above the river, passing a large white pine and an opening where we watch the river flow over beautiful red sandstone. The sunlight reflecting on the water gives this scene a kaleidoscope look–a speckled pattern, ever changing, of red, blue, and yellow. The trail then heads back down to the river where there are large *boulders* of basalt, whitish *granite*, and pinkish *monzonite*. Red sandstone outcrops on the river bottom, and downstream is a large, reddish-colored boulder pile left by some long-ago flood.

Nine: Drunken Staircase, Snake Tree, and Tiny White Pines

Moving away from the river we climb up a "drunken" staircase, walk past a large white pine, to a cedar grove and the cedar root "snake" tree, a tree with numerous roots across the trail. The various plants through here are full and green and pretty. Moving on we have views of pinkish-colored basalt, which forms tall, impressive cliffs, before coming to an overlook from which we can see a small, lacy cascade of water flowing over reddish basalt. This is waypoint 9.

At this point thick vegetation covers all surfaces. There are also tiny black spruce, cedars, and white pines–and we do mean tiny. These are this year's seedlings, and in the case of the spruce, they have a star-shaped appearance from above with their single needles circling around the small stem.

Ten: Flow Contacts and the Forest Primeval

Staying above the river we walk through a dense cedar forest with a few large white pines and birch mixed in; the trail is crossed by lots of tree roots. This section feels like the forest primeval: thick-growing lichens, dense trees, mossy carpets, and a warm wind singing through the cloud-caressed trees.

Crossing over a basalt lava flow with small plagioclase feldspar crystals, we find an *outcrop* of reddish-colored basalt (red color due to oxidation of iron-rich minerals) with amygdules that are filled by calcite, quartz, and thomsonite; however, many of the amygdules are empty as the minerals filling them have weathered out. This outcrop is at the junction with a small trail that leads to the river, and this represents waypoint 10. Taking the trail to the river we come to the top of a pahoehoe lava flow. Across the river from it is a contact between this flow top and the *massive* base of the overlying flow. The contact, well exposed, is sharp and undulating and can be followed for a short distance downstream.

Eleven: Hidden Falls

Passing a boulder-filled creek the trail continues above the river to an opening with a view of a water cascade over a basalt lava flow; there is a massive basalt cliff on the opposite side of the river. From here we cross another snake den of tangled tree roots before returning to the edge of the

234

river and an outcrop of reddish basalt with feldspar crystals and sparse amygdules.

Continuing on we walk along the river through a cedar forest over more tree roots; there are large white pine here with birch and spruce. Waypoint 11 is the junction of the hiking trail with a spur trail that goes to the Hidden Falls. The trail to Hidden Falls is 0.3 miles long.

Twelve: Big White Pine Campsite and Slippery Bridge

The Superior Hiking Trail heads uphill and away from the river through a cedar, spruce, and birch forest, followed by a ridge walk before heading downhill to a bridge across a small creek. Outcrops in and along the creek bottom are amygdaloidal basalt, and this is the same flow as the one at waypoint 10. The bottom of the creek is composed of solid rock and would surely make a wonderful water chute, which I am sure it is in the spring. The bridge across the creek, if not covered in wire mesh, is very, very, very slippery–dangerously so.

From the creek our uphill walk continues to the spur trail to the Big White Pine campsite (waypoint 12). There are enormous yellow birch through here.

Thirteen: Thousand Year-Old River Channel

The trail continues up and down through a forest of paper and yellow birch with some spruce; the understory is mountain maple and hazel. Cross a boulder-jammed creek that represents an old channel of the Cascade River, one that formed when the river was much younger, higher, and fiercer. This river channel is overlain by gravel deposits of the Cascade River Delta, indicating the channel must have formed several thousand years ago.

From the boulder-filled creek the trail heads uphill and becomes relatively flat before descending over wooden steps and tree roots to waypoint 13, a bridge across another small creek. The outcrop here represents the top of a basalt lava flow; it's amygdaloidal with most of the amygdules filled by either pinkish zeolite and/or calcite. This flow top is overlain by a layered, broken rock, one that looks like potato chips. The broken pieces contain small rock fragments (dominantly basalt and clay-rich sedimentary rocks) that are set in a fine-grained matrix composed of a green clay mineral, plagioclase feldspar, and quartz. Though the origin of this deposit is not known, it most likely represents a mudflow deposit.

Fourteen: Cut Log Campsite

The steep ascent up and out of the creek is via wooden steps that appear to have been constructed for someone who is at least ten feet tall! At the top there is a short walk to Cut Log campsite, which is located beside a giant felled white pine; this is waypoint 14. Surrounded by ash trees, the campsite contains another large felled pine. The two pine trees appear to have been abandoned after being cut down many years ago

Fifteen: Hop Across Creek

From the campsite the trail passes through a maple-birch forest, which changes into one of spruce and birch as we near a small creek.

After the creek it's back into a maple forest with some yellow birch to waypoint 15, another boulder-filled creek that is crossed by walking or hopping on the boulders. However, the creek is small enough so we can simply jump across it.

Sixteen: Elbow Tree, Waterfall, Long Slump, and County Road

We continue on through a dominantly maple forest with big ash trees to another boulder-filled creek after which we enter a more mixed forest of spruce and birch along with maple "elbow" trees. The first elbow tree is right in the trail corridor, but no one has removed it so there it stands for all to ponder. A bit further down the trail, we find another tree growing horizontally out from a stump before it bends its elbow upwards!

We come to a creek that drops over a dramatic and steep waterfall down to the Cascade River. The drop is close to vertical and well over 60 feet. Below the falls is a deep water pool and here the river cascades over a basalt lava flow; all-in-all it is very, very pretty. From here we pass a major *slump* that extends down to the river. There is a wooden fence along the trail marking the site of the slump, which must be 60-70 feet from the top to the river. The valley floor is filled with maple and pine, and the colors are gorgeous. From the slump it's a short walk to waypoint 16, which is Cook County Road 45.

Seventeen: Cascade River Bridge and Parking Lot

Walk 0.3 miles east on County Road 45 (to the right) crossing the bridge over the river, then continuing on to the Superior Hiking Trail parking lot. Hiking trail signs (waypoint 17) tell us it is 3.8 miles back to Highway 61 on the Cascade River Loop trail or 5.5 miles northeast to the Bally Creek Road.

Eighteen: Graffiti and Lavas

The Cascade River loop trail continues under the bridge, and both the bridge and nearby outcrops are adorned with much "art" work, otherwise known as grafitti. Walking along the river through a cedar forest, we cross over numerous planked sections with lots of tree roots across the trail. Waypoint 18 is beside an outcrop in the river with a small rapids and a nice little waterfall. The outcrop is an amygdaloidal lava flow with the amygdules varying from 20-50%. These are filled by pale green *epidote*, white calcite, and white, pinkish-white, and pink zeolite minerals (thomsonite and/or laumantite). A high cliff of basalt in the distance is composed of the massive part of the lava flow that overlies the amygdaloidal flow we are standing on.

There is abundant wild lettuce, meadow *rue, sensitive fern, wood anemone, goldthread*, and *cow parsnip* here.

Nineteen: Potholes and Blueberries

Just down the river from waypoint 18 are two spectacular potholes in the basalt; these are located very close to the bottom of the cascade. Satellite reception is terrible through here with accuracy around 100ft. There are two shrubby plants of note through here: the familiar *blueberry* and the less common yew.

Twenty: Falls and Slump

The trail continues along the river to the large slump and waterfall that was viewed from above at waypoint 16. Now we are at the base of the waterfall, which is waypoint 20. The rock cliff is composed of two lava flows; the flow bottoms are massive and thick, and the tops are amygdaloidal and thin. The outcrop in the river is amygdaloidal basalt.

Twenty-One: Horizontal Potholes

The cedar forest and tree root-lined trail continue past an amygdaloidal basalt outcrop to waypoint 21, four horizontal potholes bored into the basalt lava on the opposite side of the river. The potholes are just above the water level, and there are numerous boulders and cobbles sitting inside them. The potholes occur at or near the contact between the top of an amygdaloidal lava flow and the massive base of the overlying flow. The contact is sharp and undulating, and can be followed down river from the potholes. The potholes look like caves or the burrows of large animals. They formed from swirling eddies or whirlpools of water which, with the help of pebbles and cobbles, abraded away areas of the basalt that had large gas holes or abundant, closely spaced small ones. There are more large cedars here, and one-sided *pyrola*.

Twenty-Two: Jumble Creek and Steep Climb

Continue along the river over a root-lined trail to a small creek from which point we again turn away from the water and head uphill. At the top we immediately descend back to the river where there is a basalt cliff on the opposite side and, on this side, a cedar tree growing straight out over the water. Then, like musical topography, it's uphill again past an amygdaloidal basalt outcrop to the top and a private property sign near an area where the trail is covered by wooden planks.

Remaining above the river, we walk through a cedar and spruce forest with numerous planked sections over hillside seeps. Pass a boulder-filled creek clogged with a tangled mess of trees and logs. The creek has to work hard to move all this stuff in the spring before it can rest during the remainder of the year. From here it is downhill and across a narrow but steep gully with a noticeable slump above it. The boulders in the slumped material are the same composition as those seen in the tangled stream, and this slump is probably the source of both boulders and trees. Waypoint 22 is at the top of a horrendous steep climb up dozens of poorly spaced wooden steps (hopefully these have been redone!).

Twenty-Three: Murphy Mountain

Passing through a spruce-birch forest the trail has fewer tree roots as it follows the ridge top. There are partial views across the river to the opposite hillside. Through an opening in the forest we have a nice view of Murphy Mountain to the northeast (waypoint 23).

Twenty-Four: Nice Walk

We now have a nice, long walk through a spruce-birch forest with scattered cedar groves as the trail remains away from the river. After passing a Superior Hiking Trail sign and crossing a dry creek, the forest changes to one dominated by cedars, yellow birch, and big pine trees. There are buckets of white pine cones along here–kind of bonanza if you're a squirrel. Continuing the pleasant walk through a white pine woods with cedar and spruce the trail follows the edge of the Cascade River Valley. Along here we find steep drop-offs and numerous partial river views. Waypoint 24 is at the sign marking the end of private land.

Twenty-Five: Trout Creek and Red Sandstone

Continuing to walk along the edge of the valley we pass the junction with a trail to a not-so-nice overlook, before entering a dark, cedar-dominated forest with some spruce. It's then downhill to Trout Creek. The creek contains little water, but it sure has a lot of large boulders and pieces of red sandstone. The campsite is slowly being undercut by the creek, and in the near future there will be no more camping here. Waypoint 25 is at the bridge across Trout Creek. There is sandstone in the creek both above and below the bridge. The sandstone has beautifully preserved ripple marks and *mud cracks*, and is *hematite* red in color. The sandstone is 1.1 billion years old, and these preserved textures indicate it was once a sandbar that formed from the accumulation of sand grains in a stream. Imagine what this area would have looked like way back then. There would have been no life, which also means no vegetation; it would have been a dark, barren landscape composed of ragged and rolling lava flows criss-crossed by streams and rivers on their way to some far distant sea. Add bubbling hot springs, hissing steam vents, red glowing lava, and the smell of sulfur, and Dante's vision of hell would be found right here in Minnesota.

Twenty-Six: Cascade River

From Trout Creek it is a short walk to the Cascade River (waypoint 26) and an outcrop of red sandstone. The sandstone is well-bedded and breaks into flagstone-like pieces.

Twenty-Seven: Slump and Old River Channel

Once again the trail turns away from the river and heads uphill (there is a bench at the top) where it winds along the ridge top to waypoint 27, a state park sign and a large river slump. The slump occurs right at a bend in the river and has exposed an old river channel, which consists of a layer of large boulders sitting on top of a basalt lava flow. This channel is older than the Cascade River Delta and was created by a younger and stronger river.

Twenty-Eight: You Are Here, Large Slump, and the Delta

Continue above and away from the river along a wide, gravel trail to a "you are here sign" followed closely by a second "you are here sign" which is waypoint 28. At this point the trail really does get hard to follow, for the ground has slumped away into the river. There is a lot of gravel on the trail, from pea-size to cobbles, and this represents part of the old Cascade River Delta deposit.

Twenty-Nine: Around the Slump

The trail follows a ski trail around the slump area. Waypoint 29 is where the ski trail rejoins the hiking trail just above a narrow gorge in the river.

Thirty: Waterfalls and Basalt Gorge

It's downhill via wooden stairs to a nice view of water falling over a lava flow. Continue past the bridge across the river to an overlook of the river and basalt gorge seen on the first part of this walk. This is waypoint 30.

Thirty-One: Parking Lot

Continuing downhill and down river we come to another rocky, noisy overlook of the basalt gorge. From here it is a short walk back to Highway 61 and the parking lot.

This is a grand loop hike, although at 7.8 miles it is fairly long. If one doesn't mind the distance there is a ton to see–from sandstones, thomsonite, delta deposits, and pahoehoe lavas to white pine, yellow birch, glorious fall colors, rock cedars, 96 steps, and, in the spring, lots of wildflowers. Most of all, however, this hike is centered on the spirited Cascade River–both its powerful past and busy present.

Judge C.R. Magney State Park

Introduction

Sound, sight, and mystery are the essence of Judge C. R. Magney State Park. The sound is the Brule River as it rushes around a rocky bend only to encounter a large knob of solid rock that splits the river in half. In protest the river emits a furious roar as the divided parts are sent hurtling over a rocky ledge. This is where sight becomes important, for the frothy water cascades, falls, and tumbles some 50 or 60 feet with half of it vanishing into a large, round pothole called the Devil's Kettle, and the other half ending up at the bottom of what we call "Half a Devil's Kettle." This is a large, semi-circular rock structure that was once similar in shape to the Devil's Kettle, but it has had its down stream side removed by the erosive power of the energetic river.

The mystery lies somewhere inside the Devil's Kettle and can be summed up as "where in the world does all that water go?" There is no sign of it reappearing anywhere downstream, nor is there any obvious place where it empties into the lake–yet all water must run downhill, mustn't it? So therein lies the deep, dark mystery of the Devil's Kettle. My idea is of a "plumbing" system beneath the pothole that recycles the water upstream, while Steve thinks it goes to China.

Both the Devil's Kettle and "Half a Devil's Kettle" are bowl-shaped depressions "carved" into the bedrock floor of the stream. The Brule River performs this feat by abrading the bedrock, especially when the water is moving fast and there is lots of it. The river uses sand grains, pebbles, and cobbles as its major grinding and cutting tools. Where there is a combination of a natural depression in the rock (such as a fracture, joint, or gas cavity) and eddies or swirling water, there is an opportunity for sand, pebbles, and cobbles to get into the depression and be rapidly spun around and around by the water. This turns the sand and pebbles into effective drills. Over time the depression grows larger and deeper or, in this case, very large and really deep.

The bedrock that has been drilled out and eroded to make the Devil's Kettle and "Half a Devil's Kettle" is called the Devil's Kettle Rhyolite; a thick, pink-colored felsic lava flow that is exposed for over a mile along the Brule River. This lava flow is responsible for the waterfalls and white water rapids along the river as well as the picturesque gorge of Gauthier Creek. The top of the flow is exposed near the bottom of the gorge. This is a difficult place to get to but does expose the amygdaloidal flow top that exhibits nice flow banding. The top is reddish-brown in color due to oxidation of the iron-rich minerals in the rock.

The rhyolite turns out to be like a thick slab of cheese in a whole wheat sandwich, for it is bounded on top and bottom by basalt lava flows. Both the rhyolite and the basalts belong to a succession of lava flows collectively called the North Shore Volcanic Group. These lava flows erupted out of the Mid-Continent Rift some 1.1 billion years ago. The basalt lavas form "picnic rock" to the north of the Devil's Kettle, and the rocks exposed along the lake shore.

The other interesting geological aspects of the park are the old beaches left by Glacial Lake Duluth, and the abandoned channels of the Brule River. The beaches formed several thousand years ago as the water level in the lake fell due to the continued melting back of the Laurentide Ice Sheet and the uncovering of topographically lower areas. The old river channels represent a time when the Brule River flowed at a higher elevation. As the water level in the lake went down, the gradient of the river increased, and it created new channels by eroding downward as it attempted to find the easiest, most direct route to the lake.

The river's official name is the Bois Brule, which is a French interpretation of the Ojibwe name for the river. In Ojibwe the name means "burnt forest" and indicates Native Americans, at some time in the dim past, experienced what people who lived around here did in 1935 when a forest fire burned 10,000 acres of land. The Brule is sometimes called the Arrowhead and is, along with Gauthier Creek, a good place to fish for brook and rainbow tout.

The park is located 14 miles northeast of Grand Marais on Highway 61 and was established as Bois Brule State Park in 1957 when 940 acres along the river were set aside for public use. The park was renamed Judge C.R. Magney in 1963 when the Minnesota State legislature selected it as a memorial to the late Judge Clarence Magney who had been a justice of the Minnesota Supreme Court and a strong advocate of and for Minnesota State Parks, especially along the North Shore. His efforts and influence helped establish eleven parks in the state as well as numerous road waysides. Over time the park has expanded from the original 940 acres to the present size of 4,674 acres. In this aspect the history of the park is related to Naniboujou Lodge. The land was originally purchased by a group of wealthy investors who built the lodge and intended to build cabins and use the land for hunting. However the Great Depression hit, the investors lost their money, so only the lodge ended up being built. The land on the north side of the highway (the park) was eventually sold to the state.

This section of the walking guide contains three walks that concentrate on the park's geology as well as the Brule River and its mysterious Devil's Kettle.

Judge C.R. Magney State Park

Walk 1: Devil's Kettle and Picnic Rock

Walk Logistics

Start and End: Judge C.R. Magney State Park parking lot

Getting There: From Grand Marias take Highway 61 past the Kadunce River and County Road 14 to Judge C.R. Magney State Park at the Brule River. Turn left into the park and proceed to the parking lot. State Park permit is needed.

Walk Distance: 2.5 miles to Devil's Kettle (round trip); 8.0 miles to Picnic Rock II (round trip).

Difficulty: Tennis Shoes to the Kettle, Hiking Boots to Picnic Rocks

Safety Concerns: Boulders on trail and in places trail is crossed by numerous tree roots.

Worth a Longer Look: Waypoints 5, 6, 9, 14, 15

This walk is a modified version of walk 29 in a "Walking Guide to the Superior Hiking Trail: Natural History, Scenery, and Other Trail Features."

Waypoint-to-Waypoint

One: Parking Lot

We are in the parking lot (waypoint 1) of Judge C.R. Magney State Park on a clear, sunny day with the temperature a crisp 38 degrees, but it is supposed to climb all the way to 70 by this afternoon. Ours is the only car in the parking lot; too bad, for it's a great fall day to be outside. Hiking up an active and ever-changing North Shore river makes it even better.

Two: Bridge Over the Brule River

It's a short walk from the parking lot past a plaque with a brief biography of Judge C. R. Magney to waypoint 2, the bridge across the Brule River. There is an *outcrop* of dark, *massive basalt* in the river.

Three: Old River Channel and the Cross Rock

Crossing the bridge head upstream on a wide gravel path with a few larger *cobbles*. The line of *boulders* to the right of the trail represents an old river channel formed when the Brule River was flowing at a much higher level. The channel was abandoned as the river cut down through *glacial till*, deposits of *Glacial Lake Duluth*, and volcanic rock during the last several thousand years.

Waypoint 3 is at the start of a large *tree zoo*, an area that has been fenced off

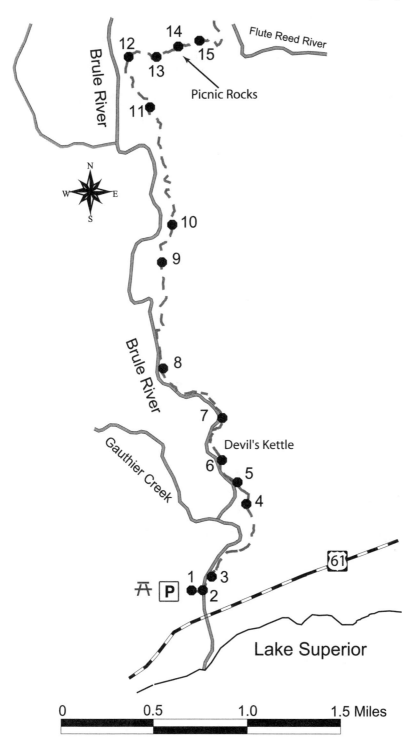

Judge C.R. Magney State Park
Walk 1: Devil's Kettle and Picnic Rocks

to protect white pine from hungry deer and rabbits A *glacial erratic* called the cross can be found here. It gets this name because it contains two intersecting *quartz* and feldspar veins that form a distinct cross shape. The veins are different ages–we know this because one cuts and offsets the other.

Four: Slumps, Meanders, and Glacial Erratics

Continue upstream on the wide path over gravel beach deposits exposed as water levels in Glacial Lake Duluth fell. These gravel beaches represent temporary shorelines of this ancient lake. Boulders seen here have been weathered out of the glacial till that is exposed further up the trail. Come to a fenced area where the river bank is *slumping* into the water. At this point the trail is a hundred feet above the river. A large glacial erratic of tan weathering, massive basalt sits here. It's kind of neat trying to picture this large rock sitting on a barren gravel beach on the shores of Glacial Lake Duluth.

Continue up the trail with partial views of the river and small waterfalls. Climbing a set of wooden steps continue along the wide, gravel trail as it moves away from the river to avoid a large *meander* and the erosion and slumping associated with it.

At waypoint 4 there is a nice view of the meander bend and a small waterfall with a pool at its base. A lot of *bedrock* is exposed in the river because of the low water level. The forest along this trail section contains some nice aspen, birch, and spruce, with a few white pine.

Five: Upper Falls and the Devil's Kettle Rhyolite

It's just a short walk up the trail, past the old steps, to the new steps that lead down to Upper Falls. Walk down the long, steep set of wooden stairs, then along a wooden boardwalk to waypoint 5, a short set of stairs that leads to a large outcrop of *rhyolite* lava at the base of Upper Falls. With the low water levels the river has separated into several "fingers," and these flow rather lazily over the rhyolite to cascade into the pool below. A nicely curved "three-quarter" *pothole* occurs at the base of the falls.

The rhyolite lava flow, pale red in color due to trace amounts of the iron oxide mineral *hematite*, contains small crystals of tabular-shaped, cream-colored feldspar (4-7%) and square to round glassy quartz (2-5%). The rock is pitted where the feldspar has weathered out. The rhyolite has a "hackly" or rough-textured weathered surface and is called the Devil's Kettle Rhyolite.

Six: Devil's Kettle

From waypoint 5 walk up another set of wooden stairs that goes above the falls; on the opposite side of the river is a cliff of rhyolite. Come to the junction with a hiking club trail and the trail to Devil's Kettle. The outcrop

244

exposed at the junction is similar to the rhyolite at waypoint 5, but here it is breaking into angular to rectangular and/or irregular chunks. The rough weathered surface and the way it breaks apart are due to numerous *spherulites*, the white spots throughout the rock, and these are an indication that this rock was once composed of volcanic glass.

There is a great view from here of Devil's Kettle Falls. Above the falls the river divides as it plunges over the rock rim with one branch flowing down and through what was once a sixty-foot-deep pothole that has had its downriver side eroded away. The other branch fountains into a beautiful round pothole or kettle and is never seen again. How deep the pothole is, no one seems to know.

Take the hiking club trail to the viewing platform directly above the Devil's Kettle (waypoint 6). The view is more than impressive with water pouring into the cavity; imagine what this looks and sounds like in the spring.

Seven: River Bars and Boulder Islands

The wide trail continues up and along the river to a gravel bar with larger cobbles at each end and *pebbles* and smaller cobbles in between. This gravel bar occurs on the inside bend of a large meander and is probably reworked each and every spring. Once past the gravel bar the wide hiking trail becomes narrow, bouldery, and root-crossed. Continue up the river past another gravel bar to waypoint 7, the start of a boulder-filled island and a large meander in the river. The island begins on the meander bend and ends where the meander ends. The boulders on the island and in the river come from erosion and slumping of the river banks; some of the basalt boulders have large weathered out *amygdules*. Massive rhyolite lava continues to outcrop on the opposite bank.

Eight: Oxbows, Spill-Over Channels, and a Huge Pine Stump

Continuing upriver through a cedar and ash-dominated forest, cross a small stream that seems to be in a great hurry to reach the river, and walk through a cedar grove to yet another meander and gravel bar. From this point the trail moves away from the main channel of the river to follow a "spring flood" spill-over channel. The banks of the "spill-over" are crammed with boulders and cobbles that represent glacial till with the finer material, the sand and clay, washed out. These banks are undercut and slump into the river during spring runoff. The trail moves back to the river passing through a cedar grove with pink-looking rhyolite outcropping on the opposite bank.

Once again the trail leaves the river, but this time it follows an old *oxbow* that is filled in with boulders, alders, spruce, and cedar to waypoint 8, the end of the oxbow. An enormous stump of what we call the Three Magi White Pine is found here. We named it this because a large spruce, small birch, and tiny fir are all growing out of it.

Nine: Glacial Lake Red Clay

From the Three Magi White Pine continue up the river with the banks crammed full of cobbles and boulders that, like the spill-over channel, represent glacial till, with most of the finer silt and clay material washed away. The forest is made up of cedar, spruce, birch, and balsam fir with large white pine stumps scattered throughout. The white pines were cut around 1900 and were part of northern Minnesota's once great white pine forest.

Pass a bench intended for little people, followed by a sharp bend in the trail from which it's uphill and away from the river. As you climb notice how the trail and hillside change from boulder-rich glacial till (left when the ice melted away) to the red clay deposits of Glacial Lake Duluth (which formed from the glacial meltwater). The change occurs where the trail makes a sharp turn at a large spruce tree.

Waypoint 9 is at a distinct break in the slope of the hillside and represents an old shoreline of the glacial lake.

Ten: Large Aspen and Glacial Till

Continue uphill, with the trail composed of red clay, walking past an area with large aspen trees and a planked-over wet section to waypoint 10, a nice view back down the river. From here a small meander can be seen along with a hillside of red maples and yellow aspens and birch. Just before waypoint 10 the trail leaves the red clay deposits and is back in glacial till; the elevation here is 1050 feet.

Eleven: White Pines and the Lightning Tree

From waypoint 10 it is a long walk (0.75 miles) with gentle ups and downs as the trail bends and twists above, but parallel to, the river. This walk is through a nice section of white pines. Cross two boulder-filled streambeds (dry) and come to waypoint 11, an old lightning struck white pine with only the charred black bottom part left.

Twelve: Large Rock Cliff

Crossing a small, boulder-filled stream head gently uphill through aspen, spruce, and birch woods with some white pine and one dense, dark grove of small spruce and aspen to waypoint 12, a view of a big hill to the left (1400 feet high). A large mass of dark grey, *columnar-jointed* basalt is exposed along the front of the hillside. The Brule River is far below and winds around the bottom of the hill.

Thirteen: Pahoehoe Lava

Continuing uphill come into a large, open area composed mostly of lichen-covered, brownish-grey to tan-colored basalt. On a fresh surface the rock is grayish-green with conchoidal fractures and few amygdules. Down slope, near the end of the clearing, we can see what looks like a billowy flow surface and this may represent the top part of a *pahoehoe* lava flow. The amygdules, hard to see on a weathered surface covered with lichen and moss, are round, up to 0.5 inches in diameter, and quartz-filled.

Fourteen: Picnic Rock

Still heading uphill come to a large, grassy opening with a great view of Lake Superior and a long exposure of the same lava that is at waypoint 13. Here the rock breaks into flat or square pieces. With white pine trees, the view, and the nice grassy area, this makes a great picnic spot. For this reason the basalt exposed here is called the Picnic Basalt Flow and the opening is called Picnic Rock I.

Fifteen: White Pines and Columnar Joints

Just uphill from here is another large opening. Here the Picnic Basalt Flow breaks into columnar-shaped pieces and, at the end of the opening, there is a columnar-jointed piece of basalt across the trail. The basalt lava also contains 1-2% lath-like grayish-green *plagioclase feldspar* crystals up to 0.5 inches long.

Waypoint 15 is at an old, white pine lined road that cuts across the opening. This is another nice picnic spot, so we name it Picnic Rock II.

From here, after a leisurely lunch, we retrace our route to the state park parking lot. The other option is to continue on the Superior Hiking Trail and complete Walk 29 in the Walking Guide to the Superior Hiking Trail.

Judge C.R. Magney State Park
Walk 2: Wildflower Loop

Walk Logistics

Start and End: Judge C.R. Magney State Park parking lot

Getting There: From Grand Marias take Highway 61 past the Kadunce River and County Road 14 to Judge C.R. Magney State Park at the Brule River. Turn left into the park and proceed to the parking lot. State Park permit is needed.

Walk Distance: 1.2 miles   **Difficulty:** Tennis Shoes

Safety Concerns: None

Worth a Longer Look: Waypoints 7, 9

Waypoint-to-Waypoint

The best time for this walk turns out to be in the spring or early summer. Though we did not see any on our walk we have been told there are coral root orchids and pink ladyslippers along this trail

One: Parking Lot

It is yet another nice fall day with the temperature in the mid-forties, but by noon it should be in the lower sixties. Once again we have the parking lot to ourselves and feel very fortunate to not only have the freedom and time to hike on such a day as this but to be able to do it in a setting that I think is just one step removed from true wilderness.

Waypoint 1 is in the parking lot.

Two: Trail Junction

Walk to the west end of the parking lot and follow the path to the sign for the Superior Hiking Trail. At the sign there is a trail junction with the park trail for the wildflower loop going to the right past a maintenance shed, and the Superior Hiking Trail going to the left toward Gauthier Creek and the Kadunce River. The trail junction is waypoint 2.

Three: Delta Deposits

The trail, composed of gravel, goes uphill passing a camping area below and to the right. In walking along we go past park interpretive signs for wild *strawberries*, balsam fir, and *raspberries*. Also seen along this trail section are large-leafed *aster*, *buttercups,* and *ox-eye daisies*. In the spring there will be *rose-twisted stalk*.

248

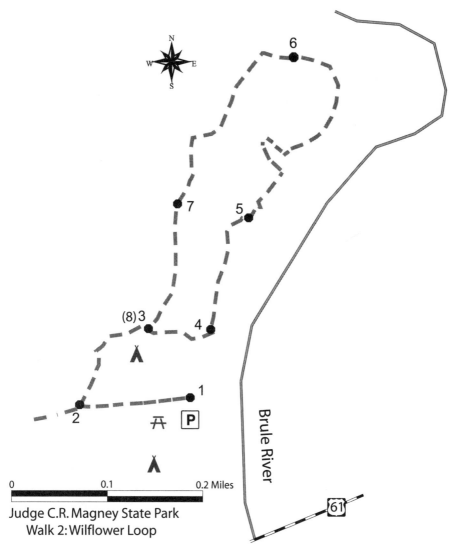

Judge C.R. Magney State Park
Walk 2: Wilflower Loop

The gravel on the trail represents part of a *delta* deposit built by the Brule River as the water level in *Glacial Lake Duluth* fell when the Laurentide Ice Sheet melted off the land and, in so doing, uncovered lower and lower outlets for the lake. The *pebbles*, *cobbles*, and sand in the delta came from the weathering of *glacial till* deposits upriver. The delta was built around 8000 years ago, since then the river has cut down to its present level. The land we are standing on is about 705 or 710 feet above sea level, and the river below us it at an elevation of about 635 feet. This means the river has cut down through the delta sediments some 70 feet in the last 8000 years at this particular spot.

Waypoint 3 is at the junction with the start of the loop trail. The forest through here is dominantly balsam fir, spruce, and paper birch.

Four: 46) Optical Illusion and White Pines

The trail is relatively flat as it goes by a sign for *honeysuckle* and past numerous, small white pines to a bench and a park interpretive sign for prickly *wild rose* (waypoint 4). In the spring there may be *wood anemone,* rose-twisted stalk, *Canadian mayflower, blue bead lily, and bunchberry* along this section. There is a partial view of the lake and the Brule River Valley from the bench. Optical illusion or not, from this spot it looks to me as if the lake is just about level with us!

Five: Ancient Beach and Fall Colors

The trail follows the edge of the river valley going gently uphill over cobbles and boulders that are dominantly *rhyolite* and *basalt* in composition. These *boulders* represent the coarse size fraction of the delta deposit and are an indicator that this is close to the place where the river entered the glacial lake (the river would deposit the largest material first). This means the shoreline of the old glacial lake is not far off.

Continue uphill to Waypoint 5, which is at a bench with a nice view to the southeast of the Brule River Valley and sparkling Lake Superior. The valley sides have lots of yellows and browns from birch, aspen, and poplar leaves, and some maple red mixed in with the green of the fir, spruce, cedar, and pine.

In walking uphill to the bench we notice a change in the composition of the material on the trail with the boulders and cobbles giving way to a sandy gravel. This material represents part of one of the beaches of Glacial Lake Duluth. Numerous beaches formed at different elevations as the water level dropped. As this happened, lake waves washed over the exposed delta deposits and reworked them to form nice beaches. So 8000 years ago this would have been a great spot-right on the beach with the cold lake not more that 5 or 10 feet away.

Thus far, in walking up this trail, we have gone from a gravel-rich to a boulder-rich delta deposit, and then onto a beach composed of the wave-washed and sorted delta gravel.

Six: Meander and Leaf-Less View

From the bench (and the former beach) the trail continues uphill with the sandy gravel giving way to boulders and cobbles composed dominantly of basalt, rhyolite, and *diabase*. These represent the coarse delta material that was above the reach of the waves when the water level fell. This material thus stood high and dry and was never reworked.

Pass an interpretive sign for *sarsaparilla* as the trail goes through a spruce, balsam fir, aspen, and paper birch woods with mistletoe in some of the birch trees. The trail then bends to the left as it continues to follow the edge of the river valley, which here is curving around a large *meander* in the Brule River.

Waypoint 6 is where a narrow path joins the main trail from the right. Following the path a short distance brings us to the edge of the valley. From here we can hear the river and, if the leaves were off the trees, we would have a very nice view.

Seven: Lily of the Valley and a Beach Lunch

Continue on, passing an interpretive sign for *starflowers* which are accompanied by bristly *clubmoss* as the trail moves away from the river to head down the opposite side of the loop. After starting out in boulders and cobbles of the delta (a wide variety of rock types including basalt, rhyolite, *granite*, and *monzonite* can be found here) the composition of the material on the trail changes into the sandy gravel of the beach. So, on the return journey, we are walking in the opposite direction from the "high and dry" delta deposit down onto the wave-washed beach, arriving just in time for lunch at the beach.

Waypoint 7 is at the interpretive sign for wild lily of the valley or Canadian mayflower.

Eight: Flood Plain

Continue downhill through a spruce, balsam fir, and paper birch forest past an interpretive sign for paper birch to waypoint 8, which is the same as waypoint 3. From this point we retrace our route back to the parking lot, which was built on an old *flood plain* of the river.

Judge C.R. Magney State Park
Walk 3: Gauthier Creek Loop

Walk Logistics

Start and End: Judge C.R. Magney State Park parking lot

Getting There: From Grand Marias take Highway 61 past the Kadunce River and County Road 14 to Judge C.R. Magney State Park at the Brule River. Turn left into the park and proceed to the parking lot. State Park permit is needed.

Walk Distance: 3.0 miles   **Difficulty:** Walking Shoes

Safety Concerns: Waypoint 4

Worth a Longer Look: Waypoints 4, 7, 8, 9

Waypoint-to-Waypoint

One: Parking Lot and the Visitor

We are back in the parking lot after hiking the wildflower loop and it remains a beautiful sunny fall day. Believe it or not, ours is still the only vehicle in the parking lot. I guess that is a good thing for we returned from our morning hike to find a black bear wandering amongst the picnic tables! After one look at us, its amazed and startled expression meeting two amazed and startled expressions, the bear took off in a mad, headlong dash for the trees and vanished before we could do more than gasp. Wow-I think it was a big bear and its coat seem to shine, so it was obviously well-fed.

Two: Superior Hiking Trail

To start this walk, go to the west end of the parking lot and take the Superior Hiking Trail to the junction. This is waypoint 2.

Three: Spherulites and Glacial Lake Duluth

Continue on the Superior Hiking Trail (to the left). After a short distance the trail makes a right turn onto a wide, grassy trail/road. Follow this uphill along Gauthier Creek, which is on the right. It is an easy walk with large aspen and ash trees to admire as the trail goes over the top of *outcrops* of the Devil's Kettle *Rhyolite*. The outcrops are weathering to kibbles and bits (see *diabase weathering*). This is due not to the usual *ophitic* texture found in the *basalts* and *diabases*, but to the *spherulites* found in this rhyolite lava flow.

Spherulites are round areas in the rock that are composed of radiating arrays of tiny, elongate crystals formed by the high temperature devitrification of

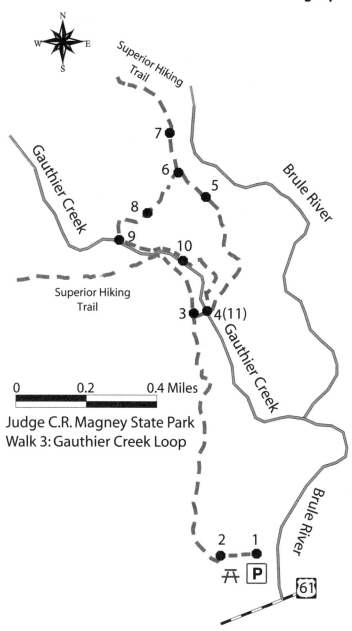

Judge C.R. Magney State Park
Walk 3: Gauthier Creek Loop

glassy volcanic rocks. Spherulites form in rocks that cooled from hot magma to solid rock so quickly that individual minerals had no time to form and grow. When that happens, an amorphous glassy mass called obsidian or volcanic glass is formed. With time the glass slowly changes (devitrifies or becomes crystalline) to form fine-grained minerals or crystal fibers. In rhyolitic rocks the crystal fibers are generally composed of *potassium feldspar* and *quartz.* Spherulites typically have diameters of 0.1-1 inch, but they can be much larger (up to 8 inches). Isolated spherulites are generally spherical in shape–thus the name. They weather out of the rock to form kibbles, which then break down to bits.

After crossing a small creek with a city-like culvert it's uphill to the junction (waypoint 3) between the Superior Hiking Trail and the Gauthier Creek Loop Trail.

Just before coming to the trail junction the material composing the walking path turns to reddish clay. This fine-grained sediment represents thick clay deposits that formed in the quiet part of *Glacial Lake Duluth* (below wave depth), and since the elevation here is 880 feet it represents a time when the lake was at its maximum size and depth. This would have been prior to the formation of the *delta* and beach deposits (see walk 2), and just after the Laurentide Ice Sheet melted off this part of the world.

Four: Gauthier Creek and Drop Pools

From the trail junction follow the Gauthier Creek Loop Trail to the right, and walk to Gauthier Creek (waypoint 4). We find the bridge across the creek sitting beside it so we cross over via boulders that are sticking out of the water. At this time of year it is no problem, but in the spring it might be a different, wetter story.

To cross we have lots of *boulders* to choose from, for the creek is chock-a-block full of them. They, along with the *cobbles*, are composed dominantly of basalt and rhyolite, and there is an outcrop of the rhyolite just downstream at a bend in the creek. The exposure is a lava flow and is the same material that forms the Devil's Kettle. It contains visible small, tabular potassium feldspar and grey quartz crystals. Upstream there is a small, low log dam across the creek; this is one of several along the stream. Their purpose is to allow drop pools to form and provide quiet places for trout to rest as they move up and/or downstream.

There is a trail junction on the opposite side of the creek that represents the start of the loop walk. Follow the trail to the right.

Five: White Pine Zoo

From the junction walk up a gentle slope then along a wide, grassy trail through a paper birch, spruce, balsam fir, and balsam poplar woods. Continuing uphill, pass a stand of white pine with a white pine "zoo" behind them. The purpose of such *tree zoos* or enclosures is to protect young trees from hungry deer and moose, which love to eat them. They will happily snip off the terminal buds thus making sure the tree doesn't grow any taller or take part in the seeding of the forest. Moose also love the small, supple branches of the mountain maple, which is sometimes called moose maple. Possible that's why the Ojibwe refer to moose as twig eaters.

254

Go around a bend in the trail before coming to a large fenced-in area constructed (in 2000) to keep deer and moose out and the white pine in. This is waypoint 5. The dominant trees through this area are spruce, balsam fir, cedar, aspen, and balsam poplar.

Six: Old Shelter

Continue along the tree enclosure which is fenced on both sides of the trail. There are large aspen trees through here and a few nice white pine. The steep slope to the right goes down to the Brule River, which we can hear but not see. Waypoint 6 is at an old shelter that is overgrown with grass and surrounded by bushes that are starting to look as though they would like to make use of it. There is a trail junction here with the loop trail going off to the left and a spur trail continuing up the river valley.

Seven: Tunnel View

Take the spur trail that heads up the valley. Along the trail are partial views down to the river and to the opposite valley side, which is showing off its fall colors. Waypoint 7 is at a bench with a lovely "tunnel" view down the Brule River to Lake Superior. This view is worth our walk up here but we decide no one needs go any farther. The rest of this mini-loop is on a grassy trail with no views; return to waypoint 6.

Eight: Spruce and Fir

Back at the shelter take the trail to the right (left on way up) walking downhill and crossing a small stream. The tree zoo ends just before the downhill begins.

From the creek, walk uphill then along a level trail that passes through dark, dense balsam fir and spruce woods before heading downhill to a wooden bridge over a small stream (now dry). This is waypoint 8.

The way to tell the difference between a balsam fir and a spruce is to shake hands with each of them and examine the bark. The balsam fir has soft, flat needles (which is why the Ojibwe used them for bedding material under their blankets or furs), and the bark is bubbly. The spruce has stiff, sharper needles (not a good night's sleep on these) and the bark is cracked and checkered.

Nine: Boulders Galore

From the creek the trail heads uphill then levels out as it takes us through dark and dense balsam fir and spruce woods and thickets. The trail then enters a more open spruce, aspen, paper birch forest before heading downhill and following the side of Gauthier Creek to a bench beside the creek (waypoint 9). The creek at this point is full of large, round boulders of basalt, *granite*, and rhyolite. The edges of the creek are lined with similar boulders, and the boulders come from erosion of the *glacial till*. The water has undercut the stream banks, removing the finer clay and silt-size material and carrying it away downstream. As this happens, the large boulders embedded in the till, as well as smaller cobbles and pebbles, become less and less secure until, one fine day, they fall, roll, or tumble into the water. The smaller rocks will be moved slowly downstream, but the larger stones, like those now in the creek, remain where they come to rest. In a large flood they may be rolled or moved to the stream edges or travel a short distance downstream to form concentrations or piles of boulders.

Ten: Creek Terrace

Continue along the side of the creek on a wide, grassy trail. The bank to the left of the trail is an old *river terrace* of the creek, and to the right is an outcrop of the Devil's Kettle Rhyolite. Walk by another low, wooden dam in the creek and then up, onto a second stream terrace with the first one still to the left. There is another log dam forming another drop pool immediately to the right of the trail, and this is waypoint 10.

We hear a grouse drumming not too far away and Steve tells me the sound reminds him of springtime in the north. It sounds like a motor starting up in the distance, "put....put....put...put..put..put, etc." with the "puts" getting closer together.

Eleven: Leaning Cedar

The trail now moves away from the creek, crossing a bridge over a small stream that flows into Gauthier Creek. Pass by a large, leaning cedar tree and boulders of *gabbro* to arrive at the trail junction that represents the start of the loop, and this is waypoint 11 as well as waypoint 4.

Recross the creek and walk back to the Superior Hiking Trail. Follow the Superior Hiking Trail back to the parking lot.

Grand Portage State Park

Introduction

Grand Portage State Park is a place of history, both human and geological, and much of that history is centered on the Pigeon River that flows through the park.

The geological history of the park is rich and complex. It contains the oldest rocks found in any of the state parks along the North Shore, and it is the only North Shore park where the geology is not dominated by 1.1billion-year old igneous lava flows and intrusive rocks. Instead most of the rocks are 1.8 to 1.9 billion-year-old sedimentary rocks that were formed in the same narrow basin as the iron ore deposits on the Mesabi and Gunflint Iron Ranges. Called the Rove Formation, these sedimentary rocks are composed of siltstones, sandstones (a kind called greywacke) and shales. The shales are dark grey to black in color because they contain organic material derived from decomposition of the abundant life forms that lived in the ocean waters that filled the basin. Back then the principal life form was a kind of blue-green algae (actually cyanobacteria) called a stromatolite.

The sedimentary material making up the Rove Formation was deposited mostly by turbidity currents or submarine mud flows; these great turbulent underwater surges of sediment-laden water periodically rushed down the slope of the basin and out onto its flat floor covering the area with a layer of sand, silt, and mud. The sediment came from the erosion of granitic bodies and volcanic rocks to the north and west of what is today the park. The rifting event that formed the basin went on for about 200 million years; the sediments composing the Rove Formation were deposited in the basin during the last 100 million years of that time.

As a group these sedimentary rocks go by several different names depending on where you happen to live. Here they are called the Rove Formation, on the Mesabi Range they are known as the Virginia Formation, and near Duluth they are the Thomson Formation. In Wisconsin they are called the Tyler Formation, and in Michigan they are the Michigamie Formation. Though they are all the same kind of rock, all the same age, all deposited in the same environment, they did form in three different basins: the Animikie, Marquette, and Huronian. Because of this, and because different geologists were mapping the different basins, it took some time to realize the rocks were all the same darn thing. Since there was no internet back when these rocks were being mapped and described, they got different names and these names have stuck.

Back 1.9 billion years ago the Mesabi and Gunflint Iron Formations were forming at the margin of the Animikie Basin in shallow water, just off shore. This was about thirty to forty miles northwest and west of today's Grand Portage State Park. Geologists refer to the place the iron ore was forming as the continental shelf, which is the submerged part of a continent on the edge of an ocean basin. The east coast of the United States is a good modern example, a place with sandy beaches, barrier islands, and warm shallow water.

Seaward of the continental shelf is what is called the continental slope, the place where the seafloor begins to dip more steeply, where water depth increases, and where a lot of turbidity currents are born. Beyond the continental slope is the continental rise, which begins at the base of the continental slope and continues outward and downward, to become the ocean floor, also called the abyssal plain. It was on the continental rise and part of the abyssal plain where turbidity currents carried the sediment that became the Rove Formation. This sediment varied from about 1000 to more than 10,000 feet in thickness, but even so it never formed a great range of mountains. Instead, something funny happened once the sediment reached the basin. Some quirk of plate tectonics caused the bottom of the basin, the continental rise, slope, and shelf, to subside at about the same rate the sediments were being deposited. So the actual thickness of sediment covering the seafloor was never very great. Most of it was buried soon after it was deposited. This particular process of planet earth, the continuous and slow subsidence of the continental rise and deposition of sediment, went on for tens of millions of years.

Geologists call such places geosynclines–large, trough-like downwarpings of the earth's crust in which thick piles of sediment slowly accumulate. It's kind of like a gigantic landfill with the bulldozers in the landfill operated by plate tectonic processes.

So as the ancient North American continent, which at that time extended from Wyoming to Maine and from Iowa to Hudson's Bay, rifted apart the Animikie Basin formed. Iron ore and chert were deposited close to the newly created shoreline and ended up forming the Biwabik, Cuyuna, and Gunflint Iron Formations. The sediment that ended up forming the greywackes, siltstones, and shales of the Rove, Virginia, and Thomson Formations was deposited in the deeper parts of the ever widening basin.

If that were the end of the story there would be no state park here today. In fact, the glacial ice would have found the soft sedimentary rocks of the Rove Formation much to its liking and would have bulldozed them as flat as a pancake; there would be no waterfalls, cliffs, rocky gorges, or high ridges. All of these scenic features are due to the relatively hard, resistant diabase sills and dikes that intruded the Rove sedimentary rocks some 1.1 billion years ago. These igneous rocks are called the Pigeon River Intrusions, and

258

they are associated with the Mid-Continent Rift, which was responsible for the lava flows and other igneous rocks seen along the North Shore. These dikes and sills are much harder than the Rove sedimentary rocks, and the glacial ice did not like them nearly as much. So the glacial ice carried away the softer sedimentary rocks and abraded and plucked the igneous rocks into ridges and rocky promontories.

It was left to the Pigeon River to complete the sculpting of the land by cutting deep into what remained of the relatively soft sedimentary rocks to form the steep-sided gorges. The diabase sills and dikes proved to be made of sterner stuff, and so the river left them standing as higher areas that became waterfalls and cliffs.

Human history, though not nearly as long as its geological counterpart–in fact in comparison it's a mere blink of the eye–has been just as important in terms of the development of this area and establishment of this park. The Ojibwe called it Git-che-O-ni-ga-ming which translates into "a great carrying place." And what a perfect name that was because the waterfalls, rapids, and high cliffs made the lower stretch of the river impossible to navigate, especially in something as fragile as a birch bark canoe. The only option for Native Americans, fur traders, and voyageurs was to "portage" around these features that are awesome to look at but a curse to anyone traveling by water. The path around these obstacles, the great carrying place, was used for hundreds if not thousands of years by the Native Americans who lived in this region. Fur traders and voyageurs who came to the area in the 1600s called it the Grand Portage. The Grand Portage is a nine-mile trail that connects Lake Superior with the Pigeon River and then continues on to an inland system of rivers and lakes that lead to the interior of the continent.

Turns out Grand Portage was a great carrying place thousands of years before the Ojibwe settled here (about 1000 years ago). Other Native Americans mined native copper on Isle Royale from 7000 to about 3500 years before the present, and they traded it across a good part of North America. Grand Portage would have been the perfect route out of Lake Superior and on to the prairies, the Yellowstone country, and north into western Canada.

In the 1700s Grand Portage became the site of the North West Fur Company's great trading post. Canoes arrived from Montreal laden with trade goods, which were then carried in 90-pound packs up the nine-mile-long trail. At the other end of the trail, a place called Fort Charlotte on the Pigeon River, the beaver pelts were unloaded from canoes coming from the trading posts to the west and north. The pelts were exchanged for the trade goods and carried back down the trail to the trading post at Grand Portage and eventually on to Montreal. The nine-mile round trip on the Grand Portage Trail took 6 to 8 hours, and many of the hardy voyageurs who packed the goods over the trail carried not one, but two ninety pound packs—each way!

Grand Portage State Park is located on the international border between Canada and the United States with the Pigeon River marking the border. The park is 7 miles north of the village of Grand Portage on Highway 61, and is immediately before the border inspection station.

The Pigeon River is the largest river along the North Shore and, after the Saint Louis River, has the largest watershed of any Minnesota River that empties into Lake Superior (610 square miles). This tends to insure an impressive flow of water in the river and makes the two major waterfalls along its course spectacular most times of the year. The first of these, High Falls (Pigeon Falls) has a drop of about 120 feet. Middle Falls, which is further upstream, has a two-step drop of some 30 feet.

The park is relatively new; it was established in 1989 through the joint efforts of the Grand Portage Band of Chippewa and the State of Minnesota. Because of this Grand Portage is a unique state park in that it is the only one not owned by the State of Minnesota. The land is leased from the Grand Portage Band, and the development and management of the park is done by the Department of Natural Resources.

This section of the book contains all the walks one can do in the park: the 0.5-mile walk to High Falls and the 3.5-mile walk to Middle Falls. Both walks are centered on the Pigeon River and its spectacular waterfalls, the sedimentary rocks of the Rove Formation, and the ridge-forming intrusive diabase of the Pigeon River Intrusions.

Grand Portage State Park
Walks 1 and 2: High Falls and Middle Falls

Walk Logistics

Start and End: Parking lot at Grand Portage State Park

Getting There: Take Highway 61 north from Grand Marais and pass Judge C.R. Magney State Park, the villages of Hovland and Grand Portage to the park entrance which is just before crossing the Pigeon River and the Canadian Customs Inspection Station. Turn left at the state park sign and park in the visitor's parking lot.

Walk Distance: 1.0 miles return to High Falls, 7.0 miles return to Middle Falls

Walk Difficulty: Tennis shoes (High Falls), Hiking Boots (Middle Falls)

Safety Concerns: See waypoint 7, 13, 17, 18, 22

Worth a Longer Look: Waypoints 3, 4, 6, 8, 12, 13, 20, 21, 25, 26, 27

Waypoint to Waypoint

One: Paved Path and Mississippi Hot

It's a late August day on the International Border, a place we don't think hot but today might change our mind. It's what I would call sultry, a Mexican-kind of sultry, humid, hot, and close. Even the wimpy breeze off Lake Superior is warm, so warm it's one of the few times all summer I would have considered wearing shorts while hiking!

Waypoint 1 is at the start of the paved path to High Falls. This is just up from the parking lot and across from the visitor's center which, for the time being, is in an old house. There is a trail that leads off to the right to a nice picnic spot overlooking the Pigeon River.

Two: Beer Hops and a Once Giant Birch

Head up the path passing the remains of an immense paper birch tree which, until it decided to rot and had to be cut down, was officially the largest paper birch in Minnesota. Waypoint 2 is at the first bench, and in this area there are wild beer hops growing. They are certainly not native to this part of the country; instead they are a legacy of the days of prohibition when the Pigeon River was crossed and recrossed many times a night. How these got here I don't know, but they have survived and possibly could be used to make ice beer (Steve's idea). Also seen along here are *Canadian mayflower, rose-*

261

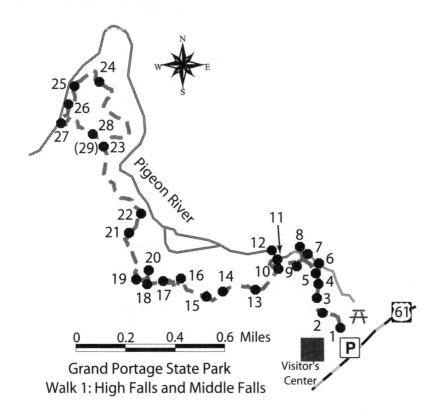

Grand Portage State Park
Walk 1: High Falls and Middle Falls

twisted stalk, large-leafed *aster*, *thimbleberry*, *sarsaparilla*, *Indian pipe*, *horsetails*, and ground cedar (*clubmoss*).

Three: The Four Seasons

Continue on the trail, passing a sign with information on the importance of each of the four seasons for the Ojibwe people. In general, for the Ojibwe, fall was for harvesting and the center of this was the harvesting of wild rice, winter was for family in small camps, spring was maple sugar time, and summer was the time people gathered together in large summer camps to garden and fish.

A park bench is waypoint 3. Another sign provides information about the fall harvesting season. There is an old foundation to the right of the trail, and in and around it are small spruce and balsam fir trees.

Four: River Estuary

It is just a short walk to another bench and another "harvest the seasons" sign, and this is waypoint 4. There is a view of the Pigeon River and the highway bridge from here.

The river at this spot looks nothing like the river that flows over the High Falls and down the twisting canyon below it. The river that flows by here ambles along through what looks like an alder and grass-filled *estuary*. In this regard the Pigeon River is like both the Gooseberry River and the Split Rock River. Back in the days of *Glacial Lake Duluth*, as the Laurentide Ice Sheet melted off the land, the ice kept uncovering outlet channels at lower and lower elevations. As this happened, the water level in Glacial Lake Duluth fell hundreds of feet; the lowest lake level was below the present level of Lake Superior. Falling lake levels meant the gradient of the Pigeon River dramatically increased, and this enabled the river to cut down through the deposits of *glacial till* and deep into the sedimentary rocks of the Rove Formation. Starting about 8000 years ago, glacial rebound caused water levels to rise, and the gradient and velocity of the river decreased. This led to the river filling in the deep channel it had cut. As the channel filled the lake level reached its present position, and ended up partly flooding the mouth of the river creating this estuary.

Five: Pigeon River

It's a short walk from waypoint 4 to a set of steps that go to the right down toward the river (waypoint 5). A dirt service road is to the left.

Six: Oxbow

Take the steps down to a dirt path, and then continue along a trail (lined with *honeysuckle*, Canadian mayflower, and clubmoss) to the river, which is waypoint 6. Here, however, we stand not on the main river channel, but on an old *meander* or *oxbow*. This oxbow is rocky and probably full of rushing water in the spring when the Pigeon River overflows its banks and fills the old channel to the brim. The boulders are dominantly *diabase,* and just upstream is a large *outcrop* of well bedded *Rove Formation siltstone*s and *shales*.

Oxbows are old meanders whose curvature has grown so extreme that only a narrow bit of land is left between the two arms of the meander; in other words, a gooseneck forms. In the spring, when the water is high and fast, a stream can erode through the gooseneck, cutting a shorter, straighter channel for itself. The new channel is referred to as a cut-off, and the abandoned meander, because of its curved or horseshoe shape, is referred to as an oxbow. Over time the oxbow is filled in by sediment and vegetation, but until that time the oxbow may become a flood channel during spring run-off.

Seven and Eight: Rove Formation and Rapids

Continue upriver on the dirt path through dense spruce, balsam fir, white cedar, and paper birch woods with red osier dogwood. There is moss hanging from the trees, and the trail is covered by numerous tree roots.

A steel marker is waypoint 7. Just beyond the marker is another trail junction. The path to the left leads to the paved trail to High Falls, and the path to the right leads to the river. Follow the path to the river, which is waypoint 8.

At the river's edge is a large exposure of bedded siltstones and shales. These tan, rusty red, and grey rocks are eroding along bedding planes, and this gives them an irregular, step-like look with the shales weathering away faster than the siltstones (Steve calls it "fractal fracturing"). This kind of weathering is responsible for the small set of rapids seen here. The individual beds are less than 0.5 inches thick and, just like the North Shore lava flows, the beds are titled toward the lake. On the opposite side of the river is a steep rock wall, and in this exposure the grey siltstones stand in relief compared to the softer, rusty, darker shales.

Nine: Trail Junction

From the river it is a short walk back to the dirt path. We then head straight ahead up the wooden stairs to the paved path, which is waypoint 9.

Ten: Glacial Till

Continue on the paved trail passing well-exposed banks of glacial till with *boulders* and *cobbles* of *basalt*, *diabase*, siltstone and shale. The till exposed here is part of the *ground moraine* that covers a good portion of the park. Till is not layered or bedded, and is poorly sorted, which means that large rocks occur next to small ones; fine sand, silt, and clay hold it all together. These two features are what distinguish till from the other major kind of glacial deposit, which is called outwash.

Walk past another bench and another "harvesting the seasons" sign to yet another bench, which is at the junction of the High Falls Trail and the Middle Falls Trail. This is waypoint 10 and there is an outhouse here.

Eleven: Viewing Platforms

Continue along the paved trail through dense balsam fir to a wooden boardwalk beyond which is a junction (waypoint 11). The stairs to the left go to what is known as the upper viewing platform, and the walkway straight ahead leads to the lower viewing platform. From here we most definitely hear the roar of the falls.

Twelve: High Falls and the Great Dike

Go straight ahead to the lower viewing platform for a spectacular view of the High Falls (waypoint 12). Today the river is mimicking the Brule River– it is divided into two separate branches that tumble down opposite sides of the waterfall. In the spring it would be a much different story with a solid sheet of water hurtling over the rough rock face to crash into the pool at the bottom before racing away downriver.

264

The steep, curving, rocky canyon downstream of the falls has been cut deep into the sedimentary rocks. In contrast the "Great *Dike*" that forms the falls has defied the river's erosive power and stands some 120 feet above the pool. The steep cliff on the opposite side of the river is in Canada, and along its base can be seen cement walls that represent the remains of the "flume" system that was once used to transport logs past the waterfall and down the river to the lake. The flume was constructed in 1899 to prevent valuable timber from shattering as it went over the falls, and also to stop logjams that commonly formed at the base of the falls.

Return to the stairs and walk up to the upper viewing platform. From here the cement walls of the flume and even parts of the old wooden structure that contained the logs is visible. The day we are here a picnic table sits on the rocks below the falls just above the water on the Canadian side. Why and how it got there are the obvious questions. The table is in a spot difficult to access, and surely it would be no better than a rotten log at surviving a trip over the falls. Steve thinks it was delivered by boat, but if so why? Either way the table will someday be part of the lake.

From this high perch we look down on the Great Dike, and we can clearly see it is what is called a multiple dike–one dike intrusive into another, or two dikes for the price of one. The thinner dike has beautiful exposed *columnar cooling joints* that are at right angles to the contact between the two dikes. The contact is nicely exposed and can be seen to the right, below the cement wall of the flume.

From this upper platform, if we drag our eyes away from the falls and turn around, Pigeon Point and Lake Superior are visible in the distance.

Ten (again) Trail Junction

From the upper viewing platform go back down the stairs and along the boardwalk to waypoint 10, the junction between the High Falls and Middle Falls trails. If walking only the High Falls section, take the paved path back to the visitor's center and parking lot

Thirteen: Delta and Green Tags

To continue on to Middle Falls follow the path that goes past the outhouse. A park sign cautions walkers that the Middle Falls Trail is not well-maintained, so watch your step.

The Middle Falls Trail starts as a wide, gravel path through dense spruce and balsam fir with some nice size paper birch trees. The gravel on the trail is interesting because there is a large *delta* deposit to the south and east of the park, and we wonder whether this gravel is part of the delta or whether it was placed here by park personnel. The delta formed as the water level in *Glacial Lake Duluth* fell and the gradient of the Pigeon River increased.

This allowed the river to carry more sand and *pebbles*, but as it flowed into the glacial lake its velocity dropped to nothing and all the material it carried was deposited. Over time this led to the formation of a sizable delta.

Cross a wet, planked section to the start of a dirt path, and then walk uphill a short distance past two big birch trees (one has a lightning scar) and a patch of bristly clubmoss to a sign that reads "green tag #2," which we designated as waypoint 13. We assume from the blank green sign this was meant to be an interpretive trail, one that obviously never got interpreted. There appears to be *starflowers* around the green tag; *blue bead lily* and large-leafed aster also grow here.

Fourteen: White Pine and Diabase Boulder

Walk up a gentle slope passing an unmarked path to the left. The forest is more open through this area with aspen making an appearance. Pass a large white pine to the left and come to green tag #3 (Canadian mayflower), which is waypoint 14. The boulders of diabase on the trail come from the adjacent hillside.

Fifteen: Gabbro and Glacial Till

The trail is relatively flat, though it is bouldery and crossed by tree roots as it winds along a hillside of glacial till. The boulders in the till are siltstone, shale, diabase, and *basalt*. Waypoint 15 is at a large boulder of coarse-grained *gabbro* with the *plagioclase feldspar* weathering a chalky white color. Ferns seem to like this chalky white stuff, for they are growing profusely on it.

Sixteen: Wildflowers and Old Man's Beard

Walk uphill past a large old spruce tree with old man's beard. The boulders on the trail are composed of crumbly diabase, and the outcrop is diabase and is part of the "Great Dike" that forms High Falls. Canadian mayflower, round-leafed *pyrola*, bush honeysuckle, rose-twisted stalk, and large-leafed aster grow along the trail.

Continue uphill, walking past nice size spruce and aspen trees over a boulder and cobble-littered trail. These rocks come from weathering and erosion of the glacial till (with help from frost heaving). The finer silt and clay-size material, over time, is washed away and only the larger boulders and cobbles are left. Here this material is composed of gabbro, diabase, siltstone, and shale.

At the hilltop we find green tag #4 and this is waypoint 16. There are nice white pine and white spruce here, the spruce trees are covered in moss. Along the trail can be found Canadian mayflowers, *bunchberries*, blue bead lily, *baneberry*, *pipsissewa*, and starflowers.

266

At the hilltop the dominant cobble types are siltstone and shale of the Rove Formation. Pine needles cover the trail.

Seventeen: Rectangular Rocks and the Perfect Lunch Spot

The trail now goes steeply uphill over small rectangular to box-shaped pieces of siltstone and shale. Walk up a set of old log steps and past an outcrop of thinly bedded (<0.5 inches thick) siltstone and shale, which exhibits the same rectangular weathering pattern as the pieces that cover the trail. The weathering is due to a combination of *frost wedging* and running water. Frost in the bedding planes expands and fractures the rocks; running water washes the broken material away. Looking at the way the Rove Formation weathers, it is easy to see how the Pigeon River eroded so deeply down into it.

Opposite the outcrop are nice white pine trees along with a view of Lake Superior. The trail continues uphill, curving near the top. Green tag #5 is waypoint 17. Found close to #5 are *bearberry* and yew.

A small clearing at this waypoint is surrounded by pretty white pine trees with till boulders of diabase and pink *granite*. From the clearing and through the ring of pine trees there is a nice view of the lake, with Hat Point visible to the left and ahead. This promontory, composed of a diabase *sill*, gets its name from the voyageurs paddling to Grand Portage from Montreal. They would stop at the point to clean up and don their finest clothes and feathered hats before loudly and lustily singing their way around the point and into the great trading post. For the voyageurs this was important stuff, for all eyes would be on them and the way they paddled their Montreal Canoes. To perform badly was something that would not be lived down for a very long time.

There is a split log bench in the clearing, and this makes for a lovely picnic spot. In fact, one could visit the High Falls and then walk up here for a romantic lunch before heading back to the parking lot.

Eighteen: White Pine and Rove Rocks

From the "perfect" lunch spot continue along a bouldery and root-crossed trail through nice white pines, followed by a short uphill section with rock steps that go past a large white pine to an outcrop of siltstone and shale and green tag #6 (waypoint 18). The outcrop exhibits the same blocky to rectangular weathering pattern as the previous one. Nice white pine grow around the outcrop, which is covered by reindeer moss. Close to #6 are rock tripe and bearberry.

Nineteen: Spur Trail

From waypoint 18 it is a short walk to a spur trail that goes to the right. This is waypoint 19.

Twenty: Nice View

Take the spur trail and walk uphill over diabase outcrops to a large outcrop of the diabase dike that forms High Falls. This is at the hilltop, and the diabase varies from smooth to lumpy weathering (see *diabase weathering*) and is reddish-brown in color. Green tag #7 (jack pine) is here and this is waypoint 20. There is a nice view of Hat Point and Wauswayugoning Bay to the south.

Twenty-One: Wow Spot

From the overlook it is a short walk on the spur trail through a grove of white pine trees over lumpy diabase to another overlook with a fabulous view to the east and north. This is waypoint 21 and this is a beautiful Japanese garden-like area on a knob with mounds of reindeer moss, and trees dwarfed somewhat by the tough conditions and thin soil. Park workers have carefully outlined a little path through this area with stones. The rocky Pigeon River is far below (here we are at an elevation of 915 feet and the river is at 820 feet), and the rolling green hills of Canada (composed of diabase) stretch away into the distance. Both jack pine and white pine are common here, along with some mountain ash. There are tons of dead birch trees adjacent to the logging road that can be seen in the distance to the north.

From the overlook return to waypoint 19 at the junction with the main walking path.

Twenty-Two: Slippery Trail and Clubmoss

Just past the trail junction is green tag #8 and an outcrop of the Great Dike, which also forms the hillside to the right. The trail goes down the hillside and, as it does, the white pine disappear and we are back in a forest of aspen, balsam fir, spruce, and birch. Walking down the hill the trail enters a dense fir and spruce woods. Going downhill the trail is relatively steep, lined by clubmoss (bristly, running, and cedar), starflowers, blue bead lily, and rose-twisted stalk. The trail, in places, is slippery, so take care. At the bottom walk through a wet, muddy area before heading back uphill into a more open forest with a return of the white pine; there are also nice large birch and aspen as well as some poplar trees. Waypoint 22 is at green tag #9.

Twenty-Three: Loop Trail

The trail is relatively flat, but it remains root-crossed as it goes through an area dominated by alder, hazel, and mountain maple to green tag #10 (balsam fir seedlings). From this point follow the winding trail through a low, muddy area and up a short slope to a section with lots of gentle ups and downs. Pass by some nice spruce trees in a dominantly poplar, aspen, fir, and birch forest. There are occasional breaks in the woods, and these openings are mostly grassy and in the spring will have a variety of wildflowers including *Mertensia*, pyrola, *bloodroot*, *marsh marigolds*, and horsetails. Horsetails are also called scouring-rush because they contain enough silica that they can and have been used to scrub dishes; they are the steel wool of the wild. Waypoint 23 is at the start of the loop or "lollipop" trail around Middle Falls.

For the quickest and most direct route to the falls, take the trail to the left. We flip a coin and end up on the trail to the right.

Twenty-Four: Moose and Middle Falls

From the junction it is about a half-mile walk through typical Canadian bush to a bench from which we can hear the roar of Middle Falls. This is waypoint 24. We are complaining about how boring this section of the trail is when we come around a bend and there, standing in the trail not more than 15 feet away, is a big bull moose. This magnificent creature is dark brown in color and has a nice rack of antlers. Fortunately the moose has other things on its mind, for it seems to completely ignore us and, lifting its head high in the air, emits a fire siren kind of snort and takes off in the direction of the river. The moose simply vanishes into the thick brush, leaving both of us amazed at its quickness and grace. To say that this makes the hike worthwhile (without seeing Middle Falls) is a bit sacrilegious, but boy, did this make the hike worthwhile! Wildflowers seen here include *sessile bellwort*, bloodroot, *trilliums*, and *wood anemones*.

Twenty-five: Cascade and a Deep Pool

From "moose corner" walk by the bench and continue through the thick forest (thick for us, but not the moose), which is composed of spruce, fir, and birch with lots and lots of moose maple (what else) along with hazel and alder. Waypoint 25 is at a spot where we get a nice view of Middle Falls from the edge of the river. At Middle Falls water flows over a diabase dike into a wide pool at the bottom. On this day the water forms silky fingers and broader white sheets as it cascades down the 20-to 30-foot high falls, hesitating a brief moment at the prominent rock step about half-way down. At the bottom the water splashes rather lazily into the deep, dark pool. The falls are not as spectacular as High Falls, but they are very pretty, especially when framed against a horizon dominated by aspen with cedar and spruce along both sides of the river and a deep blue sky overhead.

Waypoint 25 is at green tag 14.

Twenty-Six: Small Niagara

From this point continue along the river bank toward the waterfall, passing above a cobble and boulder beach and an outcrop of diabase to waypoint 26, a junction with a path to the right that goes down to the river. The falls are directly above us and, from the rocky diabase outcrop on the river bank, we watch the water splash, cascade, and slide over the diabase, which has a distinct knobby-looking surface.

Above the falls is a wide expanse of flat diabase, which the water flows across before going over the falls. At the moment it is extremely pretty. A fine mist is rising up off the water above the falls, kind of reminding me of a very miniature Niagara–all that is needed to complete the picture is a small version of the Maid in the Mist.

A sign at this spot marks the US-Canada border. The high ridges across the river (in Canada) are diabase in composition.

Twenty-Seven: Chutes and Cooling Joints

Continue upriver, passing a boulder beach in a spruce, fir, and aspen forest with some large white pine. There is a small weathered outcrop of diabase to the right along the river's edge (waypoint 27), and the water has eroded a small chute into the diabase. Here white churning water is whisked into the chute and swept quickly through it to continue its journey toward the falls. There are good examples of cooling joints along the edge of the chute, and these are horizontal so they look like steps or columns that have been tilted on their side. These joints are smaller versions of the one forming the "step" in Middle Falls. The diabase exposed here contains fine, disseminated yellow pyrite (fool's gold) and some chalcopyrite (a copper-iron-sulfide); it is also cut by *calcite* veins.

Twenty-Eight: Closed In Trail

The trail turns away from the river and goes up a short, gentle slope where it levels out. It is bouldery and closed-in on both sides by moose maple, alder, small balsam fir, and spruce with some paper birch and a few large aspen. Distributed through here are rose-twisted stalk, bunchberry, ground pine (clubmoss), pyrola, starflower, honeysuckle, wood anemone, Canadian mayflower, large-leafed aster, and sarsaparilla. Waypoint 28 is at green tag #11.

Twenty-Nine: Return Trip

From waypoint 28 it is a short walk back to the start of the "lollipop" loop trail around Middle Falls, and this junction is waypoint 29 as well as waypoint 23. From here follow the trail back to the junction between the High Falls Trail and the Middle Falls Trail. Turn right and walk down the paved pathway past the visitor's center back to the parking lot.

Geological Terms and/or Features

Aa Lava Flow: Aa is one of the two kinds of lava associated with the subaerial part of shield volcanoes. The word is Polynesian for "lava you can not walk on in bare feet" (if you do you say aa a lot). This kind of basalt lava has a jagged and rubbly flow top composed of pieces of angular lava. Such flow tops form because aa lava is very sticky (viscous) and thus flows so slowly it piles up at its front in much the same manner a carpet does when slowly pushed into a wall. This leads to a rough, angular, broken surface. Aa lava flows can also be vesicular, and these gas cavities tend to be contorted indicating volcanic gas was escaping as the lava flow slowly moved over the ground.

Agate (Lake Superior): A translucent, cryptocrystalline variety of quartz (chert) characterized by a variety of colors arranged either in alternating bands or stripes, irregular clouds, or swirls. Agates occur as the filling of gas cavities (vesicles) in volcanic rocks, dominantly basalt.

Amygdaloidal: General name for a volcanic rock that contains numerous amygdules.

Amygdule: (Greek for almond-shaped): Gas cavities (vesicles) in a lava flow that have been filled by one or more minerals. The holes vary in size from pinheads to the rare watermelon-sized one.

Anorthosite: A rare, coarse-grained igneous rock composed of more than 85% plagioclase feldspar; other minor constituents are apatite, magnetite, ilmenite, olivine, and pyroxene. Most anorthosites are older than 1 billion years; they are also found in the outer crust of the moon (which is why they are often called moon rocks). The origin of these unusual rocks remains controversial. One of the more common explanations is that anorthosite forms in large cooling and crystallizing bodies of hot molten rock (magma chambers) that have the overall composition of basalt. As the magma cools, plagioclase feldspar crystals form. These have a specific gravity (density) that is less than the magma they crystallized from, about 2.76 compared to 3.15. Being lighter than the magma, the feldspar rises or floats to the top of the magma chamber where it collects to form a solid layer of almost pure plagioclase. Later intrusions (like the Beaver River Diabase) can easily disrupt and fragment this layer, picking up pieces (xenoliths) of anorthosite on the way toward the earth's surface. The anorthosite found in the state parks occurs as inclusions or xenoliths in the Beaver River Diabase.

Aphanitic: A term that means the minerals in a rock are too small to be seen without using a magnifying glass or jewelers loupe.

Argillite: A compact rock derived from the mild metamorphism of mudstone or shale. Argillite is more highly compacted then either of these, but it lacks the planar or thin sheet-like layering of slate.

Banded Gneiss: A metamorphic rock composed of alternating bands or layers of dark (pyroxene, biotite) and light (quartz, feldspar) minerals. The bands vary from less than 1/8 inch wide up to more than a foot; they form due to segregation of light and dark minerals under conditions of high temperature and pressure.

Basalt: A dark-colored (usually dark grey, dark green, or black), extrusive (lava flow) volcanic rock. Minerals commonly found in basalt include plagioclase feldspar, pyroxene, and, less commonly, olivine. Minor minerals are ilmenite and magnetite. Basalt is the most common volcanic rock on earth with most of the oceanic crust (ocean floor) composed of this material.

Beach Terrace: A flat, horizontal or gently sloping surface formed when an old shoreline has been isolated by lowering water levels.

Beaver Bay Igneous Complex: A series of roughly contemporaneous sills, dikes, and irregularly shaped intrusive masses that are dominantly diabase to gabbro in grain-size (same chemistry and mineralogy). Minor rock types include monzonite and quartz monzonite. These igneous intrusive rocks occur along the North Shore of Lake Superior between Gooseberry Falls State Park and Grand Marais, and can be traced inland for 15-25 miles. These rocks are related to the 1.1 billion year old Mid-Continent Rift and represent magma chambers to, and feeders for, some of the basalt lava flows of the North Shore Volcanic Group.

Beaver River Diabase: This is the most common intrusive rock in the Beaver Bay Igneous Complex. It occurs as sills, dikes, and sheet-like masses from south of Beaver Bay all the way to Grand Marais. These dark rocks are the intrusive equivalents of basalt and are commonly ophitic. They are dominantly fine-grained, but medium-grained varieties also occur; these typically represent slower cooled centers of large dikes/sills or sheet-like intrusive masses. A distinguishing characteristic of this unit is the small to large, round to angular xenoliths of anorthosite and basalt that are found throughout it (also see diabase).

Bedrock: The solid rock that underlies soil, glacial deposits, gravel, and/or other superficial material. Rock that is part of the crust of the earth.

Boulder: A rock fragment greater than 10 inches (256 mm) in diameter (about the size of a volley ball). Typically somewhat rounded as the result of glacial or river transport.

Calcite: Composed of calcium carbonate ($CaCo_3$), this is a common mineral found in amygdules, and it is the main constituent of limestone. Calcite is commonly white or gray, fizzes in dilute hydrochloric acid, and forms rhombohedral-shaped crystals.

Chert: Either a hard, dense cryptocrystalline (cyrpto meaning hidden) sedimentary rock or a filling in an amygdule. Chert is composed of quartz crystals that are too small to be seen without the aid of a microscope. Typically, chert has a conchoidal fracture (cracks like glass creating smooth, spoon shaped surfaces). Usually white or cream-colored, though it can be black (flint) and red (jasper).

Cobble: A rock fragment between 3-10 inches (64 and 265 mm) in diameter; the fragment is typically rounded or abraded as the result of glacial and/or water transport.

Columnar Joints: See cooling joints.

Cooling Joints: A type of fracture pattern resulting from the thermal contraction of hot volcanic, or near-surface intrusive rocks as they cool and crystallize. Commonly seen as evenly spaced, elongate, pentagonal or hexagonal columns oriented perpendicular to the cooling surface. Columnar jointing is common in all compositions of lava flows, although it is generally best developed in mafic (basalt) lava flows; it also occurs in diabase sills and dikes. Classic examples of cooling joints are Devil's Post Pile in California and Devil's Tower in Wyoming.

272

Cross-bedding: Beds or layers in a rock that tilt at an angle to the original horizontal surface upon which the sediment accumulated. Cross beds form during deposition of sediment (sand-silt) from a changing river or ocean or wind current and are common in deltas, gravel bars, and beach deposits.

Cuesta: An asymmetric ridge with a long, gentle slope on one side (this parallels the tilt or dip of the surrounding or underlying strata) and a steep cliff-like or blunt-nose-shaped face on the other side formed by frost-wedging and glacial plucking. The resultant hill ends up looking like one of the teeth on an old wood saw. An example of a cuesta is Look Out Mountain in Cascade State Park.

Delta: A fan-shaped deposit at the mouth of a river formed by deposition of sediment (sand, pebbles, and silt) carried by the river. Deposition occurs when the river flows into a larger body of water (lake or the sea) and the velocity of the water dramatically decreases; the water loses its power and the sediment it is carrying falls out.

Diabase: A dark, igneous intrusive rock formed from hot, molten magma that never quite reached the earth's surface. Instead the magma is injected along existing rock contacts and cools below ground, more slowly than if it had flowed onto the surface. A diabase thus forms the middle part of a triumvirate with deeper gabbro and shallower basalt. See diabase formation.

Diabase Formation: Diabase, basalt, and gabbro have similar mineralogy and chemistry, but basalt is a lava flow and cools quickly so it has smaller crystals and a finer grain size; its crystals are visible only with a microscope. Gabbro is a deep intrusion and cools slowly so it has larger crystals and a coarser grain size; its crystals are easily seen with the naked eye. Diabase is a shallow intrusion that cools slower than a lava flow and faster than a deep intrusion; the crystals are between basalt and gabbro in size and can be seen with a magnifying glass. So, like good old basalt and hardy gabbro, diabase is made up of grey to greenish-gray plagioclase feldspar, and a black to greenish-black kind of pyroxene called augite, with or without a little bit of glassy green olivine and black, metallic magnetite and/or ilmenite. "Crossing over" is a good name for this middle rock because it represents a change from deep gabbro to basalt lava and most likely represents direct feeders for surface lava flows.

Diabase Weathering: What gives ophitic diabase, gabbro, and the ophitic basalt lava flows their character? It's the different looks they take on as they weather or break apart. There is: "smooth and even," "lumpy," "crumbles" and its friends–"kibbles and bits." This last rock material is the size and shape of dry dog food and gives the trail a "gravelly" look and feel.

Dike: A tabular-shaped igneous intrusion that cuts across layers (bedding, flow contacts, etc.) in the intruded rock.

Epidote: A soft calcium-iron-aluminum silicate mineral with an apple green color. Epidote is a common mineral in amygdules.

Estuary: An estuary is a "drowned river mouth." These are common along the east coast of the United States with Chesapeake Bay and Delaware Bay being good examples. The Split Rock River, Gooseberry River, and Pigeon River estuaries are the result of these three rivers downcutting through basalt and rhyolite lavas at the end of the last Ice Age, some 7000 years ago. From that time on, the level of the water in the lake rose and flooded the mouth of the rivers. Since then the lake has managed to remain high enough to maintain the estuaries.

Exfoliation or Unloading Fractures: The process by which horizontal sheets, plates, concentric shells, or pieces of rock, from less than one inch to several feet in thickness, are successively spalled or stripped from the surface of an exposed rock mass. The rock mass ends up with a saucer or onion skin appearance. Exfoliation is the result of differential stresses within the rock, often caused by slight pressure differences between the exposed rock at the surface and the rock lying just below the surface (more pressure on it). This unloading causes expansion and splitting of the rock forming horizontal fractures. These features are most common in rhyolites and granites.

Fault: A fracture or crack along which there has been displacement of one side relative to the other, movement is parallel to the fracture or crack

Flint: A dark grey or black variety of chert.

Flood Plain: The flat part of a river valley that is covered by water when the river overflows its banks.

Flow Banding: Layering in a rhyolite lava that results from shearing of viscous lava during flow. Flow bands are often contorted and folded and are commonly represented by color variations, which are due to differences in mineral content, vesicularity of the layers or alternating layers of volcanic glass (dark) and spherulites (light-colored spots).

Frost-Wedged: See frost wedging

Frost Wedging: This is a process by which water fills fractures and cracks in the rock, freezes, and expands by as much as 10%. This causes the cracks or fractures to enlarge just a tiny bit, and, after hundreds or thousands of freeze-thaw cycles the rock breaks into angular fragments. These fragments then slide, roll, or fall to the bottom of a cliff or hill to produce piles of rock debris called talus.

Gabbro: A dark-colored igneous intrusive rock that, mineralogically and chemically, is the equivalent of basalt and diabase. Gabbro has a coarser grain-size than either basalt or diabase because of slower cooling. See diabase formation.

Glacial Erratic: Large boulders (house-size to end table-size) carried in glacial ice and left behind when the ice melts away. These are the "how did that get there" rocks– large rocks sitting on hills, in the middle of swamps, in open fields, or in thick woods. The boulders may have been carried for hundreds of miles, or they may be from just down the road.

Glacial Lake Duluth: This meltwater lake formed about 11,000 years ago when the Laurentide Ice Sheet melted back over the southern and southeastern edge of the Lake Superior Basin. Meltwater became trapped between the edge of the ice sheet and the edge of the basin. This lake was smaller but deeper than present day Lake Superior with shorelines at elevations of 1,000 to 1,100 feet (today's Lake Superior is at about 600 feet). Glacial Lake Duluth drained to the south down the Brule River (in Wisconsin) and the St. Croix Valley into the Mississippi River. The lake lasted until the ice sheet melted back over Sault Ste. Marie and uncovered a topographically lower area. This led to catastrophic floods down what today is the St. Mary's River.

Glacial Plucking: A process whereby meltwater at the base of glacial ice (formed from pressure melting) seeps into broken and fractured rock and freezes solid. In doing so the frozen water attaches the broken rock firmly to the bottom of the glacier. As the ice flows forward the stuck piece of rock is pulled or peeled off the bedrock as easily as a tooth is pulled by attaching it by a string to a doorknob then slamming the door shut. This process, over time, creates small and large basins as well as whalebacks.

Glacial Striations: Fine parallel scratches or grooves in bedrock formed by rocks embedded in the glacial ice. As the ice flows over the land, the rocks are dragged across the bedrock leaving fine parallel marks behind. From these you can tell in which direction the ice was moving.

Glacial Till: Till is a wonderful Scottish word that means "stiff rocky ground," which is exactly what the hardy northeastern Minnesota farmers found when they tried to dig into it. Deposits of till are composed of sediment and rock deposited directly from the melting ice; in other words the ice melts away and leaves behind a lot of what it carried.

Deposits of till are not layered or bedded, and they are said to be poorly sorted, meaning large and small rocks occur side-by-side. This gives till a much different look than the other kind of glacial deposit–outwash–which forms from sediment carried in the waters that flow away from the front of a melting glacier. Outwash deposits are layered or bedded and relatively well-sorted.

Landforms composed of till are called moraines. There are three kinds of moraines: end, terminal, and ground. Most of the till along the North Shore is part of a ground moraine, a blanket of till that covers the countryside, fills in depressions, and smoothes out the landscape. Think of New England and the rolling, rocky pastures enclosed by stone fences and you have a picture of what ground moraine looks like.

The red color of the till is due to finely crushed and pulverized bits of sedimentary material that filled in the Lake Superior Basin when volcanic activity came to an end about a billion years ago. These rocks–sandstones, shales, and siltstones–formed what are called "red bed" deposits, assemblages of continental bedded sedimentary rocks that are red or maroon in color because they contain small amounts of the red iron oxide mineral hematite. During the last Ice Age the glaciers found these rocks to their liking, and not only scooped them out of the basin like children scoop seeds out of a pumpkin at Halloween, but in doing so, pulverized them. The final glacial product was red silt-clay-and sand-size particles distributed throughout the till.

Gneiss: See banded gneiss.

Granite: One of the most common kinds of igneous intrusive rocks, and a major component of the continental crust. Granite contains at least 20% quartz and has more potassium feldspar than plagioclase feldspar. It is the intrusive equivalent of rhyolite.

Ground Moraine: See glacial till.

Hematite: A common iron mineral (Fe_2O_3) that occurs in two distinct forms:) A soft, brick-red earthy variety (common along the hiking trail), and a much harder metallic black variety with platy crystals.

Iron Formation: A sedimentary rock that contains at least 15% iron. The iron can occur in oxide minerals (magnetite and hematite), as carbonate minerals (ankerite and siderite), or as sulfide minerals (pyrite). The main silicate minerals in iron formations are chert and jasper.

Jasper: A red variety of chert

Magnetite: A common iron mineral (Fe_3O_4) that strongly attracts a magnet. Magnetite has a metallic luster, is black in color, forms small octahedral crystals, and is relatively hard (6) on the Moh's scale.

Massive: A term applied to rocks of any origin that are more or less featureless in texture and fabric.

Meander: Pronounced sinuous curves or bends in a river that look much like switchbacks on mountain highways. These form most commonly in rivers that have gentle stream channels flowing across fine-grained sediment and/or glacial till.

Mid-Continent Rift: Some 1.1 billion years ago, when Minnesota was truly the center of the continent, the west got sick and tired of the east and tried to separate, much like Africa and South America did 200 million years ago. Hot molten magma rose upward from deep with the earth, and as it approached the surface, it caused the crust to arch or bow upward, and then split open like an overcooked sausage. A great crack formed, one that spread from the Lake Superior region down what is now the St. Croix River Valley and on through Minnesota, Iowa, and clear to the edge of the continent, which was somewhere in Kansas. This great crack or rift is referred to as the Mid-Continent Rift.

Hot molten rock poured out of this growing crack year after century, lava flow upon lava flow, thicker and thicker until a pile of basalt lava some 2-10 miles deep covered the Lake Superior Region. You would not, however, have needed to strain your neck or use high-powered binoculars to see the top of the lavas, for the rift widened and deepened at about the same rate lava was being extruded. Overall the topography remained pretty flat. The volcanic eruptions went on for about 23 million years and, since lava is about as sticky as wet cement, the greatest amount of lava piled up close to the eruptive source (the rift). The tremendous weight of this rock pile caused the land to sag downward for hundreds and hundreds of feet. This tilted the lavas some 10-20 degrees to the southeast (in Minnesota) and led to the formation of the Lake Superior Basin.

The lavas are dominantly basalt (pahoehoe and aa) with lesser amounts of rhyolite. Overall, the lavas can be likened to pancake batter spreading out over a hot grill, and this kind of eruption gave rise to stacked pancakes or sheets of lava called plateau or flood basalts.

The eruptions were not continuous, and during quiet periods streams and rivers flowing into the basin carried sediment that blanketed the surface of the flows with sand, silt, and clay. With resumed volcanic activity the sediment was covered up, and eventually became what are called interflow sedimentary rocks (sandstones and siltstones).

Not all of the magma erupted at the surface as lava; much of it remained below ground to form igneous intrusive rocks. Erosion has partly exposed many of these, with the three largest intrusive groups being the Duluth Complex, the Beaver Bay Complex, and the Pigeon River Complex.

After 23 million years rifting came to a halt, probably because the heat source in the earth's crust had expended its energy, and/or because a great continental collision started along what was the east coast. Called the Grenville Orogeny (mountain building event), it produced the ancestral Appalachian Mountains, and possibly the pressure of this collision prevented the rift from continuing to widen. In effect it may have squeezed the rift to death.

Monzonite: A relatively rare igneous intrusive rock that contains no quartz and has just about equal amounts of plagioclase feldspar and potassium feldspar.

Mud Cracks: Irregular fractures in a crudely polygonal pattern that formed by shrinkage of clay, silt, or mud, generally during drying under surface conditions.

Mudstone: A dark, fine-grained sedimentary rock composed of compacted clay and silt.

North Shore Volcanic Group: The name given to a thick (2-8 mile) sequence of 1.1 billion year old lava flows with minor interflow sedimentary rocks that occurs along the North Shore of Lake Superior from Duluth to Pigeon River. All of the volcanic rocks exposed in the state parks belong to this group. These rocks range in composition from basalt (most common) to rhyolite. The volcanic rocks were all erupted from the Mid-Continent Rift.

Obsidian: Volcanic glass, typically black in color and of rhyolitic composition. Glass is characterized by conchoidal fractures. It forms from the rapid cooling or quenching of magma or hot lava, leaving no time for individual minerals to nucleate and grow.

Olivine: A vitreous, olive green mineral that is a minor component of gabbro, diabase, and basalt. It is composed of iron, magnesium, and silica.

Ophitic Texture: From the Greek word meaning a stone spotted like a serpent, ophitic is a texture seen in mafic igneous rocks (basalt, gabbro, or diabase) in which large pyroxene crystals (augite) enclose much smaller crystals of plagioclase feldspar. The large pyroxene crystals are separated from each other by fine-grained areas of plagioclase feldspar with some olivine and magnetite. This gives the rock a mottled black and gray look. The larger pyroxenes are more resistant to weathering than the intervening feldspar-rich areas and so end up as "raised lumps" throughout the mafic rock. It is this texture that gives many of the diabases, and some of the basalts seen on the trail their interesting weathering characteristics.

Orthoclase Feldspar: A white or pink potassium feldspar ($KAlSi_3O_8$). Orthoclase is a common rock-forming mineral in granitic rocks.

Outcrop: Bedrock exposed at the earth's surface.

Oxbows or Cut-Off Meanders: Once a meander forms in a stream the curvature of the meander grows until it becomes so extreme that only a narrow bit of land is left between the two arms of the meander; in other words, a gooseneck forms. In the spring, when the water is high and fast, a stream can erode through the gooseneck, cutting a shorter, straighter channel for itself. The new channel is referred to as a cut-off, and the abandoned meander, because of its curved or horseshoe shape, is referred to as an oxbow. Over time the oxbow filled in by sediment and vegetation. Cut-offs are important;

over the last 176 years the Mississippi River has become 242 miles shorter because of its ability to cut off meanders.

Pahoehoe Lava: Pahoehoe, Polynesian for "lava you can walk on in bare feet," is associated with the subaerial part of shield volcanoes and with plateau lavas. Pahoehoe lava flows are distinctive because, being less viscous than aa, they have a billowy or ropey to shelly upper surface. As pahoehoe lava flows over the ground, the upper part of the flow is air cooled and becomes stickier, or more viscous, than the center part. The hot center then drags or pulls the sticky part, and this action forms either a billowy or curving rope-like surface. At times so much gas is escaping from the lava that it builds up under the sticky top and exerts enough upward force to break the top into shell-like slabs (shelly pahoehoe). Both billowy and ropey pahoehoe lava flows can be seen along the North Shore.

Palisade Head Rhyolite: See pyroclastic flows.

Pebble: A rock fragment between 4 and 64 mm in size (about the size of peas to dumplings). Typically rounded during ice or water transport.

Pegmatite: A very coarse-grained igneous rock that typically occurs as dikes or veins. Commonly composed of quartz, feldspar, and biotite.

Phenocrysts: The term refers to large crystals in a much finer-grained rock. Crystals form as lava begins to cool well beneath the surface. As they grow larger, the magma, due to a sudden pressure release, rises rapidly toward the surface where it begins to cool quickly. The end result is large crystals (phenocrysts) in a very fine-grained rock (called a porphyry). This kind of rock occurs as either lava flows or near-surface intrusions.

Pigeon River Intrusive Complex: The term refers to a series of diabase dikes and sills, along with larger gabbroic masses, that have intruded the Rove Formation (sedimentary rocks), the Gunflint Iron Formation, and the rocks of the Beaver Bay Igneous Complex. These rocks outcrop from just south of Hovland to the Canadian border and are responsible for the waterfalls on the Pigeon River.

Pipe Amygdule: Elongate, cylindrical zones of amygdules that extend vertically up through a lava flow ending in a vesicle cylinder. These reflect the rise of gas bubbles through a cooling lava, most commonly basalt. May be caused by the flow of lava over wet ground with the water flashing to steam and rising up through the flow.

Plagioclase Feldspar: This cream to gray-colored mineral is one of the most abundant minerals in the earth's crust and is therefore an important rock-forming mineral. It is composed of sodium, calcium, aluminum, and silica. The ratio of calcium to sodium leads to several different varieties of plagioclase feldspar. Crystals are usually tabular to lath-shaped.

Potassium Feldspar: See orthoclase.

Potholes: Potholes are bowl-shaped depressions "carved" into the bedrock floor of a stream or cut into the side walls of valleys and gorges. The flowing water performs this feat by abrading the bedrock, especially when it is moving fast and there is lots of it. It uses sand grains and pebbles as its major grinding and cutting tools. Where there is a combination of a natural depression in the rock (such as a fracture, joint, or gas cavity)

278

and eddies or swirling water, there is an opportunity for sand and pebbles to get into the depression and be rapidly spun around and around by the water. This turns the sand and pebbles into effective drills. Over time the depression grows larger and deeper. In a lot of potholes beautifully polished and rounded pebbles and cobbles can be seen, many of which represent the drill bits that help make the hole.

Pumice: Solidified fragments of cooled, highly vesicular (>60% gas holes) rhyolitic magma or lava generally formed during explosive eruptions. The highly vesicular nature of pumice (looks like Swiss cheese) results from large volumes of gas rapidly expanding within a depressurized magma. The low density of pumice permits it to float on water for extended periods of time. Size is highly variable, though the vast majority is ash-size (dust). Pumice is the main component of explosive volcanic eruptions.

Pyroclastic: From Greek meaning fire-broken, this refers to processes resulting from the explosive fragmentation of a magma or lava. Pyroclastic eruptions occur because magma is much like Pepsi Cola. The plastic pop bottle sitting on the store shelf contains a dark liquid with a cap on it. By looking at it there is no way to tell there is a lot of gas (carbon dioxide) dissolved in the liquid. However, pick the bottle up, gently shake it, and a few small bubbles form. If you shake it vigorously then take the top off, you have a frothing, foaming mess spewing everywhere.

An explosive volcanic eruption is much the same. Magma has a lot of gas dissolved in it and, like the pop, the gas is held in the liquid because of pressure; the bottle cap on the Pepsi and the overlying column of rock on the magma. As magma rises up to shallower levels of the crust, pressure decreases (like gently shaking the bottle), and small gas bubbles begin to form. The higher and faster the magma rises, the quicker and more rapid the gas comes out of solution, much like vigorously shaking the pop. Remove or breach the cap and there is instantaneous pressure release, and the gas froths out, tearing the magma apart and generating an explosive eruption. The torn-apart bits of magma are called pumice.

Pyroclastic Flows and the Palisade Head Rhyolite: The Palisade Head rhyolite, which is exposed from Beaver Bay to Little Marais, is an enigmatic unit that has characteristics of both lava flows and pyroclastic flow deposits. Though evidence exists for both origins, the widespread distribution of this unit, the lack of flow breccias and vesicles (gas cavities or, in older rocks, amygdules), and the presence of pumice at its base is more characteristic of high temperature pyroclastic flow deposits.

Pyroclastic flows are mixtures of pumice, gas, and air that are dense enough to travel over the ground (flow) at high speeds (> 60 mph and up to 250 mph) for great distances (up to 200 miles from source). A large part of the deposit is composed of pumice, which ranges from bread loaf through donut hole to peanut-size with most fragments the size of breadsticks that have been run over several times by a semi-truck (volcanic ash). If the eruption temperature is high enough, the pumice can be so hot on deposition that, in the center of the flow, this material welds or fuses together to form a homogenous glass. The temperatures may actually be hot enough to cause this glass to flow during final cooling. It is thus possible for flow bands and folds to form in this kind of pyroclastic flow.

The only evidence of the pyroclastic origin of such rocks is preserved in the much more rapidly cooled tops and bottoms of the deposit. Though very poorly exposed, this is where relict pumice is found in the Palisade Head Rhyolite.

It should be stressed that temperatures high enough to cause this "welding" phenomena and flow folding are far from the norm; most pyroclastic flows retain ample evidence of their origin.

Pyroxene: A common dark-colored mineral typically found in basalt, diabase, and/or gabbro. Forming four-and eight-sided prismatic crystals, it is composed of iron, magnesium, and silica (Si_2O_8). Pyroxene is another of the rock forming minerals. It comes in several varieties depending on the iron/magnesium ratio. The most common of these is augite, from the Greek meaning "bright," for its shiny, black crystal faces.

Quartz: Crystalline silica (SiO_2); one of the most common minerals in the earth's crust. Quartz occurs as clear, purple (amethyst), pink (rose), and/or black (smoky) hexagonal-shaped crystals and as irregular masses. It also occurs in microcrystalline form which, depending on color, has been given the names flint (black), chert (cream), and jasper (red). Quartz is the main constituent of Lake Superior agates.

Rhyolite Lava Flows: Rhyolite is the extrusive equivalent of granite and the complete opposite of the dark basalts seen along most of the trails. Where basalt is dark-colored and composed of dark minerals such as pyroxene and olivine, rhyolite is light-colored (pink to gray) and composed of light-colored minerals such as quartz, potassium feldspar, and plagioclase feldspar. The rhyolite lavas seen along the North Shore are the same age as the basalt lavas, but they make up only a small percentage of the rocks the hiking trails cross. Rhyolite lava is much more viscous than basalt lava, and is erupted at a much lower temperature. The combination of these two factors means rhyolite, as a lava, does not travel far from where it is erupted–0.5 to a few miles at most. In fact, rhyolite is often so viscous it piles up right over the volcanic opening to form an inverted bowl-shaped feature called a lava dome. Rhyolite flows are thick and may have cooling joints, spherulites, and flow banding.

River Terrace: A level or step-like surface breaking the continuity of the slope above a river or creek, the terrace represents an old flood plain.

Ripple Marks: Elongate ridges of sand spaced at a uniform distance from each other. Ripples form in shallow water by wave action or currents and are preserved in sedimentary rocks.

Rove Formation: A group of sedimentary rocks that formed between 1.9 and 1.8 billion years ago, at the same time and in the same narrow elongate basin as the iron ore deposits on the Mesabi Iron Range. The Rove Formation is composed dominantly of greywackes, siltstones, shales, and mudstones that formed over a 100-million-year time span.

These sedimentary rocks, as a group, go by several different names. Along the North Shore they are called the Rove Formation, on the Mesabi Range they are known as the Virginia Formation, and near Duluth they are the Thomson Formation. In Wisconsin, they become the Tyler Formation, and in Michigan they are the Michigamie Formation. Though they are all the same kind of rock, all the same age, and all deposited in the same environment, they did form in three different basins: the Animikie, Marquette, and Huronian. Because of this, and because different people were mapping the different basins, it took geologists some time to realize the rocks were all the same. Since there was no Internet back when these rocks were being mapped and described, they got different names and the names have stuck.

Think back 1.9 billion years ago, back to when the iron formations were forming in warm shallow water off shore from sandy beaches. These beaches were about 30-50 miles from what is now the North Shore. The iron ore was forming on a continental shelf, which is the submerged part of a continent on the edge of an ocean basin. The east coast of the US is a good modern example, a place with sandy beaches, barrier islands, and warm shallow water.

Seaward of the continental shelf is something called the continental slope, the place where the seafloor begins to dip more steeply and water depth increases. Beyond the continental slope is the continental rise-the transition zone between the continental slope and the ocean basin proper, called the abyssal plain. It was on the continental rise and part of the abyssal plain where turbidity currents carried the sediment that ended up forming the rocks of the Rove Formation. In the Animikie Basin these sedimentary rocks vary from about 1000 feet to more than 10,000 feet in thickness, but they never formed a great range of mountains. Instead something funny happened to them once they reached the basin. Some quirk of plate tectonics caused the bottom of the basin, the continental rise, slope, and shelf, to subside at about the same rate the sediments were being deposited. So the actual thickness of sediment covering the seafloor was never very great. Most of it was buried soon after it was deposited. This particular process of planet earth, the continuous and slow subsidence of the continental rise and deposition of sediment, went on for tens of millions of years. So, as North America's first supercontinent, which has been named Kenoraland, rifted apart, a basin named the Animikie formed. Layers of iron ore and chert, now known as the Biwabik, Cuyuna, and Gunflint Iron Formations, were deposited close to the newly created shore, while the greywackes and siltstones of the Rove, Virginia, and Thomson Formations were deposited in the deeper parts of the ever widening rift.

Sandstone: A sedimentary rock composed of sand-size grains that are most commonly quartz. In the North Shore Volcanic Group, the sand-size grains are dominantly plagioclase feldspar and pyroxene.

Sawtooth Mountains: The name given to prominent hills along the North Shore of Lake Superior from about Tofte to Grand Marais; the hills have long, gentle slopes in the direction of the lake (the way the lava flows dip), and steep cliff-like or blunt-nosed shapes on the opposite side. This gives the hills the profile of teeth on a wood saw. The hills that make up the Sawtooth Mountains are composed of an intrusive rock we call the Star Wars Porphyry and/or basalt lava flows.

Schist: A medium-to coarse-grained metamorphic rock that exhibits a parallel alignment of platy or prismatic minerals.

Shale: A fine-grained sedimentary rock composed of clay flakes. Shale forms due to lithification (hardening and compaction) of mud.

Sill: A tabular-shaped igneous intrusive rock body that parallels the planar structure (flow contacts, bedding, or layering) of the surrounding rocks.

Silt: A detrital particle finer than sand and coarser than clay

Siltstone: A sedimentary rock composed of silt-size grains of feldspar, quartz, and clay.

Slate: A metamorphosed shale that tends to break into thin planar pieces.

Slumps: Slumps are one of the more common forms of "mass wasting," which is defined as the down slope movement of rocks and/or soils, especially soft, loose stuff like clay or silt, under the influence of gravity. Slumps can be identified because the head, or beginning, of the slump has a crescent-shaped scarp. Trees hanging over the edge of the scarp and big cracks in the trail also help. Slumps usually involve several separate blocks which, together, look like giant steps going down a hillside. Each block is composed of unconsolidated material that moves as a single mass but only about as fast as a lazy turtle. The material never goes very far–unless it reaches a river, that is.

The slumping along rivers on the North Shore typically occurs above meanders. The velocity of the flowing water is not uniform around a menader. In meanders the higher velocity water, as well as the more turbulent water, is on the outside of the curve, which, in this case, is the slump side of the stream. This higher velocity water erodes away the glacial till at the base of the slope, most often during spring run-off, leaving the material in the stream bank unsupported. It eventually gives in to the pull of gravity and slumps downward. This loss of slope stability happens in stages leading to a kind of domino effect that, in the end, produces step-like blocks. As long as there is a meander and the stream is actively eroding its banks, the slumped area will continue to grow.

Spheroidal Weathering: Chemical weathering turns an angular block-shaped rock into a rounded rock. Weathering is more intense on the edges or corners of block-shaped pieces than on the smoother rock faces and thus, over time, the edges and corners are worn away, leaving a round shape.

Spherulite: Rounded, radiating arrays of crystal fibers produced by the high temperature devitrification of volcanic glass. These form in rocks that cooled from hot magma to solid rock so quickly that individual minerals had no time to form and grow. When that happens an amorphous glassy mass called obsidian or volcanic glass is formed. With time glass slowly changes or devitrifies to form fine-grained minerals or crystal fibers. In rhyolitic rocks the crystal fibers are generally composed of potassium feldspar and quartz, whereas in mafic rocks the fibers commonly consist of plagioclase feldspar and/or pyroxene. Spherulites typically have diameters of 0.1-1 inch, but they can be much larger (commonly up to 8 inches). Isolated spherulites are generally spherical, but adjacent spherulites may impinge upon one another to produce long chains that are often aligned with flow foliation.

Split Rock River Rhyolite: The Split Rock River Rhyolite is a pink to red, fine-grained lava flow that may contain 2-5% easily visible, tabular-shaped, white plagioclase feldspar crystals. The pink or red color comes from the abundance of potassium feldspar in the rock. This lava flow forms steep cliffs on the shore of Lake Superior south of the Split Rock River, along and in the Split Rock River, and in nearby streams. The cliffs and high towers are largely the result of weathering of the rhyolite along vertical cooling joints and numerous, closely space horizontal fractures that give the rock a "flagstone" look. These horizontal fractures occur in the upper 5 to 15 feet of the rhyolite and are due to a process called unloading or exfoliation. This characteristic feature of the rhyolite has given rise to many names including "shingle parting," "stacked saucers," and "split rock." This feature is the reason for the name of the river. Locally there are also 2-8% quartz-filled, elongate, and contorted amygdules near the top of the flow. Spherulites (small whitish spots) can be seen in some outcrops, and represent a texture that developed as the lava slowly changed from dense volcanic glass (obsidian) to a wholly crystalline rock.

Talus: An apron of rock rubble at the base of a slope. Along the Superior Hiking Trail the most important process that causes the rocks to break loose and begin their down slope journey is frost wedging.

Terrace: See river terrace.

Tortured Basalt: A name given to distinctive basalt lava flows found within the state parks that break into angular or flagstone to step-like surfaces. These form due to weathering along numerous fractures that crisscross the rock at various angles. The name comes from the fact that the rock ends up looking like it has been given a very rough time by planet earth.

Unconformity: A break or gap in the geological record; this gap may represent a month or a billion years or longer.

Unloading: see exfoliation.

Vesicle: See gas cavity.

Vesicle Cylinder: Round to irregular-shaped areas in the tops of lava flows that contain abundant amygdules. These features form from concentrations of gas rising up through a cooling lava along cylindrical-shaped pathways.

Whaleback: A tapered, blunt-nosed hill formed when pieces of rock (in a highly fractured rock) are pulled away by overriding ice (see glacial plucking). Generally this process is most pronounced on the down ice side of irregularities on the outcrop surface. So named because the bedrock exposure ends up looking like the back of a whale headed out to sea.

Xenolith or inclusion: As magma (hot molten rock) is injected into, through, and around pre-existing rocks, much like cream is injected into doughnuts, the intruded rocks are bent or arched upwards, as well as being shouldered aside. As this takes place, small to very large pieces of the pre-existing rocks are broken off and completely surrounded by the intruding magma. Depending on the composition and temperature of the magma, some of these pieces will be assimilated or completely melted by the intruding magma, but many will be preserved as alien (strange) pieces of rock, totally different in appearance and composition than the material they are entombed in. The name xenolith comes from the Latin words meaning xeno for stranger and lithos for rock. They have been compared to raisins in oatmeal, only these raisins vary in size from dimes to larger than football stadiums.

Zeolites: A group of more than 40 hydrous silicate minerals composed of varying amounts of sodium, potassium, calcium, and aluminum. Zeolites are best known for their occurrence in holes in volcanic rocks where they have precipitated out of warm groundwater at low temperature. The most common zeolite minerals seen are: thomsonite (white to cream-colored or pink, often fibrous or radiating), laumantite (massive and white or pink), and white stilbite.

Some Common Wildflowers and Shrubs in the State Parks Along the North Shore

Aster, Blue-Fringed (Aster ciliolatus): A member of the Daisy Family this 2 to 4 foot-tall plant has a purple stem with blue radiating flowers and a yellow disc. Grows in dry soils blooming from August to September.

Aster, Large-Leafed (Aster macrophyllus): Daisy Family, also called "lumber jack toilet paper," because the basal leaves are large (4 to 8 inches wide), rough, and heart-shaped. The plant is 1 to 5 feet tall with violet or whitish ray flowers. Plant stems are a pale purple color. Blooms late July to late August and is part of the Canadian carpet. Ojibwe hunters are said to have smoked the leaves before embarking on a hunt because they believed the smoke attracted deer and moose.

Aster, Purple (Aster patens): Daisy Family with lobes of short, oblong, toothless leaves. The purple flowers occur at the ends of slender branchlets and have 15 to 25 rays. Grows 1 to 3 feet tall. Blooms August and September

Aster, Purple-Stemmed (Aster ciliolatus): This 2 to 7 foot tall plant has blue or purple-rayed flowers, a bristly, purple stem, and rough, toothed leaves. Found in swamps and wet thickets. Blooms July through September.

Aster, White (Aster umbellatus): This 2 to 7 foot-tall plant of the Daisy Family has flat-topped clusters of white flowers with relatively few rays. Disks are yellow. Leaves are lance-shaped with rough edges.

Baneberry (Actaea rubra): A member of the Buttercup Family, this 1 to 2 foot-tall plant has white, 4 to10-petaled flowers that occur in tight, oblong clusters. Leaves are divided and then subdivided into sharply toothed leaflets. The fruit consists of a cluster of red or white berries, each with a red stalk and a black or purple "eye," which leads to the nickname of doll's eyes. Berries, leaves, and roots are poisonous. Blooms late May to early June.

Bearberry (Arctostaphylos uva-ursi): Uva in Latin means "a bunch of berries" and ursus is "bear," and yes bears do love to eat bearberries. This plant is a trailing shrub of the Heath Family and has reddish bark and small, paddle-shaped, evergreen leaves. The egg-shaped, white to pink flowers are in terminal clusters. Berries are red. Native Americans used the dried leaves for tobacco; they called it kinnikinnick. Bearberry tea was used to treat kidney stones, inflammation of the urinary tract, and headaches. Blooms mid-May into early June in dry, often sandy soils. Look for it on outcrops, rock ledges, and beneath pine trees.

Bellwort, Sessile (Uvularia sessilifolia): Also known as "wild oats," this 4 to 12 inch-tall plant has nodding pale yellow flowers. Leaves are attached directly to the stem. Blooms late April through May. The young plant shoots are a good substitute for asparagus, and Ojibwe hunters carried the root as a charm to attract white-tailed deer and moose.

Birdfoot Trefoil (Lotus corniculatus): A member of the Pea Family, this 6 to 24 inch-tall plant has clover-like clusters of yellow flowers. The leaves are in 5 parts: 3 clover-like leaflets and 2 that look like a large appendage at the base of the leafstalk. Slender seed pod suggests a bird's foot and thus the name. Blooms mid-June through August.

Bird's-Eye Primrose (Primula mistassinaca): This plant, considered an Artic relict, is found along the North Shore of Lake Superior. Growing out of fractures and crevices in the volcanic rocks the plant has notched, 5-petaled, delicate purple flowers that perch at the top of short stems. Blooms late May to early July.

Bloodroot (Sanguinaria canadensis): One of the earliest spring flowers to bloom. The plant has a large lobed-leaf that wraps itself like a shawl around the 6 to 12 inch stalk, which bears the very pretty 8- to 10-petaled, white flower. The leaf remains long after the flower has vanished. Broken stem emits an orange juice that the Ojibwe used as a dye for baskets and clothing. The juice does contain alkaloids and can be toxic. Blooms from late April to late May.

Blue Bead Lily or Clintonia (Clintonia borealis): Also known as "corn lily," this 6 to 14 inch-tall plant has 2 or 3 shiny, parallel-veined basal leaves and yellow, bell-shaped flowers on a leafless stalk. Has poisonous blue berries, but young leaves taste like cucumber. Blooms from mid-May through June; berries conspicuous from July to August.

Blueberry, Low Bush (Vaccinium angustifolium): Low, woody shrub some 10 to 20 inches tall that can be found in open, rocky areas, especially in old burn areas. The leaves are shiny, alternate, and without teeth, while the urn-shaped white flowers hang down in loose clusters. Blooms late May to mid-June with berries ripe in early to mid-July.

Blue-Eyed Grass (Sisyrinchium montanum): This plant is not really a grass but a member of the Iris Family with blue flowers that open only in the afternoon. Buds of the blooming plant look like thin strands of grass with blue-tipped ends. The blue flowers have 5-7 petals with a yellow "eye" in the center. Blooms May to June in open meadows.

Blue Flag Iris (Iris versicolor): Also called wild iris, this 2 to 3 foot-tall plant with graceful, sword-shaped leaves (very distinctive) has curved, violet-colored flowers that are deeply veined. Found in marshes and along the edges of lakes. Blooms from mid-June to mid-July. The Ojibwe always carried a small bit of the plant with them when they went berry picking for they believed it would keep snakes away.

Bracken Fern (Pteridium aquilinum): This fern can grow over 3 feet tall with fronds that branch once or twice giving the appearance of compound leaves. The triangular-shaped fronds have many spatula-shaped leaflet-like segments that have their edges rolled under. The stem at the base is dark brown and hairy becoming straw-colored and hairless toward the top. Found in acid soils in both old-growth and new pine forests as well as in abandoned pastures and along forest margins.

Brown-eyed Susan (Rudbeckia hirta): This is a sun loving flower that is 12 to 30 inches tall and has brown "disk flowers" surrounded by yellow "ray flowers." Also known as black-eyed Susan this original wildflower of the prairie blooms from July to September.

Buckwheat (Fagopyrum sagittatum): White or pink flowers in branching sprays, the 1 to 2 foot-tall plant has arrowhead-shaped leaves and swollen sheaths where attached to the reddish stem. Blooms June through August.

Buckwheat, Climbing False (Polygonum scandens): Similar to above, but the plant is a twining vine.

Bunchberry (Cornus canadensis): Part of the Dogwood Family this 3 to 8 inch plant has 4 white bracts (modified leaves adjacent to the flower) that surround the center cluster of tiny greenish flowers giving the appearance of a single pretty blossom. Leaves are in a whorl of 6, and the fruit is scarlet-colored and pulpy with a slightly sweet taste. The root was used for infant colic and the leaf for tea to ease aches and pains. Blooms from late May to late June, berries appear in mid-July.

Buttercup, Common (Ranunculus acris): This is the most familiar and most common of the 36 buttercup species. The 2 to 3 foot-tall plant has 5 to 7 glossy, overlapping yellow petals (buttercups) with bushy stamen. The leaves are deeply cut into 5 to 7 unstalked segments. Fields and meadows; blooms late May through July.

Butterwort (Pinguicula vulgaris); This 2 to 5 inch-high, carnivorous plant has yellowish, ground-hugging, basal leaves and purple flowers. It is an artic plant that lives in crevices and rock surfaces along Lake Superior's North Shore. Its sticky leaves trap, dissolve, and absorb insects. Its name may come from the slimy feel of the leaves (like fat was poured over them). Flowers bloom in July.

Canadian Carpet: Refers to a small number of plant species that comprise the vast majority of ground cover in a boreal forest. Species include blue bead lily, Canadian mayflower, bunchberry, twinflower, pyrola, starflower, Indian pipe, wintergreen, pipsissewa, ladyslipper, spotted coralroot orchid, and large-leafed aster.

Canadian Mayflower (Maianthemum canadense): The Latin name means May blossom of Canada, plant also known as "wild lily of the valley." This 3 to 6 inch-tall plant has 2 to 3 heart-shaped leaves and clusters of 4 pointed white flowers. Berries are white with spots but turn pale to ruby red in the fall. Likes moist woods and commonly found in spruce-fir forests. Flowers from mid-May to June. Native Americans used the plant to cure headaches, sore throats, and kidney problems.

Chickweed (several varieties): Chickweed is a 4 to 16 inch-tall plant with small, white flowers that have 5 petals. The petals are so deeply cleft that flowers often seem to have 10 petals. Leaves are in pairs. An excellent source of vitamin B.

Cinquefoil, Dwarf (Potentilla canadensis): This 2 to 4 inch-tall plant has cream-colored to yellow 5-petaled flowers with radially, 5-parted leaves that are wedge-shaped and toothed. Flowers and leaves rise from runners that are on separate stalks. Runners can be 6 to 20 inches long. Stems are silver and hairy. When chewed, the leaves are an excellent source of vitamin B. Blooms May to June.

Cinquefoil, Rough-Fruited (Potentilla recta): A member of the Rose Family this 1 to 2 foot-tall plant has pale yellow 5-petaled flowers in a flat, terminal cluster. These are attached to an erect, very hairy stalk with many-branched leaves. Leaflets are 5 to 7 inches long and relatively narrow. Native Americans made a tea of the leaves and used it to treat diarrhea. Blooms mid-June through July.

Cinquefoil, Shrubby (Potentilla fruticosa): This is a bushy, 1 to 2 foot-tall shrub with silky leaves (whitish underneath) and woody stems; leaf segments are toothless, and the yellow flowers have 5 petals. Blooms July to mid-August and likes cold, exposed rock ledges.

Cinquefoil, Tall (Potentilla arguta): A member of the Rose Family, this 1 to 3 foot-tall plant has white or cream-colored 5-petaled flowers that occur in flat-topped clusters. Leaflets 7 to 11, toothed and downy underneath. Blooms late June through July.

Cinquefoil, Three-Toothed (Potentilla tridentata): A member of the Rose Family, this 1 to 10 inch-tall ground-hugging plant has white 5-petaled flowers, and 3 shiny leaflets with 3 rounded teeth at the tip. The leaves turn deep red in the fall. Common in rocky crevices. Blooms mid-June through July.

Clematis, Purple (Clematis verticillaris): A member of the Buttercup Family, this climbing vine has pretty, bell-like purple flowers with 4 sepals. Flowers are "downy" inside and out; leaves are in groups of 3. Rocky woods and open slopes. Blooms late May through June.

Clubmoss, Bristly (Lycopodium annotinum): A common ground cover in the boreal forest. These are short (up to a foot tall), stiff, evergreen plants with straight, sharply pointed leaves at right angles to the stem. Likes acid soils.

Clubmoss, Ground Cedar or Pine (Lycopodium complanatum): This kind of clubmoss looks like a small cedar tree. The stem branches are made up of scale-like leaves, flatted and fanned out in one direction. Cones (1-4) occur on 3 inch stems looking like the arms of a candelabra.

Clubmoss, Running (Lycopodium clavatum): Also known as "running pine," this plant has long, forking horizontal stems that create a maze over the ground. Straw-colored strobiles (a group of modified leaves at the end of a stem) occur in pairs atop a single stalk. Leaf tips end in threadlike hairs. Found under aspen and fir trees. Spores were used to stop bleeding.

Clubmoss, Shining (Lycopodium lucidulum): Bright green stems up to 10 inches tall. These may branch 3 times. Leaves are of unequal size and toothed at tips.

Coltsfoot (Tussilago farfara): This 6 to 15 inch-tall plant has a stalk with reddish scales and a bristly yellow flower that looks like a dandelion. Flower appears before the leaves. Blooms mid-April through June.

Columbine (Aquilegia canadensis): A member of the Buttercup Family, this plant has drooping red bell-shaped flowers with 5 long, curved spurs (they look like Bung's hat in the Wizard of Id). Very distinctive, have been called the "eye candy of the wildflower world." Blooms early May through June, and likes rocky or gravelly areas with partial to full sun.

Corydalis (Corydalis): Small (6 to 16 inches) plants of the poppy family that have finely cut leaves and narrow, yellow, tubular flowers with a hollow spur. Several varieties grow along the trail, but all love sun, grow on rocks, and in sand and gravel. Native Americans placed the root on wood coals and inhaled the smoke to "clear the head." Blooms in June.

Cow Parsnip (Heracleum maximum): This large (4 to 10 foot-tall) plant is a member of the Carrot Family and has leaves commonly over a foot wide that are divided into 3 maple-shaped segments. Stem is hollow and may be 2 inches thick at the base. White flowers occur in umbrella-like clusters, are woolly and rank smelling. Likes moist ground. Native Americans ate the cooked root to relieve upset stomachs; the root, when dried, can be used as a salt substitute. Blooms late June through August.

Cowslip: See Marsh Marigold.

Dewberry or Dwarf Raspberry (Rubus pubescens): This 3 to 6 inch-tall plant has 3 leaflets that resemble strawberry leaves. The red fruit is a cluster of juicy droplets that resemble a raspberry. These are edible but not great tasting; also fruit is not easy to remove from the plant. Blooms early May to early June.

Dutchman's Breeches (Dicentra cucullaria): A member of the Bleeding Heart Family, this 5 to 9 inch-tall plant has white or pink nodding flowers with long, triangular spurs. The spurs resemble the legs of tiny "pantaloons" or "breeches" that appear to hang upside down as if on a clothesline. Leaves are finely dissected and bluish-green. This is a close relative of the bleeding heart. Native Americans used the leaves to make tea (possibly because of its repute as a powerful love potion). Blooms mid-April to mid-May.

Fireweed (Epilobium angustifolium): A member of the Evening Primrose Family, this 3 to 5 foot-tall plant has slender spikes of many purple-pink, roundish flower petals, drooping flower buds, and reddish seedpods angling upwards. Leaves alternate. Flowers open from the bottom of the plant upward and, as the saying goes, when "fireweed blooms at the top, summer is over." Loves disturbed soil, roadsides, gravel pits, burn areas; blooms July through mid-August.

Golden Alexander (Zizea aptera): Part of the Parsley Family, this 1 to 3 foot-tall plant has small yellow flowers in compound umbrella-like clusters. Lower leaves are heart-shaped and un-divided; upper leaves are divided into 3 to 5 leaflets. Blooms April through May.

Goldenrod (Solidago species): over 10 varieties of goldenrod can be found in the parks, but all have yellow-rayed blossoms in clusters with either plume-like leaves that are parallel veined or feather-veined. Blooms July to late August.

Ground Cedar: See Clubmoss, Ground Cedar.

Goldthread (Coptis groenlandia): A member of the Buttercup Family; 3 to 5 inches tall. The plant has 5 to 7 white petal-like sepals and 15 to 25 stamens. The plant has shiny, dark, evergreen leaves with 3 leaflets and bright yellow roots. Blooms in May; prefers cool woods and bogs.

Hairy Rock Cress (Arabis hirsuta): A member of the Mustard Family, this 1 to 2 foot-tall plant has oblong to paddle-shaped basal leaves in rosettes; stem leaves are narrow and clasping. White 4-petaled flowers occur in small clusters. Blooms May to June.

Harebell (Campanula rotundifolia):Also called bluebell, this 6 to 18 inch-tall plant has blue-violet, bell-shaped flowers that are ½ to ¾ inch long. The leaves are narrow or hair-like. Blooms from late June to mid-August.

Hawkweed, Orange (Hieracium aurantiacum): A member of the Composite Family, orange hawkweed is also called "devil's paintbrush." The 8 to 24 inch-tall plant is very hairy with leaves forming a basal rosette. Plant has deep orange flat-ray flowers with yellowish centers. Called hawkweed because it was once believed hawks ate the flowers to improve their vision. Blooms mid-May through July. There is also a yellow-flowered variety.

Hepatica (Hepatica americana): This 4 to 6 inch-tall plant of the Buttercup Family has rounded, 3-lobed leaves, hairy stalks, and 6 to 10-petaled white, pink, or blue flowers. Blooms from mid-April to late May; can be seen blooming amongst patches of melting snow.

Honeysuckle (Lonicera): Honeysuckles are mostly 1 to 5 foot-tall woody shrubs and vines with oblong to heart-shaped or oval opposite leaves. Flowers are bell-shaped or funnel-like, yellow to orange, with 5 stamens (male organs tipped by pollen). Several different varieties. Blooms May to August.

Honeysuckle, Bush (Diervilla lonicera): This 1 to 4 foot-tall plant has sharp-pointed, toothed leaves and yellow funnel-shaped flowers that are tinged in red. Blooms June to August.

Horsetails (Equisetum species): Also called "Indian Tinker Toys" (because the stem can be pulled or popped apart at nodes) this non-flowering plant has reddish-brown, scale-like leaves (called teeth) at nodes that are clumped together in threes. The stiff, hollow stem has a ridge-like surface with spicules of silica on the ridges. This makes the plant rough enough to file fingernails or scrub pots. The stem is topped by a spore-producing cone. The plant name comes from the vegetative shoots that appear feathery due to long, wispy branches. Moist, wet areas.

Indian Pipe (Monotropa uniflora): Also called "corpse plant" and "ghost flower," this is a member of the Wintergreen Family. It is 4 to 10 inches tall and has waxy, translucent stems from which a nodding white or pink flower hangs. Leaves are scale-like. The plant has no chlorophyll and obtains its food like a mushroom. The clear sap was used by Native Americans to help clear up cloudy vision. Blooms July and August.

Jack-in-the-Pulpit (Arisaema triphyllum): A member of the Dragon Arum family, which includes philodendron, this unique plant has a fleshy, club-shaped spike (Jack) that is gracefully covered by a flap-like green or purplish-brown sheath (the pulpit). There are 1 or 2 long stalked leaves that are 3-parted; the fruit is a cluster of scarlet berries. Blooms mid-May to mid-June. The Ojibwe tell a wonderful story about this plant and the little people who inhabit the forest.

Joe-Pye Weed (Eupatorium purpureum): Daisy Family, 3 to 5 feet tall, with pinkish-purple flower heads in round-topped clusters. Narrow, short-stalked leaves in whorls of 3 or 4. Gives off vanilla odor when bruised or crushed. Named after Joe Pye, a Native American doctor who treated early colonists for typhoid fever with this plant (or so the story goes). Blooms July through mid- September.

Juneberry (Amelanchier species): Member of the Rose Family, also known as serviceberry, this shrub is 5 to 15 feet tall and has spectacular white drooping flower clusters that turn parts of the hiking trails into virtual "gardens." The flowers have 5 long petals, and the leaves are oval and toothed. Also slender reddish buds. Blooms late May into June. Huckleberry-like fruits ripen in July.

Labrador Tea (Ledum groenlandicum): This evergreen shrub, a member of the Heath Family, is a 1 to 3 foot-tall plant with white or pinkish flowers in terminal clusters. The leaves are leathery with rolled edges and are "rusty-woolly" on the under surfaces. Native Americans used the leaves for tea, and they also chewed the leaves. Likes bogs; blooms from late May through June.

Leatherleaf (Chamaedaphne calyculata): A member of the Heath Family, this 1 to 2 foot-tall shrub has pinkish-white, bell-shaped flowers in one-sided clusters. Evergreen leaves are leathery with dot-like scales on both upper and lower surfaces. Blooms May through early June.

Marsh Marigold (Caltha palustris): Part of the Buttercup Family, also known as "cowslip," this is an early spring flower found in wooded, swampy areas and along the edges of creeks. The 8 to 24 inch-tall plant has large yellow flowers (1 to 2 inches) with 5 to 9 petals and round or kidney-shaped glossy leaves. Native Americans mixed the root with maple sugar and used this concoction to relieve coughs; they also used the raw root to heal minor wounds. However, eating the plant can cause heart inflammation. Blooms late April through May.

Mertensia (Mertensia virginica): Part of the Forget-Me-Not Family, this plant is also known as "Virginia Bluebells." It is 1 to 2 feet tall, and has blue, trumpet-like flowers that are pink when in bud. The leaves are oval, smooth, and well-veined. Found in moist woods and bottomlands; blooms from late April through May.

Mullein, Common (Verbascum thapsus): A member of the Snapdragon Family, this 2 to 7 foot-tall plant has a club-like flower head with yellow, 5-petaled flowers and large "flannel" textured leaves that look like they flow into the stem. Blooms July through mid-September in fields and along roadsides.

Orchid, Coralroot (Corallorhiza species): several different varieties of Coralroot orchid grow along the park trails; all have "lipped" flowers and parallel-veined leaves. They lack green pigment and bear their pink, red, and white flowers on a leafless stalk. Most varieties bloom June to late-July.

Orchid, Ladyslipper, Pink (Cypripedium acaule): Also called Moccasin Flower, this member of the Orchid Family is a 6 to 15 inch-tall plant with a distinctive heavily veined, pink "pouch." The plant also has 2 oval basal leaves with parallel veins. Likes cool, shady, mossy, or rocky areas. Blooms mid-May to late June. The root was used to ease tooth pain.

Orchid, Ladys Slipper, Yellow (Cypripedium calceolus): Another member of the Orchid Family, this is a 1 to 2 foot-tall plant an inflated yellow lip (slipper) and 2 lateral petals that are long, twisted, and brownish-green. Likes bogs, wet woods, shady swamps. Blooms June through mid-July.

Ostrich Fern (Matteuccia struthiopteris): Named for the frond's resemblance to the plume of an Ostrich. This fern grows to heights of 3 to 8 feet; the fronds increase in width at the top. In the spring rootstalks send up tightly coiled new leaves that resemble the head of a violin; these are called "fiddleheads."

Ox-Eye Daisy (Chrysanthemum leucanthemum): A white daisy with a yellow disk; leaves are dark, narrow, irregular; and bluntly toothed. Grows to heights of 18 to 30 inches. Plant was used by Native Americans as a stimulant. Blooms June to mid-August.

Pearly Everlasting (Anaphalis margaritacea): This 1 to 2 foot-tall plant, a member of the Daisy Family, has white flowers in tubular heads and terminal clusters. Numerous silver-white bracts surrounding single flowers give the plant its name. Leaves are long and narrow. Blooms from late July into August.

Pipsissewa (Chimaphila umbellata): This 6 to 12 inch plant of the Wintergreen Family has a terminal cluster of waxy white to pinkish flowers, each with a ring of reddish anthers (enlarged part of the stamen that holds the pollen). Dark, shiny toothed leaves radiate in whorls from the stem. Pipsissewa is Cree for "breaks into small pieces." Grows in dry woods; blooms mid-May to late June. Used by Native Americans to treat sore eyes and skin irritations.

Pitcher Plant (Sarracenia purpurea): This 12 to 18 inch-tall bog plant has red, pitcher-like, heavily veined leaves that are usually half-filled with water. The flaring lips are lined with downward pointing bristles that help trap insects. The nodding, globular red flower is on a separate stalk. Insects fly or crawl into the pitcher and fall into the water at the bottom and drown. Then they are ingested by the plant. Blooms June to early July.

Purple Vetch (Vicia americana): Part of the Legume Family, this 2 to 3 foot-high vine has violet-purple, pea-like flowers that occur in loose racemes (long cluster of flowers arranged singly along a stalk). Blooms mid-May through early July.

Pussytoes (Antennaria canadensis): A member of the Daisy Family, this 5 to 12 inch-tall plant has small white, woolly flowers in a cluster at the top of the stem. Basal leaves, which have 1 main nerve, are larger than leaves on the stem. Blooms late April to early June.

Pyrola (Pyrola species): There are several different species of pyrola to be found along the park trails. The leaves of this plant have analgesic properties and Native Americans used it to treat cuts, sores, and rheumatism.

1. One-Sided Pyrola (Pyrola secunda) is an 8 inch-high plant with all the flower stalks attached to one side of the long stem. White flowers are small, waxy, and cup-shaped. Basal leaves are rounded and not toothed. Blooms mid-June through July.

2. Round-Leaved Pyrola (Pyrola rotundifolia) is an 8 to 18 inch-tall plant with fragrant white to rose- colored flowers that occur at the end of the long stem. Leaves are shiny and round. Blooms May through July.

3. Shinleaf Pyrola (Pyrola elliptica) is a 5 to 10 inch-tall plant that has large (up to 3 inches), elliptical leaves that are flattened at the end, and not pointed. Bluish white, cup-shaped flowers at the top of the long stalk. Blooms mid-June through July.

Raspberry (Rubus idaeus): This tall bush has 5-petaled white flowers and prickles or sharp spikes on the canes. Blooms June to early July; berries typically ripen late July and August.

Rose-Twisted Stalk (Streptopus roseus): A member of the Lily Family, this 1 to 3 foot-high plant has a zigzag stem, parallel-veined leaves, and six-pointed pink, bell-like flowers that hang singly from leaf axils. The fruit is cherry red and translucent. Blooms mid-May through June; likes acidic soils. Another name for this plant is "scootberry," because eating the berries makes you "scoot" to the bathroom a lot.

Rue, Early Meadow (Thalictrum dioicum): A member of the Buttercup Family, this 1 to 2 foot-tall plant has drooping or dangling clusters of 4 or 5-petaled greenish-white flowers with purple tips. Blooms late April to May.

Rue, Tall Meadow (Thalictrum polygamum): Taller (3 to 8 feet) and later blooming (June through July) than early meadow rue. Leaves are divided, then subdivided into many roundish, 3-lobed leaflets. Plumes of white flowers lack petals.

Running Pine: see Clubmoss, Running.

Sarsaparilla, Wild (Aralia nudicaulis): Part of the Ginseng Family, this plant has large, 3-branched leaves (each with 3 to 5 leaflets) with white, round, umbrella-like flower clusters below the leaves on a separate stem. Leaves start off a burgundy color then slowly turn green. Has blue-black berries that ripen in mid-July. This is a close cousin to wild ginseng and, supposedly, was the root used in the original root beer, or the drink called sarsaparilla. Blooms mid-May through late June.

Sensitive Fern (Onoclea sensibilis): So named because it is sensitive to cold, the fronds of this fern wither rapidly after a frost or after being cut. This is a 15 to 30 inch-tall fern with a single blade that is deeply cut, but not all the way to the stem. Has a lacy network of veins that covers the single blade. Tips of leaflets are blunt. The hollow structure in which spores are produced is on a totally separate stalk, which is much shorter than the fronds. Likes wet areas.

Snowberry (Gaultheria hispidula): A member of the Heath Family, this low, creeping plant has small, alternate, oval leaves along the stems. Flowers are white, tiny, 4-lobed, and bell-shaped. Fruit is a white berry tasting of wintergreen. Blooms May through July. Ojibwe name for this plant is waaboozaba, and they used it for cuts, burns, and to cure tapeworm.

Solomon's Seal (Polygonatum biflorum): A member of the Lily Family, this 1 to 3 foot-tall plant has paired, greenish-yellow flowers that dangle beneath the elongate leaves. Flowers are arranged alternately on the stem. Berries are blue-black. Blooms early May through June.

Sphagnum Moss: Called peat moss or the "shag carpeting of the Canadian Shield," these are stout, thick-leaved mosses that vary from red to pink to dominantly green in color. The stems may be 8 inches long with 5 branches at each node. This particular moss can absorb up to 27 times its weight in water. Found in floating bogs, cedar swamps, sedge mats, and spruce swamps.

Springbeauty (Claytonia virginica): A member of the Purslane Family and also called "fairy spuds" (the tubers resemble a small potato with many protruding eyes). This plant has smooth, linear leaves halfway up the 4-10 inch-tall stem. Flowers have 5 petals and are white to pink with darker pink veins. Found in moist woods blooming from mid-April through May.

Starflower (Trientalis borealis): A member of the Primrose Family with two 6 to 7-pointed, star-like, white flowers on thin stalks above a whorl of 5 to 9 shiny, tapered leaves. Found in wooded areas blooming from mid-May through June. Also called "Star of Bethlehem" and, in Sweden, "wood star."

Strawberry, Common or Meadow (Fragaria virginiana): A member of the Rose Family, this wild strawberry is similar to the domestic version. The 3 to 6 inch-tall plant has hairy, 3-toothed leaflets on a slender stalk. The 5-petaled white flowers occur in a flat cluster on a separate stalk. Plant spreads by runners. Blooms late May through June; berries ripen mid-June into July. Seeds are embedded in pits in the red fruit.

Strawberry, Wood (Fragaria vesca): Similar to the common strawberry, but flowers and fruits are smaller and on stems that are taller than the leaves, which are more pointed. Fruit is more elongate and the seeds are on the surface of the fruit, not in pits. Blooms May to mid-July.

Sundew (Drosera rotundifolia): This 8 to 10 inch-tall plant has small, white flowers on one side of a long stem. Round basal leaves have reddish, glandular bristles that exude a sticky juice. When the sun shines on this plant, the leaves look like they are covered with sparkling dewdrops. When an insect lands on one of these, the bristles close to capture the unwary creature. Blooms mid-June through July. Native Americans used the leaves to treat different kinds of coughs as well as asthma.

Sunflower, Common (Helianthus annuus): This 7 to 10 foot-tall plant of the Daisy Family has a yellow flower head with reddish-brown disk florets. The leaves are heart-shaped, toothed, and resinous with slender stalks. The stem is rough and hairy. Blooms July through September. There are many varieties and sizes of sunflowers including wood sunflowers, which are 2 to 6 feet tall.

Sweet Cicely (Osmorhiza claytoni): Part of the Parsley Family this 1 to 3 foot-tall plant has a round stem and wide, fern-like leaves. Both leaves and stem have soft, white hairs. The leaves are bluntly toothed, and the lower ones are large (a foot or more in length). The white flowers are small and occur in flat-topped clusters. The roots have a sweet licorice odor. Blooms May to June.

Tansy (Tanacetum vulgare): This member of the Daisy Family grows 2 to 3 feet tall and has many small button-shaped, yellow flower heads in a flat-topped cluster. Fern-like leaves are finely divided. Strongly scented plant (sometimes called "stinkweed"). Likes waste areas, roadsides, and open fields. Blooms from late July through mid-September. The Ojibwe used the root for ear drops and the leaves as a fever suppressant, and the dried leaf was chewed for sore throats.

Thimbleberry (Rubus parviflorus): This is a waist-high bush (2 to 4 feet) with large, maple-like leaves and big, fragile, 5-petaled, white flowers. The raspberry-like fruit develops in August. The berries easily fit over the end of your finger like a thimble. Also called salmonberry. Blooms mid-June to mid-July.

Tree Zoos: Visitors to North Shore Parks will notice two kinds of fencing. The first is wire fencing around individual trees. The purpose of this is fairly clear—it protects the young trees from being eaten by deer or moose. The second kind is wire fencing that encloses large areas. These are called "exclosures" or, by us "tree zoos." These have been used for both research and management. Most of them are now used as management tools to allow young trees to grow high enough so that they escape the deer. Sometimes young trees are planted inside these areas and sometimes natural seedlings are just protected.

292

Whitetail deer love the terminal (top) buds of young white pines, and anything they can chew on a white cedar. Deer populations are currently very high on the North Shore. In the winter, the whitetails migrate toward Lake Superior, and concentrate near the shore. This has resulted in a situation where very few young cedars or pines survive. The forest consists mostly of older trees with no replacements in sight. Park managers use the exclosures to protect the young trees until they are a couple feet higher than deer can reach. That's higher than you might think, because deer sometimes have packed snow to stand on. Once trees are tall enough, the fencing can be removed. Deer will still feed on the trees–there are few accessible white cedars in the parks with any foliage left that deer can reach–but if they can't nip the tip off, the trees will probably grow to escape them.

Exclosures can do more than protect young trees. They have also been used a research tools. In the western states, where cattle can graze on much public land for a nominal fee, this grazing has been a perennial political issue. Exclosures have been used to keep cattle out, and help answer the question "What would this ecosystem be like without cattle grazing?" Such exclosures have been used to answer similar questions in Minnesota, but the animal being exclude is usually deer. One past study involved white cedar regeneration in Tettegouche State Park. A current study in the park is birch regeneration on undisturbed versus scarified soil. Later a controlled burn may be added to the mix.

Trillium, Large-Flowered (Trillium grandiflorum): Trillium is Latin for "three". Same as nodding trillium, but the flowers are much larger and stand upright between the 3 leaves. Blooms May to early June. Flower turns pink as it ages.

Trillium, Nodding (Trillium cernuum): Three broad leaves and 3 showy white or pink petals. The single flower dangles below the leaves. The plant is 10 to18 inches tall and likes acid woods. Blooms from late April to early June.

Twinflower (Linnaea borealis): Part of the Honeysuckle Family this fragrant, dainty plant has small, pink, bell-shaped flowers that occur in pairs at the top of thin, 3 to 6 inch-tall stalks. The leaves of this creeping plant are small, paired, and rounded. Likes mossy areas; flowers in June.

Violet, White (Viola incognita): This 1 to 5 inch-tall plant has white 5-petaled flowers atop a bare stem. The leaves arise from the base of the flower stem. Blooms May to mid-June.

Violet, Wooly Blue (Viola sororia): This 3 to 8 inch-tall plant has blue or violet, 5-petaled-flowers with white centers. There are numerous leaves with blades up to 4 inches wide. Found in damp woods and meadows. Blooms May to early June.

Violet, Yellow (Viola pubescens): This 4 to 10 inch-tall plant has 5-petaled yellow flowers. Both leaves and flowers arise from the main stem. There are 1 to 5 basal leaves, which are broad and smooth. Blooms May through early June. The flowers and leaves may be eaten raw in salads.

Wild Rose (Rosa species): Two varieties are found along the North Shore. Flowers are 5-petaled white or pink, with many stamens. Prickly variety has pink flowers on a bush that is waist high and covered by prickles. Smoth variety has a smooth stem. Rose hips are the fruit of the rose plant; these ripen to a deep red or orange color in August. Rose hips are a great source of vitamin C.

Wintergreen (Gaultheria procumbens): Part of the Heath Family and also called teaberry, this 3 to 6 inch-tall plant has waxy, pinkish-white flowers that are urn-shaped. Leaves are oval, thick, waxy, and dark green. The edible red berries form in late summer but ripen in the fall. Berries taste and smell of wintergreen, and the crushed leaves are the source of oil of wintergreen. Blooms mid-July to late August.

Wood Anemone (Anemone quinquefolia): Also known as windflower, this member of the Buttercup Family has deeply cut, dark green leaves divided into 3 or 5 leaflets. The plant is 4 to 8 inches tall and has a 5-petaled white flower that closes up on cloudy, cool days (hence one of its other names—"drops-of-snow"). An early spring flower blooming late April through mid-June. Native Americans made a tea of the roots and used this to ease headaches and prevent dizziness.

Wood Sorrel (Oxalis montana): This 6 inch-high plant has pink or white flowers, strongly veined in pink, with 5 petals. The leaves are divided into 3 inversely heart-shaped leaflets that look like shamrocks. Blooms May through July with the young leaves having a lemony flavor.

Yarrow (Achillea millefolium): A member of the Daisy Family, this 12 to 20 inch tall plant has aromatic, fern-like leaves and white to pinkish flower heads in flat-topped clusters. Although it is a composite, the 5 rays give each head the look of a 5-petaled flower. Blooms July through late September. The plant is also called bloodwort because the plant can be used to speed up the formation of blood clots.

References

Bates, R.L. and Jackson, J.A., 2004, *Dictionary of Geological Terms.* American Geological Institute, 3rd edition.

Boerboom, T.J., Miller, J. and Green, J.C., 2004, *Geological Highlights of New Mapping in the Southwestern Sequence of the North Shore Volcanic Group and in the Beaver Bay Complex.* In Severson, M. and Hein, J., eds., Field Trip Guidebook, Institute on Lake Superior Geology, Duluth, MN., p. 46-85.

Brockman, C.F., 1986. *Trees of North America.* New York, NY., Golden Press.

Fenton, H., 2000, *50 Circuit Hikes: A Stride by Stride Guide to Northeastern Minnesota.* Duluth, MN., Pfeifer-Hamilton (University of Minnesota Press).

Green, J.C. and Fitz, T.J. III, 1993, *Extensive Felsic Lavas and Rheoignimbrites in the Keweenawan Midcontinent Rift Plateau Volcanics, Minnesota: Petrography and Field Recognition.* Journal of Volcanology and Geothermal Research, V. 54, 177-196.

Green, J., 1996, *Geology on Display, Geology and Scenery of Minnesota's North Shore State Parks.* State of Minnesota, Department of Natural Resources.

Grieve, Mrs. M., 1971, *A Modern Herbal, The Medicinal, Culinary, Cosmetic and Economic Properties, Cultivation and Folk-Lore of Herbs, Grasses, Fungi, Shrubs, and Trees with all their Modern Scientific Uses.* New York, NY., Dover Publications.

Marotta, Juanita, 1971, *Minnesota's Wildflowers of the Forest, Field, and Wetland.* Published by the Author.

Marshak, S., 2004, *Essentials of Geology.* New York, NY., W.W. Norton Company.

Miller, J.D., 1988, *Geologic Map of the Silver Bay and Split Rock Point NE Quadrangles, Lake County, Minnesota.* St. Paul, Mn., Minnesota Geological Survey, Map M-65.

Miller, J. and Chandler, V. W., 1997, *Geology, Petrology, and Tectonic Significance of the Beaver Bay Complex, Northeastern Minnesota;* in Ojakangas, R.W.O., Dickas, A.B., and Green, J.C., eds., Middle Proterozoic to Cambrian Rifting, Central North America, Geological Society of America Special paper 312.

Minnesota Department of Natural Resources, 2003, *Field Guide to the Native Plant Communities of Minnesota: the Laurentian Mixed Forest Province.* Ecological Land Classification Program, Minnesota County Biological Survey, and Natural Heritage and Nongame Research Program, MNDNR, St. Paul, MN., New Brighton, MN., Printing Enterprises.

295

Morton, R. 1996, *Music of the Earth: Volcanoes, Earthquakes, and Other Geological Wonders*. New York, NY., Plenum Publishing, (Perseus, 2004).

Morton, R. and Gawboy, C., 2000, *Talking Rocks: Ten Thousand Years of Native Americans and Geology in the Great Lakes Region*. Duluth, MN., Pfiefer-Hamilton (University of Minnesota Press, 2004).

Morton, R. and Gibbs, J., 2006, *A Walking Guide to the Superior Hiking Trail: Natural History, Scenery, and Other Trail Features*. Knife River, MN., Rockflower Press.

Ojakangas, R.W.O. and Matsch, C.L., 1982, *Minnesota's Geology*. Minneapolis, MN., University of Minnesota Press.

Oldfield, B. and Moriarty, J.J., 1994, *Amphibians and Reptiles: Native to Minnesota*. Portland, OR., Timber Press, Inc.

Peterson, R and McKensey, M., 1968, *A Field Guide to Wildflowers*. New York, NY., Houghton–Mifflin Co.

Stensaas, M., 1996, *Plants and Trees of the North Woods and Boundary Waters*. Duluth, MN: Pfiefer-Hamilton.

Stensaas, M., 2003, *Wildflowers of the BWCA and the North Shore*. Duluth, MN., Kollath-Stensaas Publishing.

Stensaas, M.S., 2004, *Canoe Country Flora, Plants, and Trees of the North Woods and Boundary Waters*. Minneapolis, MN., University of Minnesota Press.

Tekiela, S., 1999, *Wildflowers of Minnesota, Field Guide*. Cambridge, MN., Adventure Publications.

Tekiela, S., 2001, *Trees of Minnesota, Field Guide*. Cambridge, MN., Adventure Publications Inc..

Tryon, R., 1980, *Ferns of Minnesota*. Minneapolis, MN., Universitry of Minnesota Press.

Water, T., 1987, *The Superior North Shore, A Natural History of Lake Superior Northern Lands and Waters*. Minneapolis, MN., University of Minnesota Press.

Ron Morton is a professor in the department of Geological Sciences at the University of Minnesota-Duluth where he has taught courses in introductory geology, physical volcanology, Precambrian geology, economic geology, earth science for teachers, and people and volcanoes. Ron has also taught for many years in the Elderhostel Program. His main areas of research are volcanic rocks and mineral resources of the Canadian Shield. Ron is also the author of "Music of the Earth" (Perseus, 1996, 2004), with Carl Gawboy "Talking Rocks" (University of Minnesota Press, 2000), and with Judy Gibbs "A Walking Guide to the Superior Hiking Trail" (Rockflower Press, 2006).

Steve Morse is a sometimes wandering naturalist, sculptor, and stained glass artist who has spent most of his career working in biology. He started with a position as an "Amoeba Farmer" raising protozoan, algal, and small invertebrate cultures for a company that supplied schools and universities. Steve holds bachelor's degrees in Art and in Fisheries Science. He moved on to working with lake trout, lake herring, and other fish on Lake Superior for the Minnesota Department of Natural Resources, along with inland crayfish studies and sturgeon radio telemetry. He considers working outdoors and working with living things to be essential ingredients in a job, and he has been lucky enough to have these elements in his career most of his life. He was born with a frog in his pocket and mud between his toes, and he hopes to die under the stars.